Electric
Circuits

The titles in this series

MACMILLAN WORK OUT SERIES

Electric Circuits

**Noel M. Morris
and
Frank W. Senior**

MACMILLAN

First published 1991 by
MACMILLAN EDUCATION LTD
Houndmills, Basingstoke, Hampshire RG21 2XS
and London
Companies and representatives
throughout the world

ISBN 0–333–51399–1

A catalogue record for this book is available
from the British Library

Printed in Hong Kong

Reprinted 1992

Contents

Preface

This book is one of a series for use by students not only as a textbook but also as a guide to good practice in the solution of problems.

The topics in the book have been carefully selected to represent the most popular areas of study in a first year undergraduate, HND, and HNC course in Electrical and Electronic engineering. Each chapter opens with a Fact Sheet containing relevant definitions, principles, theorems and supporting information. This is followed by a set of worked examples illustrating the general area of study covered by the chapter. Each chapter concludes with a selection of unworked problems (with answers). The solutions in the book are the responsibility of the authors.

The topics covered include basic electrical and mechanical units, circuit theory including mesh current and node voltage analysis (incorporating both independent and dependent sources). Alternating waveforms are introduced in a chapter on waveforms and Fourier analysis and, following the treatment of reactance, susceptance and admittance, a.c. circuits are covered in some depth, including series and parallel circuits, resonance, and frequency response. The reader is also introduced to the concept of apparent power, power, reactive VA, and power factor improvement.

Two chapters are devoted to circuit theorems, including mesh current and node voltage analysis applied to a.c. circuits, Millman's theorem, Thévenin's theorem, Norton's theorem, duality, star-mesh and mesh-star transformations, superposition theorem, reciprocity theorem, compensation theorem, and the maximum power transfer theorem. Coupled circuits and the transformer are covered, as are polyphase systems, symmetrical components, and the measurement of power. Transients and the Laplace transform are dealt with in a comprehensive chapter.

Finally, the four appendixes cover complex numbers, matrices, determinants, the use of computer software appropriate to the solution of electric circuits, and partial fractions.

It is a simple matter to watch an expert building a structure; how different it becomes when you are faced with the same problem! So it is with Electric Circuit Analysis. It is easy to read how to solve problems, but solving a problem in practice calls for special abilities. The reader should develop his/her intellectual skills by attempting to solve the problems at the end of each chapter. Each question should be carefully studied, and possible techniques for its solution should be considered (there are often several ways of solving a given problem!); there are no shortcuts to mastering the technique of problem solving. Many of the solutions in this book have been checked using computer software, but not before they have been worked out the hard way using a pen and a calculator.

The authors and publisher wish to thank the Department of Electrical and Electronic Engineering of the Staffordshire Polytechnic and the School of Information Science and Technology of Liverpool Polytechnic for kind permission to publish extracts from examination papers. The questions selected are, in general, either part questions or short questions which ask for a particular type of solution.

Finally, each author would like to thank his wife, for whom the effort was happily made, for their support and forbearance during the writing of the book. The authors would also like to thank Mr W. Roberts for information on SPICE and Andrew Senior for his assistance in the preparation of the book.

1 Basic Concepts and D.C. Circuits

1.1 Fact Sheet

(a) Mechanical Units

All units used by electrical and electronic engineers are part of the SI (Systéme International) system of units. Mechanical units are specified in terms of mass (the kilogramme [kg]), length (the metre [m]), and time (the second [s]). The basic units used are

linear velocity, $v = \delta l / \delta t$ m/s

linear acceleration, $a = \delta v / \delta t$ m/s^2

force, F = mass × acceleration = ma newtons (N)

energy or work, W = force × distance = Fl N m or joules (J)

torque or turning moment, T = force × radius = FR N m

power in a straight line, P = force × velocity = Fv watts (W) or J/s

angular velocity, $\omega = \delta\theta / \delta t$ rad/s

angular acceleration, $\alpha = \delta\omega / \delta t$ rad/s^2

rotary power, $P = T\omega$ W or J/s

(b) Electrical Units

Current (i, I)

The SI unit of current (the *ampere*, unit symbol A) is defined in terms of the force experienced between two parallel current-carrying conductors, and is defined as follows:

When a current of one ampere flows in each of two infinitely long parallel conductors of negligible cross-section placed 1 m apart in a vacuum, the force between the conductors is 2×10^{-7} N per metre length of the conductors.

1

Generally speaking, the *instantaneous value* of an electrical unit, e.g. current, is represented by a lower-case letter e.g., *i*, and the *average value* (and the *r.m.s.* or *effective value* of an alternating unit) is represented by a capital letter e.g., *I*. *Peak* or *maximum values* carry subscripts, e.g., I_p, I_m.

Conventionally, current flows from a positive charge to a negative (or less positive) charge, and the direction of flow is shown by an arrow *on the circuit* (see Figure 1.1). Electron flow is in the opposite direction.

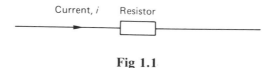

Fig 1.1

E.M.F. and Potential Difference (e, E, v, V)

The energy (be it electrical energy, mechanical energy, chemical energy, heat energy, etc) converted per unit electrical charge is known as the *electromotive force* (e.m.f.). The electrical energy which is converted into heat when a unit charge moves from one point to another in a circuit is known as the *potential difference* (p.d.) between the two points. That is

$$\text{e.m.f. or p.d.} = \frac{\text{energy}}{\text{charge}} \text{ volts (V) or joules/coulomb}$$

or

$$E = W/Q \text{ V}$$

The e.m.f. of a supply source, and the p.d. across a circuit element are shown either by means of the polarity signs + and −, or by means of an arrow by the side of the element, with the arrow head pointing towards the more positive potential; see diagrams (a) and (b) of Figure 1.2 for an e.m.f., and diagrams (c) and (d) for a p.d..

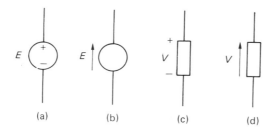

Fig 1.2

Power (p, P)

The unit of power is the *watt* (unit symbol W), and the power consumed in a direct current circuit is given by

$$\text{power (watts)} = \text{voltage (volts)} \times \text{current (amperes)}$$

The instantaneous power, p, consumed is $p = vi$ W, and the average power, P, is given by $P = VI$ W. If the power varies periodically, the average power consumed is

$$P = \frac{1}{T}\int_0^T p \, \mathrm{d}t$$

where T is the periodic time of the power waveform.

When using the current and voltage direction notation outlined earlier, a circuit element *generates power* if the current arrow on the circuit flows out of the + terminal (or the current and voltage arrows point in the same direction); see Figure 1.3(a) for an example. A circuit element *consumes power* if the current arrow on the circuit flows into the + arrow on the element (or the current and voltage arrows associated with the element point in the opposite directions), as shown in Figures 1.3(b) and (c).

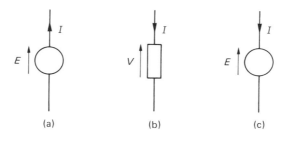

(a)   (b)   (c)

Fig 1.3

Energy (w, W)

The unit of energy is the *joule* (unit symbol J) or watt-second, and the energy consumed by a circuit is the time integral of power, that is

$$W = \int_{t_1}^{t_2} p \, \mathrm{d}t \ \mathrm{J}$$

where W joules is transferred to the circuit between t_1 and t_2. Conversely

$$p = \mathrm{d}w/\mathrm{d}t \ \mathrm{W}$$

If the average power, P, is consumed during a length of time t, then

$$W = Pt \ \mathrm{J}$$

Note: A comprehensive list of basic units is provided in Tables 1.1 to 1.4.

(c)   Ohm's Law and Resistance (*r, R*)

Ohm's law states that the voltage across a conductor is directly proportional to the current in the conductor, i.e.,

$$v = Ri \ \mathrm{V}$$

Table 1.1
Base units

Quantity	Name of unit	Unit symbol
length	metre	m
mass	kilogram	kg
time	second	s
electric current	ampere	A
thermodynamic temperature	kelvin	K
amount of substance	mole	mol
luminous intensity	candela	cd

Supplementary units

Quantity	Name of unit	Unit symbol
plane angle	radian	rad
solid angle	steradian	sr

Table 1.2
Names and symbols for the SI prefixes

Factor	Prefix	Symbol
10^{18}	exa	E
10^{15}	peta	P
10^{12}	tera	T
10^{9}	giga	G
10^{6}	mega	M
10^{3}	kilo	k
10^{-3}	milli	m
10^{-6}	micro	μ
10^{-9}	nano	n
10^{-12}	pico	p
10^{-15}	femto	f
10^{-18}	atto	a

or

$$V = RI \text{ V}$$

where the constant of proportionality, R, is called the *resistance* of the conductor. The unit of resistance is the *ohm* (unit symbol Ω).

(d) Conductance (g, G)

The conductance, G, of a pure resistor is the reciprocal of its resistance. The unit of conductance is the *siemens* (unit symbol S), and

$$G = 1/R \text{ S}$$

Also, $v = i/G$ and $V = I/G$

Table 1.3
Derived units having special names and symbols

Quantity	Name	Symbol	Expression in terms of other SI units	Expression in terms of base (and supplementary) units
frequency	hertz	Hz		$1/s$
force	newton	N		$m\ kg/s^2$
pressure	pascal	Pa	N/m^2	$kg/(m\ s^2)$
energy, work, quantity of heat	joule	J	N m	$m^2\ kg/s^2$
power, energy flux	watt	W	J/s	$m^2\ kg/s^3$
quantity of electricity, electric charge	coulomb	C	A s	s A
electric potential	volt	V	W/A	$m^2\ kg/(s^3\ A)$
electric capacitance	farad	F	C/V	$s^4\ A^2/(m^2\ kg)$
electric resistance	ohm	Ω	V/A	$m^2\ kg/(s^3\ A^2)$
conductance	siemens	S	A/V	$s^3\ A^2/(m^2\ kg)$
magnetix flux	weber	Wb	V s	$m^2\ kg/(s^2\ A)$
magnetic flux density	tesla	T	Wb/m^2	$kg/(s^2\ A)$
inductance	henry	H	Wb/A	$m^2\ kg/(s^2\ A^2)$

Table 1.4
Derived units
Most of these are expressed in terms of units in Table 1.3. Expressions in terms of the base (and supplementary) units are included.

Quantity	Name	Symbol	Expression in terms of base (and supplementary) units
dynamic viscosity	pascal second	Pa s	$kg/(m\ s)$
moment of force	newton metre	N m	$m^2\ kg/s^2$
surface tension	newton per metre	N/m	kg/s^2
heat flux density, irradiance	watt per square metre	W/m^2	kg/s^3
specific heat capacity, specific entropy	joule per kilogram kelvin	J/(kg K)	$m^2/(s^2\ K)$
thermal conductivity	watt per metre kelvin	W/(m K)	$m\ kg/(s^3\ K)$
electric field strength	volt per metre	V/m	$m\ kg/(s^3\ A)$
electric flux density	coulomb per square metre	C/m^2	$s\ A/m^2$
permittivity	farad per metre	F/m	$s^4\ A^2/(m^3\ Kg)$
current density	ampere per square metre	A/m^2	A/m^2
magnetic field strength	ampere per metre	A/m	A/m
permeability	henry per metre	H/m	$m\ kg/(s^2\ A^2)$
molar entropy, molar heat capacity	joule per mole kelvin	J/(mol K)	$m^2\ kg/(s^2\ K\ mol)$
angular velocity	radian per second	rad/s	rad/s
angular acceleration	radian per second squared	rad/s^2	rad/s^2
radiance	watt per square metre steradian	$W/(m^2\ sr)$	$kg/(s^3\ sr)$

(e) Active and Passive Circuit Elements

An *active element* in a circuit is one capable of delivering power to an external device; a battery and a generator are examples of active elements. A *passive element* is one which is only capable of receiving power; a resistor is an example of a passive element. There are, however, types of passive element, such as an inductor or a capacitor, which are capable of storing a limited amount of energy, and of returning it (or part of it) to an external element.

Additionally, active elements are capable of receiving power; for example, an accumulator receives power when it is being electrically charged.

(f) Voltage and Current Sources

Independent Ideal Sources

In an independent source, the voltage produced by the source is completely independent of the current through the source, and vice versa. There are two types of independent source, namely a *voltage source* and a *current source*. An ideal voltage source is one having zero internal resistance (or impedance if a.c.), and an ideal current source has infinite internal resistance (or impedance if a.c.).

A circuit symbol for a unidirectional (d.c.) independent voltage source is shown in Figures 1.4(a) and 1.4(b), and that for an independent a.c. voltage source is shown in Figures (c) and (d). Figures 1.4(e) and (f) respectively represent a unidirectional independent current source, and an independent a.c. current source.

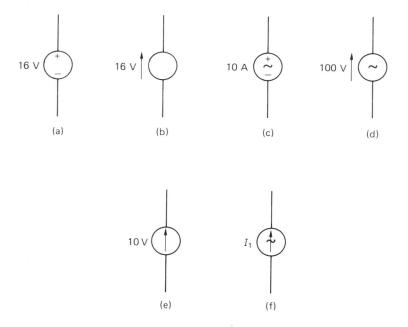

Fig 1.4

Dependent Ideal Sources

A dependent source or *controlled source*, which may either be a voltage source or a current source, is one in which the source quantity is dependent on a voltage or a current at some other point in the circuit.

Circuit symbols for the following sources are shown in Figure 1.5: (a) and (b), a unidirectional voltage source; (c) and (d), an alternating voltage source; (e), a unidirectional current source; and (f), an alternating current source. The voltage produced by the source in Figures 1.5(a) and (b) depend on an external current, the voltage produced by the source in Figures 1.5(c) and (d) depend on an external voltage; the current produced by Figures 1.5(e) and (f) depend on an external voltage.

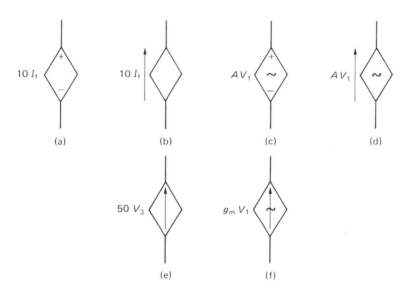

Fig 1.5

Practical Sources

These exhibit the property of internal resistance, and are represented by the combination of an ideal source (either dependent or independent) and a resistance (or impedance if a.c.) or a conductance (or admittance if a.c.). Practical sources are discussed in sections (d) to (f) of the Fact Sheet in Chapter 9.

(g) Inductors and Capacitors

These are passive elements capable of storing a limited energy for a limited time. In the case of an inductor, the energy is stored in its magnetic field; since a practical inductor is wound with wire, it has the property of resistance as well as inductance. A capacitor stores energy in the electric field between the plates.

Inductance

When current flows in the winding of an inductor, a magnetic flux is produced. When the current changes, the magnetic flux linking with the coil changes, resulting in an e.m.f. being induced in the inductor itself. This is known as the *self-induced e.m.f.*, v_L, where

$$v_L = L \frac{di}{dt} \text{ V}$$

L is the *inductance* (or *self-inductance*) of the coil, and di/dt is the rate of change of current in the coil.

The energy, w, stored in an inductor is

$$w = \tfrac{1}{2} L i^2 \text{ J}$$

Capacitance

The change in charge, dq coulombs, stored by a capacitor is

$$dq = C \, dv$$

where C is the *capacitance* in farads (unit symbol F) of the capacitor, and dv is the change in voltage between the plates of the capacitor. The current flowing through the capacitor is given by

$$i = \frac{dq}{dt} = C \frac{dv}{dt} \text{ A}$$

The energy, w, stored by a capacitor is

$$w = \tfrac{1}{2} C v^2 \text{ J}$$

(h) Mutual Inductance (M)

When the flux produced by the current in one circuit links with a conductor in another circuit, an e.m.f. is induced in the second circuit. The e.m.f. is said to be *mutually induced*; the two circuits are said to be *magnetically coupled*, and there is a *mutual inductance*, M henry, between the circuits.

More details of mutual inductance are given in Chapter 11.

(i) Double Suffix Voltage Notation

In Figure 1.6 the voltage between nodes 1 and 2 is V_x volts, and the voltage of *node 2 with respect to node 1* is written as V_{21}. With the polarity shown, $V_{21} = +V_x$. Similarly, V_{12} is the voltage of node 1 with respect to node 2, and $V_{12} = -V_x$. Also V_{31} is the voltage of node 3 with respect to node 1, etc.

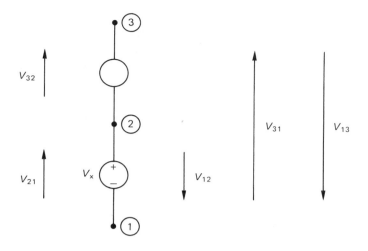

Fig 1.6

(j)   Kirchhoff's Laws

The majority of electrical circuits consist of elements which are connected together; such a circuit is known as a *lumped-constant* network, and is the type we deal with here.

A *node* in a circuit is a point where two circuit elements are physically connected together. A node where three or more elements are connected together is known as a *principal node*. The circuit in Figure 1.7(a) is redrawn in Figure 1.7(b) to illustrate the four nodes in the circuit; whilst node 3 is a simple node, nodes 0, 1, and 2 are principal nodes.

Where voltages are specified with respect to a particular node, then that node is referred to as the *reference node*. If node 0 in Figure 1.7(b) is the reference node, the voltage V_{10} can simply be specified as V_1, V_{20} can be referred to as V_2, etc.

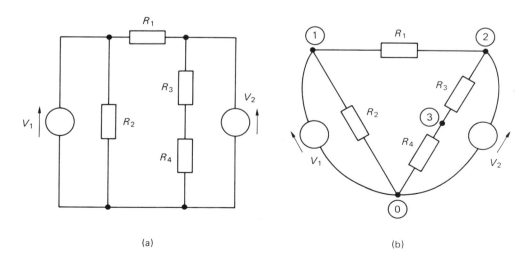

(a)

(b)

Fig 1.7

A *branch* of a network is a path between two nodes. In Figure 1.7, for example, the resistor R_3 is the element in one path, and the element R_2 is the element in another path. A *closed path* or *closed loop* or *closed circuit* (which can also simply be called a *path* or *loop*) is a path in a circuit which starts at one node and finishes at the same node, *and encounters some of the nodes once only*. For example, in Figure 1.7(b), one path (starting at node 0) contains the elements R_2, R_1, R_3 and R_4; another path (starting at the same node) contains V_1, R_1 and V_2.

Kirchhoff's Current Law (KCL)

This states that the algebraic sum of the currents entering any node is equal to the algebraic sum of the currents leaving the node, or

$$\Sigma \text{ currents entering} = \Sigma \text{ currents leaving}$$

In Figure 1.8,

$$I_1 + I_3 = I_2 + I_4$$

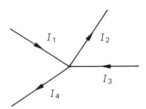

Fig 1.8

Kirchhoff's Voltage Law (KVL)

The algebraic sum of the voltage rises or e.m.f.s in any closed path is equal to the algebraic sum of the potential drops in the closed path, or

$$\Sigma \text{ potential rises} = \Sigma \text{ potential drops}$$

In Figure 1.9,

$$V_1 - V_2 = IR_1 + IR_2$$

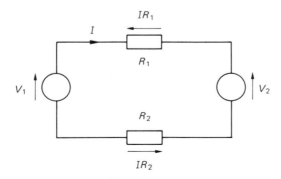

Fig 1.9

Alternatively, we may say that the sum of the potential rises and potential drops around any closed path is zero. In Figure 1.9, this results in an equation of the type

$$V_1 - IR_1 - V_2 - IR_2 = 0$$

(k) Power Consumed by a D.C. Circuit

The power consumed in a d.c. circuit is

$$P = VI = I^2R = V^2/R \text{ watt (W)}$$

where V is the voltage (V) across the circuit, I is the current (A) in the circuit, and R is the resistance (ohm) of the circuit.

(l) Energy Consumed by a D.C. Circuit

The energy consumed is

$$W = VIt = I^2Rt = V^2t/R \text{ watt s or joule (J)}$$

where t is the time in seconds.

In the case of electrical power installations, power is measured in kW and time is measured in hours, and the relation between the energy in kWh and the energy in J is

$$1 \text{ kWh} = 1 \text{ kW} \times 1 \text{ h} = 3.6 \text{ MJ}$$

(m) The Series Circuit

In a *series-connected circuit*, each element in the circuit carries the *same current*. The circuit in Figure 1.10 is an example of a series circuit.

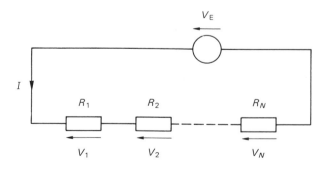

Fig 1.10

If there are N resistors in the circuit, the *equivalent resistance*, R_E, of the circuit is

$$R_E = R_1 + R_2 + \ldots + R_N \text{ ohm}$$

Applying KVL to the circuit yields

$$V_E = V_1 + V_2 + \ldots + V_N$$
$$= IR_1 + IR_2 + \ldots + IR_N \text{ V}$$

(n) Voltage Division in a Series Circuit

In a series circuit, the current drawn by the circuit is

$$I = V_E/R_E = V_1/R_1 = V_2/R_2 = \ldots = V_N/R_N \text{ A}$$

where V_E is the effective voltage across the circuit, V_1 is the voltage across R_1, etc, and V_N is the voltage across R_N, hence

$$V_N = V_E \times \frac{R_N}{R_E} = V_E \times \frac{R_N}{R_1 + R_2 + \ldots R_N} \text{ V}$$

(o) The Parallel Circuit

In a *parallel-connected circuit*, each circuit element has the *same voltage across it*. The circuit in Figure 1.11 is an example of a parallel-connected circuit. Applying KCL to the circuit yields

$$I = I_1 + I_2 + \ldots + I_N \text{ A}$$

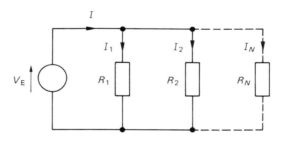

Fig 1.11

The *reciprocal of the equivalent resistance* of the parallel circuit is given by

$$\frac{1}{R_E} = \frac{1}{R_1} + \frac{1}{R_2} + \ldots + \frac{1}{R_N} \text{ S}$$

or

$$G_E = G_1 + G_2 + \ldots + G_N \text{ S}$$

where G_E is the *equivalent conductance* of the complete circuit, and G_N is the conductance of the nth branch.

In the special case of two resistors in parallel,

$$R_E = \frac{R_1 \times R_2}{R_1 + R_2} \text{ ohm}$$

or

$$G_E = G_1 + G_2 \text{ S}$$

(p) Division of Current in a Parallel Circuit

In a parallel circuit with N branches (see Figure 1.11), the voltage across the circuit is

$$V_E = IR_E = I_1R_1 = I_2R_2 = \ldots = I_NR_N \text{ V}$$

or

$$I_N = I\frac{R_E}{R_N} \text{ A}$$

Alternatively, using conductance values,

$$I_N = I\frac{G_N}{G_E} \text{ A}$$

In the special case of a two-branch parallel circuit,

$$I_1 = I\frac{R_2}{R_1 + R_2} = I\frac{G_1}{G_1 + G_2} \text{ A}$$

$$I_2 = I\frac{R_1}{R_1 + R_2} = I\frac{G_2}{G_1 + G_2} \text{ A}$$

1.2 Worked Examples

Example 1.1

An electrical motor develops a torque of 200 N m at a shaft speed of 1000 rev/min. If the motor input power is 24.6 kW, calculate the efficiency of the motor, and the heat loss per minute by the motor (assume that the motor temperature remains constant).

Solution 1.1

The power output can be calculated as follows:

$$\text{shaft speed} = 1000 \text{ rev/min} = 1000/60 \text{ rev/s}$$

$$= 1000 \times 2\pi/60 \text{ rad/s} = 104.72 \text{ rad/s}$$

$$\text{power output} = \omega T = 104.72 \times 200 = 20\,944 \text{ W} = 20.944 \text{ kW}$$

and

$$\text{motor efficiency, } \eta = \frac{\text{output power}}{\text{input power}} = \frac{20.944}{24.6}$$

$$= 0.851 \text{ per unit (p.u.) or } 85.1 \text{ per cent}$$

The power loss in the motor is $24.6 - 20.944 = 3.656$ kW and energy loss per minute $= 3.656 \times 60 = 219.36$ kW s or kJ.

Example 1.2

A direct current electrically-driven pump delivers 2 m³ of water per minute through a total head (suction and delivery) of 50 m. If the efficiency of the motor is 85 per cent, and that of the pump is 90 per cent, calculate the output power of the pump, the input power to the motor, the current drawn by the motor if the supply voltage is 500 V, and the electrical energy consumed by the pumping system during a 12-hour period. The mass of 1 m³ of water is 1000 kg.

Solution 1.2

The weight of water pumped per minute is $2 \times 1000 = 2000$ kg. Hence, the output from the pump is

$$\frac{g \times 2000 \times \text{head}}{60} = \frac{9.81 \times 2000 \times 50}{60} = 16\ 350 \text{ N m/s or W}$$

The overall efficiency of the motor and pump is
0.85 p.u. $\times$ 0.9 p.u. $= 0.765$ p.u. or 76.5 per cent.
Therefore,

$$\text{input power} = \frac{\text{output power}}{\text{efficiency}} = \frac{16\ 350}{0.765} = 21\ 373 \text{ W or } 21.373 \text{ kW}$$

and

$$\text{current drawn by the motor} = \frac{\text{power}}{\text{voltage}} = \frac{21\ 373}{500} = 42.75 \text{ A}$$

The energy consumed during a 12-hour period is
input power in kW $\times$ time $= 21.373 \times 12 = 256.5$ kW h.

Example 1.3

A battery is charged at a constant current of 10 A for 4 hours, the average terminal voltage of the battery being 20 V. Calculate the electrical charge absorbed by the battery, the power consumed, and the energy consumed.

Solution 1.3

$$\text{electrical charge} = It = 10 \times (4 \times 60 \times 60) = 144\ 000\ \text{C}$$

$$\text{power consumed} = VI = 20 \times 10 = 200\ \text{W}$$

$$\text{energy consumed} = VIt = 200 \times 4 = 800\ \text{W h}$$

$$= 200 \times (4 \times 60 \times 60) = 2\ 880\ 000\ \text{Ws or J}$$

This example illustrates the simplicity in some cases of using the more popular engineering units rather than fundamental scientific units, i.e., the W h rather than the J.

Example 1.4

In a resistive circuit, the voltage varies with time according to $v = 25 \sin 6.284ft$, where f is the supply frequency in hertz (Hz), and t is time in s. Deduce an expression for the current (i) in the circuit, the instantaneous power (p) consumed by the circuit, and the average power (P), given that the circuit resistance is 100 ohm, and the frequency is 50 Hz.

Solution 1.4

$$i = \frac{v}{R} = \frac{25 \sin (6.284 \times 50)t}{100} = 0.25 \sin 314.2t\ \text{A}$$

$$p = vi = (25 \sin 314.2t)(0.25 \sin 314.2t)$$

$$= 6.25 \sin^2 314.2t\ \text{W}$$

$$P = \frac{1}{2\pi} \int_0^{2\pi} 6.25 \sin^2 (\omega t) \cdot d(\omega t) \quad \text{where } \omega = 314.2$$

$$= \frac{6.25}{2\pi} \int_0^{2\pi} \tfrac{1}{2}(1 - \cos 2\omega t) \cdot d(\omega t)$$

$$= \frac{6.25}{4\pi} \left[\omega t - \frac{\sin 2\omega t}{2} \right]_0^{2\pi} = \frac{6.25}{2} = 3.125\ \text{W}$$

Example 1.5

An electrical circuit carries a current of 15 mA for 1 hour. If the power consumed by the circuit is 22.5 mW, calculate the energy consumed by the circuit, and the resistance of the circuit.

Solution 1.5

Energy, W = power × time = 0.0225 × (60 × 60) = 81 J

   Now,

$$\text{power, } P = VI = (IR) = I^2R$$

   Hence,

$$R = \frac{\text{power}}{I^2} = \frac{0.0225}{0.015^2} = 100 \text{ ohm}$$

Example 1.6

Calculate the power absorbed by each of the four circuit elements in Figure 1.12.

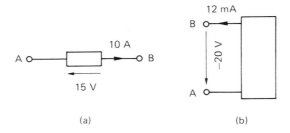

(a)   (b)

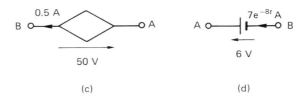

(c)   (d)

Fig 1.12

Solution 1.6

The power absorbed by each element is $P = VI$. In each diagram, the terminal indicated by the arrowhead is given the numerical potential which is written by the side of the potential arrow.

   The power *consumed* in each case is

(a) $P = 15 \times 10 = 150$ W
(b) $P = (-20) \times 0.012 = -0.24$ W
(c) $P = 50 \times 0.5 = 25$ W
(d) $P = 6 \times (-7e^{-8t}) = -42e^{-8t}$ W

   In cases **(b)** and **(d)** the *power absorbed is negative*, that is to say these two circuits *generate power* or *supply power*.

Example 1.7

Calculate the power consumed by each element in Figure 1.13.

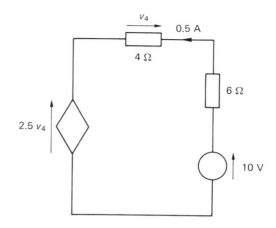

Fig 1.13

Solution 1.7

The power consumed by the resistors is as follows:

$$\text{4 ohm resistor: } P = I^2R = 0.5^2 \times 4 = 1 \text{ W}$$

$$\text{6 ohm resistor: } P = I^2R = 0.5^2 \times 6 = 1.5 \text{ W}$$

The power consumed by the 10 V independent voltage source is $P = 10 \times (-0.5) = -5$ W, i.e., it generates or supplies 5 W to the circuit. The power consumed by the voltage-controlled dependent voltage source is

$$P = 0.5 \times 2.5v_4$$

where $v_4 = 4 \times 0.5 = 2$ V. That is, the power consumed is

$$P = 0.5 \times (2.5 \times 2) = 2.5 \text{ W}$$

Note: the total power *consumed* by the circuit is

$$1 + 1.5 + 2.5 = 5 \text{ W}$$

which is equal to the power *generated* by the independent voltage source; that is, for the complete circuit, Σpower $= 0$.

Example 1.8

A voltage of $v = 200 \sin 1000t$ V is applied to (**a**) an inductor of inductance 0.1 H, (**b**) a capacitor of 0.1 microfarad. Deduce, in each case, an expression for the current i, and the instantaneous power p. Calculate the average power P consumed.

Solution 1.8

(a)   For the inductor

$$v_L = L \frac{di}{dt}$$

Hence

$$i = \frac{1}{L} \int v_L \, dt = \frac{1}{0.1} \int 200 \sin 1000t \, dt = \frac{200}{0.1} \left(\frac{-\cos 1000t}{1000} \right)$$

$$= -2 \cos 1000t \text{ A}$$

and

$$p = vi = (200 \sin 1000t)(-2 \cos 1000t)$$

$$= -400 \sin 1000t \times \cos 1000t = -200 \sin 2(1000t)$$

$$= -200 \sin 2000t \text{ W}$$

Since the power waveform is sinusoidal, the average power consumed during each cycle is zero, hence $P = 0$.

Note that:

$$\frac{1}{2\pi} \int_0^{2\pi} \sin 2\omega t \, d(\omega t) = 0$$

(b)   For the capacitor

$$i = C \frac{dv}{dt} = (0.1 \times 10^{-6}) \times \frac{d(200 \sin 1000t)}{dt}$$

$$= 20 \times 10^{-6} \times \frac{d(\sin 1000t)}{dt} = 20 \times 10^{-3} \cos 1000t \text{ A}$$

and

$$p = vi = (200 \sin 1000t)(20 \times 10^{-3} \cos 1000t)$$

$$= 4 \sin 1000t \times \cos 1000t = 2 \sin 2(1000t) = 2 \sin 2000t \text{ W}$$

As with the inductor, the average power (P) consumed during each cycle of the waveform is zero.

Example 1.9

Determine the value of I_3 in Figure 1.14.

Solution 1.9

Since the resistor values in the network are unknown, it is impossible to estimate the current distribution within the network, but KCL can be applied to the network as a whole as follows.

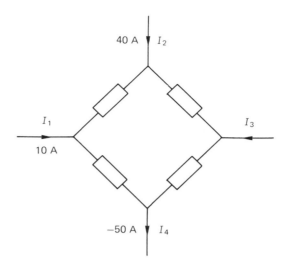

Fig 1.14

$$I_1 + I_2 + I_3 = I_4$$

or

$$10 + 40 + I_3 = -50$$

Hence,

$$I_3 = -50 - (10 + 40) = -100 \text{ A}$$

That is $I_3 = 100$ A flowing away from the network.

Example 1.10

Write down the mesh current equation for the loop ABCDA in Figure 1.15.

Solution 1.10

Starting at any point, KVL can be applied to the loop. If we commence at point A, and move around the loop in a clockwise direction until point A is reached again, we get the mesh equation

$$-20I_1 + 30(I_2 - I_1) + 2v - 10 + 40(I_3 - I_1) - 10I_1 = 0$$

where $v = -50I_2$. Alternatively, starting at point D, and moving around the loop in an anticlockwise direction, the mesh equation is

$$40(I_1 - I_3) + 10 - 2v + 30(I_1 - I_2) + 20I_1 + 10I_1 = 0$$

Example 1.11

For the circuit in Figure 1.16, calculate the values of I_1 to I_6, and the voltages V_{CE}, V_{DE}, V_{DA} and V_{BD}.

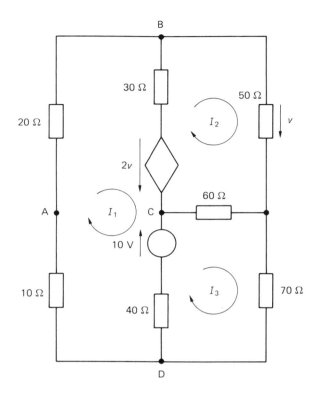

Fig 1.15

Solution 1.11

For the branch ABC,

$$R_{ABC} = 50 + 50 = 100 \text{ ohms}$$

Hence,

$$I_2 = \frac{10}{100} = 0.1 \text{ A}$$

The effective resistance of the 3-branch parallel circuit is calculated from

$$\frac{1}{R_{DE}} = \frac{1}{20} + \frac{1}{40} + \frac{1}{50} = 0.05 + 0.025 + 0.02 = 0.095 \text{ S}$$

Hence,

$$R_{DE} = 1/0.095 = 10.53 \text{ ohm}$$

For the branch ADEC,

$$R_{ADEC} = 10 + 10.53 + 60 = 80.53 \text{ ohm}$$

Therefore,

$$I_3 = \frac{10}{80.53} = 0.1242 \text{ A}$$

The current in each arm of the 3-branch parallel circuit is calculated using the technique described in section (p) of the Fact Sheet as follows.

$$I_4 = I_3 \frac{R_{\mathrm{DE}}}{R_4} = 0.1242 \times \frac{10.53}{20} = 0.0654 \text{ A}$$

$$I_5 = I_3 \frac{R_{\mathrm{DE}}}{R_5} = 0.1242 \times \frac{10.53}{40} = 0.0327 \text{ A}$$

$$I_6 = I_3 \frac{R_{\mathrm{DE}}}{R_6} = 0.1242 \times \frac{10.53}{50} = 0.0261 \text{ A}$$

Note:

$$I_4 + I_5 + I_6 = 0.1242 = I_3$$

Applying KCL to node A yields

$$I_1 = I_2 + I_3 = 0.1 + 0.1242 = 0.2242 \text{ A}$$

Referring to the inset in Figure 1.16, I_3 flows from A to C, so that E is positive with respect to C, that is

$$V_{\mathrm{CE}} = -I_3 \times R_{\mathrm{EC}} = -0.1242 \times 60 = -7.452 \text{ V}$$

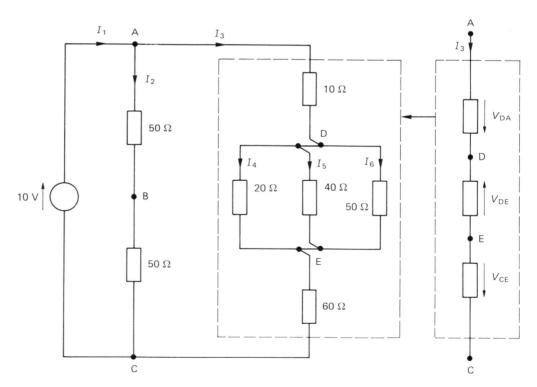

Fig 1.16

Also,

$$V_{\mathrm{DE}} = I_3 \times R_{\mathrm{DE}} = 0.1242 \times 10.53 = 1.308 \text{ V}$$

$$V_{\mathrm{DA}} = -I_3 \times R_{\mathrm{AD}} = -0.1242 \times 10 = -1.242 \text{ V}$$

Note:
$$V_{EC} = (-V_{CE}) \text{ and } V_{AD} = (-V_{DA})$$

and

$$V_{EC} + V_{DE} + V_{AD} = 10.002 \text{ V}$$

which, within the rounding errors of the calculation, is equal to the supply voltage of 10 V.

One method of calculating V_{BD} is as shown in Figure 1.17. Starting at point D in the circuit and move towards B, the equation is as follows.

$$V_{BD} = -V_{DE} - V_{EC} + V_{BC}$$

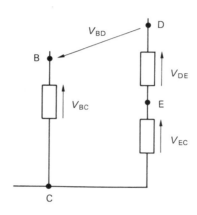

Fig 1.17

Now,

$$B_{BC} = 50I_2 = 50 \times 0.1 = 5 \text{ V}$$

Hence,

$$V_{BD} = -1.308 - 7.452 + 5 = -3.76 \text{ V}$$

1.3 Unworked Problems

Problem 1.1

A portable field transmitter is powered by a hand-operated generator. If the radiated power of the transmitter is 20 W, and the overall efficiency of the unit is 50 per cent, calculate the speed at which the crank arm must be rotated if its length is 25 cm. The operator applies a constant force of 45 N to the crank handle. What energy is required to operate the transmitter during a 5 minute transmission period?

[3.56 rad/s or 34 rev/min; 3.33 W h or 12 000 J]

Problem 1.2

The charge entering an electronic circuit is given by $10 \cos 500\pi t$ millicoulombs. Calculate the charge transferred between $t = 2$ ms and $t = 4$ ms. What is the value of charge at $t = 4.6$ ms?
[20 mC; 5.878 mC]

Problem 1.3

The voltage and current waveforms associated with a circuit element are shown in Figure 1.18. Calculate the energy absorbed by the element in the time interval shown.
[0.333 J]

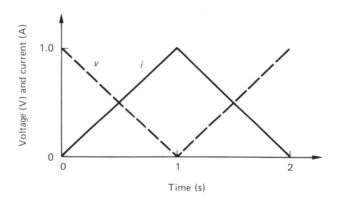

Fig 1.18

Problem 1.4

The voltage and current waveforms in Figure 1.19(a) are associated with an electrical circuit. Calculate the energy delivered to the circuit in the 2 s interval shown in the figure. Calculate also the peak power consumed, and draw the waveform of the power delivered to the circuit.
[166.67 J; 200 W; the waveform of the power consumed is shown in Figure 1.19(b).]

Problem 1.5

In Figure 1.20, calculate the value of i and v, and the power consumed by each element in the circuit.
[$i = -3$ A; $v = 1.534$ V; power consumption, 5 ohm resistor 45 W, 4 ohm resistor 0.585 W, 2 ohm resistor 72 W, 10 ohm resistor 0.61 W, 4 V source 1.53 W, $4v$ source -15.16 W, 3 A source -45 W, $2i$ source 176.82 W]

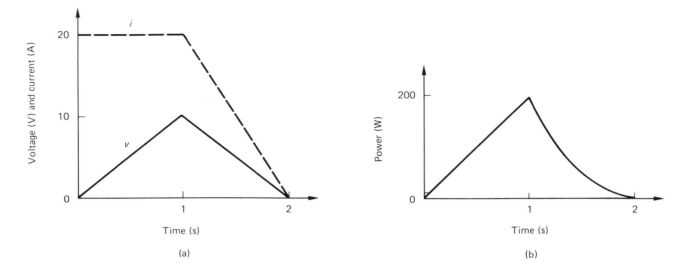

Fig 1.19

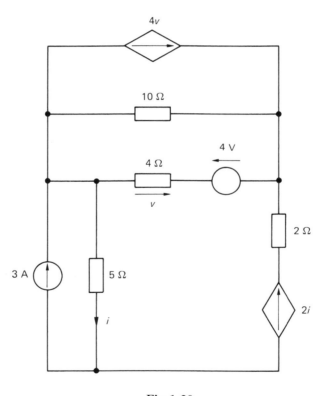

Fig 1.20

Problem 1.6

A current of $i = 10 \sin 1000t$ flows in a pure inductor of 0.1 H. What is the first instant of time after $t = 0$ that the power absorbed by the inductor is (a) 2000 W, (b) -2000 W? What peak power is absorbed by the inductor?
[(a) 0.21 ms; (b) 1.78 ms; 5000 W]

24

Problem 1.7

For the current waveform in Figure 1.21, determine the charge transferred between $t = 0$ and (a) $t = 3$ s, and (b) $t = 10$ s.
[(a) 1.5 C; (b) -10 C]

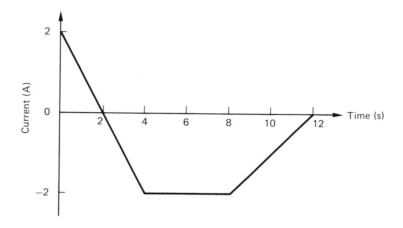

Fig 1.21

Problem 1.8

Calculate the value of R in Figure 1.22. If the voltage produced by the dependent voltage source in the circuit was reduced to $2v_1$, what would be the new value of R for the current in the 0.01 S conductance to remain unchanged?
[125 ohm; 50 ohm]

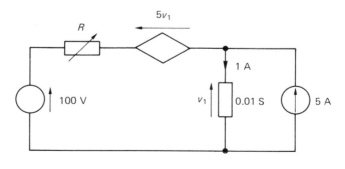

Fig 1.22

Problem 1.9

Calculate the value of V_{AB} in Figure 1.23.
[7 V]

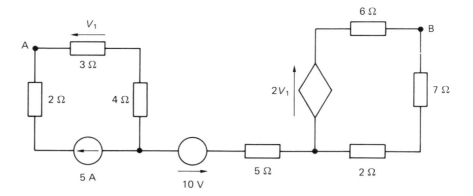

Fig 1.23

Problem 1.10

In Figure 1.24, determine the current in each element connected to node X. Also state which of the elements A, B and C absorb power and which generate power. [$I_A = -4.45$ A; $I_B = 2.385$ A; $I_C = -0.7$ A; $I_3 = 2.765$ A; B absorbs power, A and C generate power.]

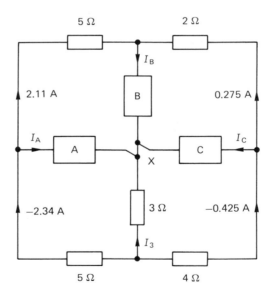

Fig 1.24

Problem 1.11

Using the methods described earlier for current and voltage division, calculate the current in each element in Figure 1.25. Calculate also V_{AB}, V_{CB}, and V_{CD}. [$I_1 = 3.644$ A; $I_2 = 0.607$ A; $I_3 = 0.749$ A, $I_4 = 0.4$ A; $I_5 = 0.349$ A; $V_{AB} = 1.82$ V; $V_{CB} = -2.43$ V; $V_{CD} = 0.24$ V]

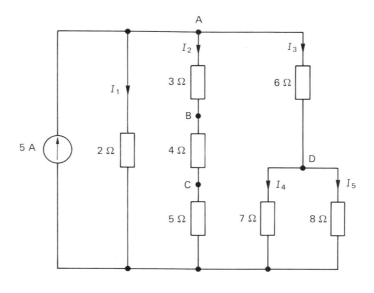

Fig 1.25

Problem 1.12

(a)   A two-branch parallel circuit containing a 12 ohm resistor in one branch, and an 8 ohm resistor in the other, draws a current of 30 A. Calculate the current in the 8 ohm resistor. (b)   A circuit comprises a 0.4 S conductance and a 0.2 S conductance in parallel with one another; if the 0.2 S conductance carries a current of 2 A, determine the current in the 0.4 S conductance. (c)   Calculate the current I in Figure 1.26.

(Staffordshire Polytechnic)

[(a) 18 A; (b) 4 A; (c) 5 A]

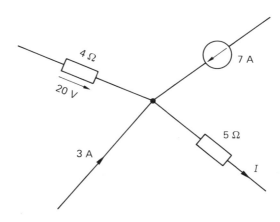

Fig 1.26

Problem 1.13

Calculate V_{AB} in Figure 1.27.

(Staffordshire Polytechnic)

[6 V]

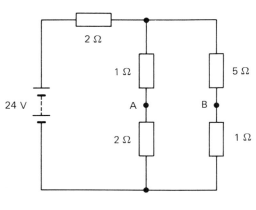

Fig 1.27

Problem 1.14

The current wave shown in Figure 1.28 flows in a series circuit containing a resistor of 2 ohm resistance, and a 2 mH inductance. Construct the waveform of the voltage across R, the voltage across L, and the total voltage across the circuit. Calculate the average value of the voltage across the circuit.

(Staffordshire Polytechnic)

[16.67 V]

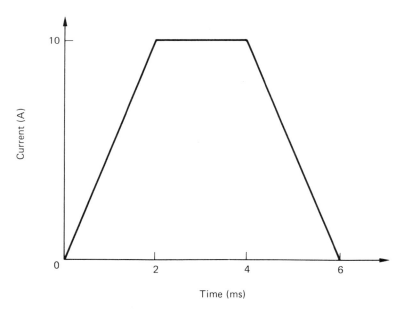

Fig 1.28

28

Problem 1.15

A circuit contains a two-branch parallel circuit, which is in series with two other resistors of value 2 ohm and 1 ohm. The parallel circuit contains a 3 ohm resistor in one branch, and a 6 ohm resistor in the other branch. If the complete circuit is energized by a 10 V d.c. source, calculate the current in each branch of the parallel circuit.

(Staffordshire Polytechnic)

$[I_3 = 1.333 \text{ A}; I_6 = 0.667 \text{ A}]$

Problem 1.16

If the supply voltage to the circuit in Problem 1.15 is changed to 24 V, and the 2 ohm resistor is replaced by a resistor R of unknown value, calculate the value of R if the power dissipated in the 3 ohm resistor in the parallel circuit is 12 W.

(Staffordshire Polytechnic)

[5 ohm]

Problem 1.17

A 2 ohm resistance is connected in series with a resistor R of unknown value to a 10 V d.c. supply. If the power dissipated in R is 8 W, calculate the two possible values of R.

(Staffordshire Polytechnic)

[8 ohm or 0.5 ohm]

2 Mesh Current and Node Voltage Analysis

2.1 Fact Sheet

(a) Mesh Current Analysis

Mesh current analysis can only be applied to a *planar circuit*, i.e. a circuit which can be drawn on a plane surface. The circuit drawn in full line in Figure 2.1 is a planar circuit. However, if the branch shown in broken line between B and E is added, the circuit becomes nonplanar, and mesh current analysis cannot be used to analyse it.

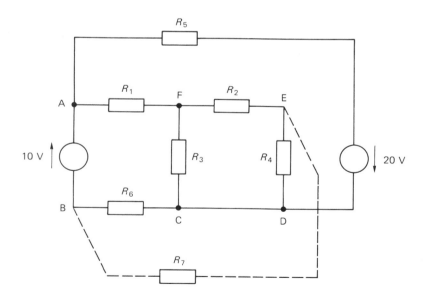

Fig 2.1

A mesh is a property of a planar circuit, and is not defined for a nonplanar circuit. A *mesh* is a loop which does not contain any other loops within it. The circuit drawn in full line in Figure 2.1 contains three meshes, namely the loops

ABCFA, FCDEF, and AFEDA. The loop ABCDEFA is not a mesh because it contains another loop within it.

A method of obtaining a set of mesh current equations for the solution of a circuit is as follows.

1. Draw a labelled circuit diagram.

2. Assign a current (I_1, I_2, ... I_N), circulating in a *clockwise direction* to each of the N meshes.

3. If the circuit contains only voltage sources, apply KVL to each mesh (see Example 2.1 and also Section (b) of this Fact Sheet for a circuit containing only independent voltage sources, or Worked Example 2.2 for an illustration containing a dependent voltage source).

4. If the circuit contains current sources, replace each source by an open circuit circuit; the mesh currents assigned in step 2 above should not be changed. Each source current should then be related to the mesh currents in step 2 above (see Worked Examples 2.3 and 2.4 for illustrations of current sources in a circuit). If a current source is a practical source (see Chapter 9 for details), it can be converted to its equivalent practical voltage source, and dealt with as outlined in step 3 above.

(b) Mesh Equations for a Network Containing Only Independent Voltage Sources

When the above steps are applied to the circuit in Figure 2.2, the following equations are obtained and, by a deductive reasoning, we obtain a method of writing the equations down by visual inspection. The mesh equations for the three loops are

$$E_A - E_B = I_1(R_A + R_B) - I_2 R_B$$
$$0 = - I_1 R_B + I_2(R_B + R_C + R_D) - I_3 R_D$$
$$-E_C = - I_2 R_D + I_3(R_D + R_E)$$

Writing the equations in matrix form gives (see Appendix 2 for details),

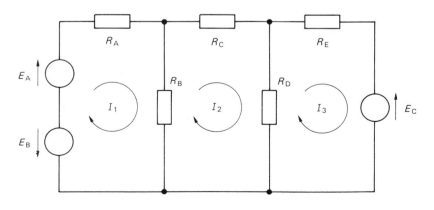

Fig 2.2

$$\begin{bmatrix} E_A - E_B \\ 0 \\ -E_C \end{bmatrix} = \begin{bmatrix} R_A + R_B & -R_B & 0 \\ -R_B & R_B + R_C + R_D & -R_D \\ 0 & -R_D & R_D + R_E \end{bmatrix} \begin{bmatrix} I_1 \\ I_2 \\ I_3 \end{bmatrix}$$

and when written in generalized matrix form they become

$$\begin{bmatrix} E_1 \\ E_2 \\ E_3 \end{bmatrix} = \begin{bmatrix} R_{11} & R_{12} & R_{13} \\ R_{21} & R_{22} & R_{23} \\ R_{31} & R_{32} & R_{33} \end{bmatrix} \begin{bmatrix} I_1 \\ I_2 \\ I_3 \end{bmatrix}$$

where E_1 is the sum of all the source voltages driving I_1, in a *clockwise direction*, i.e., $E_1 = E_A - E_B$, whilst E_2 and E_3 are the sum of the source voltages driving I_2 and I_3, respectively, in a clockwise direction.

R_{11}, R_{22} and R_{33} are the *self-resistances* of the meshes in which I_1, I_2 and I_3, respectively flow.

R_{ij} ($i \neq j$), i.e., the resistance at the intersection of row i and column j, is $(-1) \times$ the resistance which is mutual to the meshes in which I_i and I_j flow. That is $R_{12} = -R_B$, $R_{32} = -R_D$. It should be noted that for all ij, $R_{ij} = R_{ji}$.

Any element for which $R_{ij} = R_{ji}$ is called a *bilateral element*; i.e., they can be connected into the circuit in either direction, and they still have the same result. A network containing only bilateral elements is known as a *bilateral circuit*.

(c) Node Voltage Analysis

Node voltage analysis uses KCL to evaluate the voltages at the principal nodes in a circuit. The circuit is generally drawn using current sources; however, where voltage sources are involved, special techniques are involved (see the method outlined below, and the examples referred to in the text).

The basic circuit in Figure 2.3(a) is redrawn in Figure 2.3(b) to show the three nodes more clearly; in addition, the resistance values are converted into conductances.

A method of determining a set of node voltage equations for the solution of a circuit is as follows.

1. Draw a labelled circuit diagram, and mark the principal nodes on it. If there are N principal nodes, $(N-1)$ equations are needed to solve the circuit. Select one of the principal nodes as the reference node.

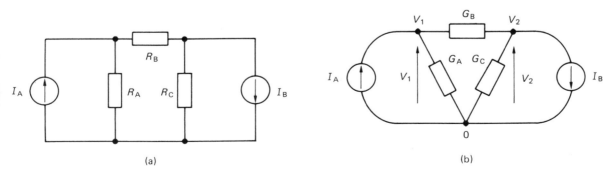

(a)   (b)

Fig 2.3

2. If the circuit contains only current sources, apply KCL to each of the
    non-reference nodes. If the circuit contains depenent current sources (see
    Worked Example 2.6), relate the source current to the unknown node
    voltages.

3. If the circuit contains voltage sources (see Worked Example 2.7), replace
    each source by a short circuit; the node voltages assigned in step 1 must
    not be changed. Each voltage source should be related to the unknown
    node voltages assigned in step 1 above. If a voltage source is a practical
    source, it can be converted to its equivalent current source (see Chapter 9
    for details) and dealt with as outlined in step 2 above.

(d)   Node Voltage Equations for a Network Containing Only Independent Current Sources

Let us determine the node voltage equations for the circuit in Figure 2.4, from
which it is possible to deduce a method of writing down the equations by visual
inspection.

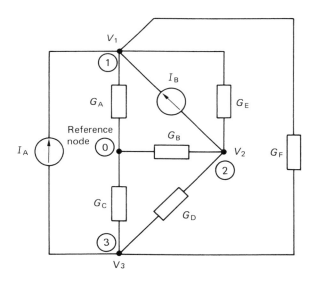

Fig 2.4

Voltages V_1 (= V_{10}), V_2 (= V_{20}) and V_3 (= V_{30}) are shown at nodes 1, 2 and 3,
respectively, and node 0 is taken as the reference node. Applying KCL to each
non-reference node in turn results in the following.

Node 1: Here, current sources I_A and I_B supply current to the node, so that
$I_A + I_B$ is shown on the left-hand side of the equation.

$$I_A + I_B = G_A V_1 + G_E(V_1 - V_2) + G_F(V_1 - V_3)$$

$$= (G_A + G_E + G_F)V_1 - G_E V_2 - G_F V_3$$

Node 2: At this node, I_B flows away from the node, so that a current of $-I_B$ is shown flowing towards the node.

$$-I_B = G_E(V_2 - V_1) + G_B V_2 + G_D(V_2 - V_3)$$
$$= -G_E V_1 + (G_B + G_D + G_E)V_2 - G_D V_3$$

Node 3: Here I_A flows away from the node.

$$-I_A = G_C V_3 + G_D(V_3 - V_2) + G_F(V_3 - V_1)$$
$$= -G_F V_1 - G_D V_2 + (G_C + G_D + G_F)V_3$$

These equations are expressed in matrix form as

$$\begin{bmatrix} I_A + I_B \\ -I_B \\ -I_A \end{bmatrix} = \begin{bmatrix} G_A + G_E + G_F & -G_E & -G_F \\ -G_E & G_B + G_D + G_E & -G_D \\ -G_F & -G_D & G_C + G_D + G_F \end{bmatrix} \begin{bmatrix} V_1 \\ V_2 \\ V_3 \end{bmatrix}$$

and when written in generalized matrix form the equations become

$$\begin{bmatrix} I_1 \\ I_2 \\ I_3 \end{bmatrix} = \begin{bmatrix} G_{11} & G_{12} & G_{13} \\ G_{21} & G_{22} & G_{23} \\ G_{31} & G_{32} & G_{33} \end{bmatrix} \begin{bmatrix} V_1 \\ V_2 \\ V_3 \end{bmatrix}$$

where I_1 is the sum of the source currents *entering* node 1, and I_2 and I_3 are the sum of the source currents entering nodes 2 and 3, respectively.

G_{11}, G_{22}, and G_{33} are the respective sums of the conductances terminating on nodes 1, 2 and 3.

G_{ij} ($i \neq j$), i.e., the conductance at the intersection of row i and column j, is $(-1) \times$ the conductance connected directly between node i and node j. It should be noted that for all ij, $G_{ij} = G_{ji}$.

(e) Input Resistance

In a network energized by a single supply source (see Figure 2.5), a knowledge of the *input resistance* or *driving-point resistance* is valuable. The input resistance, R_{in}, of Figure 2.5 is defined by

$$R_{in} = E_1/I_1$$

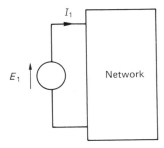

Fig 2.5

If the network has, say, three meshes, the generalized matrix form of equation is

$$
\begin{bmatrix} E_1 \\ E_2 \\ E_3 \end{bmatrix} = \begin{bmatrix} R_{11} & R_{12} & R_{13} \\ R_{21} & R_{22} & R_{23} \\ R_{31} & R_{32} & R_{33} \end{bmatrix} \begin{bmatrix} I_1 \\ I_2 \\ I_3 \end{bmatrix}
$$

and

$$
I_1 = \begin{vmatrix} E_1 & R_{12} & R_{13} \\ E_2 & R_{22} & R_{23} \\ E_3 & R_{32} & R_{33} \end{vmatrix} \Bigg/ \begin{vmatrix} R_{11} & R_{12} & R_{13} \\ R_{21} & R_{22} & R_{23} \\ R_{31} & R_{32} & R_{33} \end{vmatrix} = \begin{vmatrix} E_1 & R_{12} & R_{13} \\ E_2 & R_{22} & R_{23} \\ E_3 & R_{32} & R_{33} \end{vmatrix} \Bigg/ \Delta_R
$$

$$
= E_1 \frac{\Delta_{11}}{\Delta_R} + E_2 \frac{\Delta_{21}}{\Delta_R} + E_3 \frac{\Delta_{31}}{\Delta_R}
$$

where Δ_R is the resistance matrix of the network, and Δ_{ij} is the cofactor of R_{ij} (which is the element in row i, column j) in Δ_R (Note: care must be taken over the sign of the cofactor). Since E_1 is the only source in the network, $R_{in} = E_1/I_1$, then $R_{in} = \Delta_R/\Delta_{11}$

(f)   Transfer Resistance

In the network in Figure 2.5, which is typified by the equations in section (e) of the Fact Sheet, the current I_N (say I_2) in mesh N (mesh 2 in this case) is given by

$$
I_N = E_1 \frac{\Delta_{1N}}{\Delta_R} + E_2 \frac{\Delta_{2N}}{\Delta_R} + E_3 \frac{\Delta_{3N}}{\Delta_R}
$$

Since the network has only one driving voltage, then E_1, E_2, etc, have zero value, and

$$
I_N = E_1 \frac{\Delta_{1N}}{\Delta_R}
$$

The *transfer resistance* relating the driving voltage E_1 to the mesh current I_N is given by

$$
R_{T(1,N)} = \frac{E_1}{I_N} = \frac{\Delta_R}{\Delta_{1N}}
$$

Note that the input resistance is $R_{in} = R_{T(1,1)}$

(g)   Output Resistance

A knowledge of the *output resistance* of a network is useful in predicting circuit performance. The output resistance of the circuit in Figure 2.6(a) is calculated using the measurements in Figure 2.6(b) and (c), namely the open-circuit output voltage V_{OC}, and the short-circuit output current I_{SC}. The output resistance R_{out} is given by

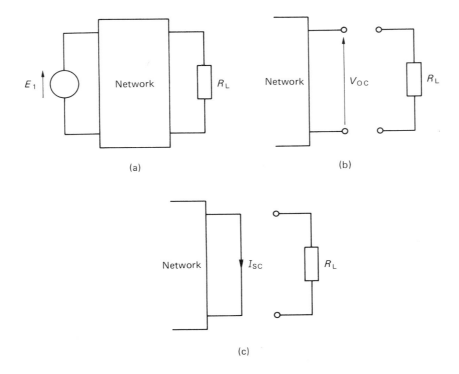

(a)

(b)

(c)

Fig 2.6

$$R_{out} = V_{OC}/I_{SC} \text{ ohm}$$

where V_{OC} is the voltage between the output terminals with the load resistor disconnected, and I_{SC} is the current which flows in a short-circuit between the output terminals of the network.

(h) Network Topology

Topology is the branch of geometry concerned with the properties of a geometrical figure, and *network topology* is concerned with the properties of an electrical circuit. In network topology, the nature of the elements between nodes is supressed, and is replaced by lines connecting the nodes; the resulting diagram is known as a *linear graph*, or simply as a *graph*.

A study of the graph of a network leads to a series of equations allowing the variables in the network to be calculated. Although network topology follows the rules of KCL and KVL, it is of great value as an introduction to the field of *state variable analysis*, in which the variables mentioned above are the state variables.

Consider the circuit in Figure 2.7(a), having six branches and four principal nodes; the corresponding graph is shown in Figure 2.7(b). The nodes are shown as dots on the graph.

In addition to the terms *node*, *branch*, *path*, *loop* and *mesh*, the following definitions are needed to describe the topology of a network:

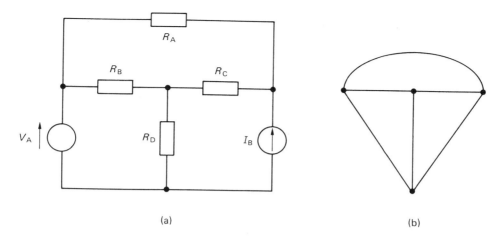

(a)   (b)

Fig 2.7

Tree (or *spanning subtree*): this is a set of branches *connecting all the nodes in the network*, but containing no loops. A network may contain several trees.

Cotree: this is the set of branches which do not belong to a given tree. Any branch of the cotree is called a *link*. There may be loops in the cotree.

In circuit analysis, we select a *normal tree*, i.e., one containing all the voltage sources in the network together with the maximum number of voltage-controlled dependent sources.

A cotree is the compliment of a tree, so that a tree and its cotree form the complete network. All the current sources together with the maximum number of current-controlled dependent sources are in the cotree.

If a network has N nodes, each tree contains $(N-1)$ branches. If B is the number of branches, and L is the number of links in the cotree, the relation between them is

$$B = L + (N-1)$$

The graph in Figure 2.7(b) has 4 nodes, and it contains more than one tree (each having 3 branches). Since there are 6 branches on the graph, each cotree contains $(6 - (4-1)) = 3$ links. Figures 2.8(a) and (c) each show a tree for the graph in Figure 2.7(b); the corresponding cotrees are shown in Figures 2.8(b) and (d).

The following rules enable us to deduce a set of node voltage equations for a network (in a few cases the rules fail, in which case other techniques must be employed).

1. Draw a graph of the network.

2. Identify a normal tree. All voltage sources (and their polarity) *must be shown on the tree* and, if possible, all voltage-controlled dependent sources should be included in the tree.

3. Node voltage equations are obtained by applying KCL to the nodes. This method generally requires $(N-1)$ equations, but the number is reduced

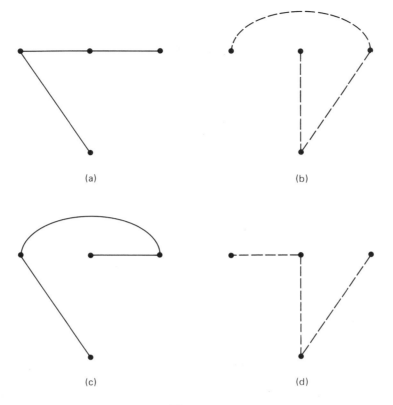

(a)   (b)

(c)   (d)

Fig 2.8

by unity for each independent or dependent voltage source in a tree branch, and is increased by unity for each dependent source that is voltage controlled by a link voltage or is current controlled. If there are current-controlled dependent sources, equations must be written for each control current in terms of the voltage variables.

The following rules allow us to write a set of mesh current equations for a network.

1. Draw a graph of the network.

2. Identify a normal tree. All current sources (and their direction) *must be shown* on the tree and cotree and, if possible, all current-controlled dependent sources should be included in the cotree.

3. Mesh current equations are obtained by repositioning, one at a time, each link of the cotree in the tree. KVL is applied to the mesh formed in the tree in this way; whilst each link has only one current flowing in it, a tree branch may have one or more link currents flowing in it. This method generally requires $(B - (N - 1))$ equations, but this value is reduced by unity for each independent or dependent current source in a link, and is increased by unity for each dependent source that is current-controlled by a tree branch current.

2.2 Worked Examples

Example 2.1

Solve the circuit in Figure 2.9 for I_1, I_2 and I_3.

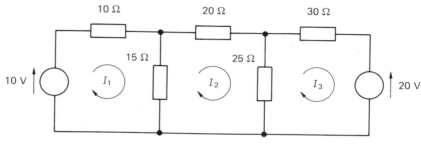

Fig 2.9

Solution 2.1

By inspection, the mesh equations for the circuit are

$$10 = 25I_1 - 15I_2$$
$$0 = -15I_1 + 60I_2 - 25I_3$$
$$-20 = -25I_2 + 55I_3$$

which may be written in matrix form as follows

$$\begin{bmatrix} 10 \\ 0 \\ -20 \end{bmatrix} = \begin{bmatrix} 25 & -15 & 0 \\ -15 & 60 & -25 \\ 0 & -25 & 55 \end{bmatrix} \begin{bmatrix} I_1 \\ I_2 \\ I_3 \end{bmatrix}$$

The 3×3 matrix is the *resistance matrix* of the network, each element in the matrix being a resistance value. The matrix is symmetrical about the major diagonal (top left to bottom right), and all elements on this diagonal have a positive value; elements not on the diagonal are either zero or negative.

Note that the matrix form could have been written directly using the method outlined in section (b) of the Fact Sheet for this chapter.

Using Cramer's rule, I_1 is determined as follows.

$$I_1 = \begin{vmatrix} 10 & -15 & 0 \\ 0 & 60 & -25 \\ -20 & -25 & 55 \end{vmatrix} \Big/ \begin{vmatrix} 25 & -15 & 0 \\ -15 & 60 & -25 \\ 0 & -25 & 55 \end{vmatrix} = \frac{19\,250}{54\,500} = 0.353 \text{ A}$$

Similarly

$$I_2 = \begin{vmatrix} 25 & 10 & 0 \\ -15 & 0 & -25 \\ 0 & 20 & 55 \end{vmatrix} \Big/ \begin{vmatrix} 25 & -15 & 0 \\ -15 & 60 & -25 \\ 0 & -25 & 55 \end{vmatrix} = -0.078 \text{ A}$$

and

$$I_3 = \begin{vmatrix} 25 & -15 & 10 \\ -15 & 60 & 0 \\ 0 & -25 & -20 \end{vmatrix} \Bigg/ \begin{vmatrix} 25 & -15 & 0 \\ -15 & 60 & -25 \\ 0 & -25 & 55 \end{vmatrix} = -0.4 \text{ A}$$

The negative sign associated with I_2 and I_3 merely imply that the current in that mesh circulates in the opposite direction to that shown in Figure 2.9, i.e., the currents actually circulate in the anticlockwise direction. However, when using the equations developed above, the values of 0.353, −0.078 and −0.4 should be used, respectively, for I_1, I_2 and I_3.

Wherever possible, it is useful to check the accuracy of the result by inserting the calculated values back into one of the KVL equations and, subject to rounding errors, the value of the e.m.f. in the loop should agree with this calculation.

Example 2.2

Solve the circuit in Figure 2.10 for I_1, I_2 and I_3.

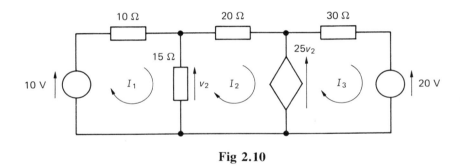

Fig 2.10

Solution 2.2

This circuit contains both independent and dependent voltage sources. Applying KVL to loop 1 yields

$$10 = 25I_1 - 15I_2$$

The dependent voltage source in loop 2 is regarded as a normal voltage source with the exception that its value needs to be related to the unknown mesh currents. Applying KVL to loop 2 gives

$$-25v_2 = -15I_1 + 35I_2$$

It should be noted that, since the dependent voltage source is ideal, it has no internal resistance, and therefore no component of I_3 appears in the above equation. Also, it is observed that

$$v_2 = 15(I_1 - I_2)$$

Inserting the above value for v_2 into the loop equation gives

$$0 = 360I_1 - 340I_2$$

And for mesh 3 the equation is

$$25v_2 - 20 = 30I_3$$

or, since $v_2 = 15(I_1 - I_2)$

$$-20 = -375I_1 + 375I_2 + 30I_3$$

and the matrix form of the circuit equations becomes

$$\begin{bmatrix} 10 \\ 0 \\ -20 \end{bmatrix} = \begin{bmatrix} 25 & -15 & 0 \\ 360 & -340 & 0 \\ -375 & 375 & 30 \end{bmatrix} \begin{bmatrix} I_1 \\ I_2 \\ I_3 \end{bmatrix}$$

Note that the 3×3 matrix is not symmetrical about the major diagonal, and some of the non-diagonal elements have positive values. This is due to the presence of the dependent voltage source in the circuit. The 3×3 matrix cannot, in this case, be described as the resistance matrix of the network because some of the elements do not represent resistances.

Solving by Cramer's rule yields

$$I_1 = 1.097 \text{ A}$$
$$I_2 = 1.161 \text{ A}$$
$$I_3 = -1.473 \text{ A}$$

Example 2.3

Using mesh analysis, calculate the currents in the meshes in the circuit in Figure 2.11.

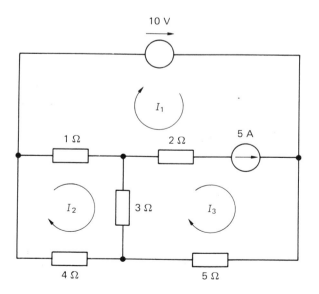

Fig 2.11

Solution 2.3

The circuit contains a 5 A independent current source in one of its branches. Following the rules laid down earlier for mesh analysis in this situation, the currents in the meshes are assigned in the usual manner as shown in Figure 2.11.

To solve the circuit using mesh analysis, the current source is initially replaced by its internal resistance, which is infinity, i.e., the current source is 'mentally' replaced by an open-circuit (see Figure 2.12). This has the effect of reducing the circuit to a 2-mesh network, one mesh carrying current I_2, and the other mesh (which is called a *supermesh*) carries currents I_1 and I_3. However, in the final analysis, both I_1 and I_3 need to be calculated, so that it is necessary to maintain their identity in the mesh equations.

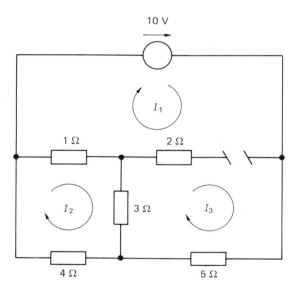

Fig 2.12

Since the 5 A source is 'mentally' replaced by an open-circuit, the reader should note that no current flows in the 2 ohm resistor at this stage. Applying KVL to the supermesh yields

$$10 = 5I_3 + 3(I_3 - I_2) + 1(I_1 - I_2) = I_1 - 4I_2 + 8I_3$$

and for mesh 2

$$0 = -1I_1 + 8I_2 - 3I_3$$

Three equations are needed to solve for the three unknown currents, the third equation being obtained by relating the current in the independent current source to the unknown mesh currents as follows

$$5 = I_3 - I_1$$

The three equations are written in the following matrix form

$$\begin{bmatrix} 10 \\ 0 \\ 5 \end{bmatrix} = \begin{bmatrix} 1 & -4 & 8 \\ -1 & 8 & -3 \\ -1 & 0 & 1 \end{bmatrix} \begin{bmatrix} I_1 \\ I_2 \\ I_3 \end{bmatrix}$$

The reader will note that the 3 × 3 matrix is not symmetrical about the major diagonal, and is due to the presence of the independent current source in the circuit.

Solving by Cramer's rule gives

$$I_1 = \begin{vmatrix} 10 & -4 & 8 \\ 0 & 8 & -3 \\ 5 & 0 & 1 \end{vmatrix} \Big/ \begin{vmatrix} 1 & -4 & 8 \\ -1 & 8 & -3 \\ -1 & 0 & 1 \end{vmatrix} = -3.214 \text{ A}$$

and

$$I_2 = 0.268 \text{ A}$$

$$I_3 = 1.786 \text{ A}$$

Example 2.4

Deduce and solve the mesh equations for the circuit in Figure 2.13.

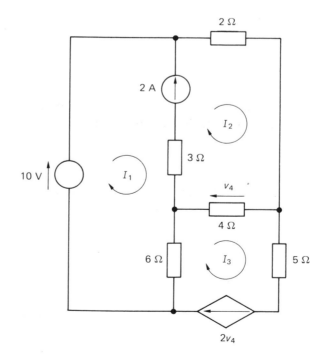

Fig 2.13

Solution 2.4

This circuit contains independent voltage and current sources, together with a dependent current source. As with Worked Example 2.3, currents are assigned to each mesh of the circuit, and each current source is replaced by an open circuit. The net result is shown in Figure 2.14, and the reader will note that we are left with one supermesh. The equation for this supermesh is

$$10 = 2I_2 + 4(I_2 - I_3) + 6(I_1 - I_3) = 6I_1 + 6I_2 - 10I_3$$

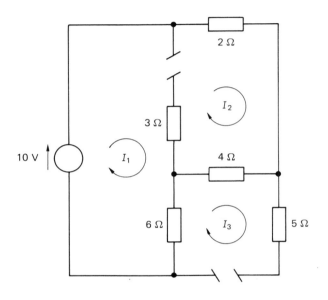

Fig 2.14

The other two equations are obtained by relating the current sources to the unknown mesh currents. For the 2 A independent current source, the equation is

$$2 = I_2 - I_1$$

and for the dependent current source, $2v_4$, is

$$2v_4 = I_3$$

Now,

$$v_4 = 4(I_3 - I_2) = -4I_2 + 4I_3$$

Hence,

$$I_3 = 2v_4 = -8I_2 + 8I_3$$

or

$$0 = -8I_2 + 7I_3$$

The corresponding matrix representation of the circuit equations is

$$\begin{bmatrix} 10 \\ 2 \\ 0 \end{bmatrix} = \begin{bmatrix} 6 & 6 & -10 \\ -1 & 1 & 0 \\ 0 & -8 & 7 \end{bmatrix} \begin{bmatrix} I_1 \\ I_2 \\ I_3 \end{bmatrix}$$

and the solution is

$$I_1 = \begin{vmatrix} 10 & 6 & -10 \\ 2 & 1 & 0 \\ 0 & -8 & 7 \end{vmatrix} \Big/ \begin{vmatrix} 6 & 6 & -10 \\ -1 & 1 & 0 \\ 0 & -8 & 7 \end{vmatrix} = 36.5 \text{ A}$$

and

$$I_2 = 38.5 \text{ A}$$
$$I_3 = 44 \text{ A}$$

Example 2.5

Determine the node voltages in the circuit in Figure 2.15(a).

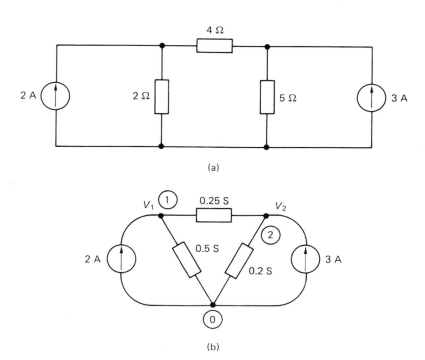

(a)

(b)

Fig 2.15

Solution 2.5

The circuit is redrawn in Figure 2.15(b) to show the three principal nodes and, at the same time, the resistance values have been converted to conductance values.

Node 0 is nominated as the reference node, and all voltages are calculated by reference to it. Thus the voltage V_1 at node 1 is the voltage V_{10}, and the voltage V_2 at node 2 is the voltage V_{20}.

Applying KCL to node 1, by inspection, yields

$$2 = 0.75V_1 - 0.25V_2$$

and applying KCL to node 2 gives

$$3 = -0.25V_1 + 0.45V_2$$

which are represented in matrix form as follows

$$\begin{bmatrix} 2 \\ 3 \end{bmatrix} = \begin{bmatrix} 0.75 & -0.25 \\ -0.25 & 0.45 \end{bmatrix} \begin{bmatrix} V_1 \\ V_2 \end{bmatrix}$$

The 2×2 matrix is the *conductance matrix* of the circuit, each element in the matrix being a conductance value. The matrix is symmetrical about the major diagonal, and all non-diagonal elements are either zero or negative.

Note that the matrix form could have been written directly by observation using the method outlined in section (d) of the Fact Sheet for this chapter. Using Cramer's rule

$$V_1 = \begin{vmatrix} 2 & -0.25 \\ 3 & 0.45 \end{vmatrix} \bigg/ \begin{vmatrix} 0.75 & -0.25 \\ -0.25 & 0.45 \end{vmatrix} = \frac{1.65}{0.275} = 6 \text{ V}$$

$$V_2 = \begin{vmatrix} 0.75 & 2 \\ -0.25 & 3 \end{vmatrix} \bigg/ \begin{vmatrix} 0.75 & -0.25 \\ -0.25 & 0.45 \end{vmatrix} = \frac{2.75}{0.275} = 10 \text{ V}$$

Where possible, it is advisable to check the accuracy of the calculations which, in this case, is relatively easy as follows. At node 2, the current of 3 A flowing into it is balanced by 2 A flowing through the 0.2 S conductance, and 1 A flowing to node 1.

Example 2.6

Using nodal analysis, calculate the voltage at nodes 1, 2, and 3 in the circuit in Figure 2.16.

Solution 2.6

The circuit contains a dependent current source, $5v_{13}$, where v_{13} is the voltage developed across the 2 S conductance. Taking node 0 as the reference node, and applying KCL to each node in turn, the following results are obtained

Node 1

$$-5v_{13} = 3V_1 + 2(V_1 - V_3)$$

but $v_{13} = V_1 - V_3$, hence

$$-5(V_1 - V_3) = 3V_1 + 2(V_1 - V_3)$$

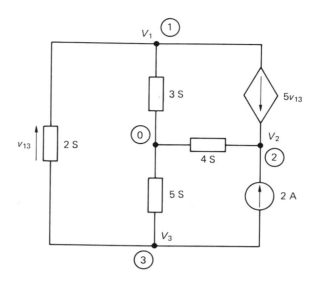

Fig 2.16

or

$$0 = 10V_1 - 7V_3$$

Node 2

$$5v_{13} + 2 = 4V_2$$

that is $5(V_1 - V_3) + 2 = 4V_2$

or

$$2 = -5V_1 + 4V_2 + 5V_3$$

Node 3

$$-2 = 5V_3 + 2(V_3 - V_1)$$

or

$$-2 = -2V_1 + 7V_3$$

The equations are presented in matrix form as follows

$$\begin{bmatrix} 0 \\ 2 \\ -2 \end{bmatrix} = \begin{bmatrix} 10 & 0 & -7 \\ -5 & 4 & 5 \\ -2 & 0 & 7 \end{bmatrix} \begin{bmatrix} V_1 \\ V_2 \\ V_3 \end{bmatrix}$$

Note that the 3 × 3 matrix is not symmetrical about the major diagonal, and some of the non-diagonal elements are positive. This is due to the presence of the dependent current source in the circuit. Strictly speaking, this matrix is not the conductance matrix of the circuit, since some of the elements are not pure conductances.

Solving by Cramer's rule gives

$$V_1 = \begin{vmatrix} 0 & 0 & -7 \\ 2 & 4 & 5 \\ -2 & 0 & 7 \end{vmatrix} \Bigg/ \begin{vmatrix} 10 & 0 & -7 \\ -5 & 4 & 5 \\ -2 & 0 & 7 \end{vmatrix} = -0.25 \text{ V}$$

and

$$V_2 = 0.634 \text{ V}$$

$$V_3 = -0.357 \text{ V}$$

Example 2.7

Using nodal analysis, determine the voltage at nodes 1, 2, and 3 in Figure 2.17(a).

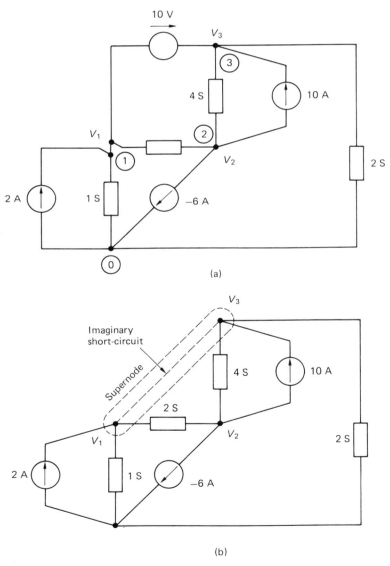

(a)

(b)

Fig 2.17

Solution 2.7

The circuit contains a 10 V independent voltage source, and it is necessary to redraw the circuit in Figure 2.17(b), with the voltage source being replaced by its internal resistance, which is zero. That is, we can mentally imagine nodes 1 and 3 being short-circuited together, resulting in a *supernode*. However, the identity of nodes 1 and 3 are not lost, since the voltages at these nodes are included in the nodal equations of the circuit.

The current flowing towards the supernode is $10 + 2 = 12$ A, and the current flowing away from it is

$$1V_1 + 2(V_1 - V_2) + 4(V_3 - V_2) + 2V_3 = 3V_1 - 6V_2 + 6V_3$$

Applying KCL to this node gives the equation

$$12 = 3V_1 - 6V_2 + 6V_3$$

Applying KCL to node 2 gives

$$-10 - (-6) = 2(V_2 - V_1) + 4(V_2 - V_3)$$

or

$$-4 = -2V_1 + 6V_2 - 4V_3$$

A third equation is needed to solve for the three unknown voltages, and this is realized from the fact that nodes 1 and 3 are, in fact, separated by 10 V, so that we may say

$$10 = -V_1 + V_3$$

The resulting equations are represented in matrix form as follows

$$\begin{bmatrix} 12 \\ -4 \\ 10 \end{bmatrix} = \begin{bmatrix} 3 & -6 & 6 \\ -2 & 6 & -4 \\ -1 & 0 & 1 \end{bmatrix} \begin{bmatrix} V_1 \\ V_2 \\ V_3 \end{bmatrix}$$

In this case, the 3×3 matrix is not symmetrical about the major diagonal, and one of the non-diagonal elements is positive; these effects are due to the presence of the voltage source in the circuit.

Solving the equations gives

$$V_1 = \begin{vmatrix} 12 & -6 & 6 \\ -4 & 6 & -4 \\ 10 & 0 & 1 \end{vmatrix} \Bigg/ \begin{vmatrix} 3 & -6 & 6 \\ -2 & 6 & -4 \\ -1 & 0 & 1 \end{vmatrix} = -4 \text{ V}$$

and

$$V_2 = 2 \text{ V}$$

$$V_3 = 6 \text{ V}$$

Example 2.8

For the network in Figure 2.18, calculate the input resistance, together with the transfer resistance between meshes 1 and 2, and between meshes 1 and 3. Hence calculate I_1, I_2, and I_3.

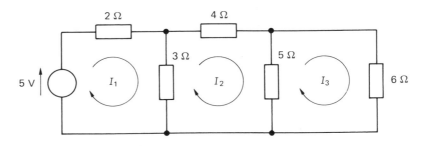

Fig 2.18

Solution 2.8

Applying mesh analysis to the network yields the equations

$$5 = 5I_1 - 3I_2$$
$$0 = -3I_1 + 12I_2 - 5I_3$$
$$0 = -5I_2 + 11I_3$$

and the determinant of the resistance matrix is

$$\Delta_R = \begin{vmatrix} 5 & -3 & 0 \\ -3 & 12 & -5 \\ 0 & -5 & 11 \end{vmatrix} = 436$$

Now

$$\Delta_{11} = (-1)^{1+1} \begin{vmatrix} 12 & -5 \\ -5 & 11 \end{vmatrix} = 107$$

$$\Delta_{12} = (-1)^{1+2} \begin{vmatrix} -3 & -5 \\ 0 & 11 \end{vmatrix} = 33$$

$$\Delta_{13} = (-1)^{1+3} \begin{vmatrix} -3 & 12 \\ 0 & -5 \end{vmatrix} = 15$$

The input resistance is given by

$$R_{IN} = R_{T(1.1)} = \Delta_R/\Delta_{11} = 436/107 = 4.075 \text{ ohm}$$

The transfer resistance between meshes 1 and 2 is

$$R_{T(1.2)} = \Delta_R/\Delta_{12} = 436/33 = 13.21 \text{ ohm}$$

and the transfer resistance between meshes 1 and 3 is

$$R_{T(1,3)} = \Delta_R/\Delta_{13} = 436/15 = 29.07 \text{ ohm}$$

Hence

$$I_1 = E_1/R_{IN} = 5/4.075 = 1.227 \text{ A}$$

$$I_2 = E_1/R_{T(1,2)} = 5/13.21 = 0.379 \text{ A}$$

$$I_3 = E_1/R_{T(1,3)} = 5/29.07 = 0.172 \text{ A}$$

Example 2.9

Construct the tree and cotree for the circuit in Figure 2.19(a). How many tree branches are there, and how many links? Write a set of equations in tree-branch voltages and solve them.

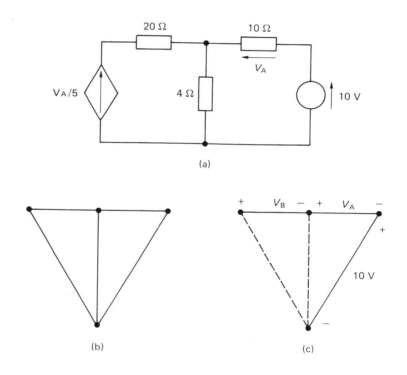

(a)

(b)   (c)

Fig 2.19

Solution 2.9

The graph of the circuit is shown in Figure 2.19(b) and, since it has 4 principal nodes and 5 branches, each tree contains

$$N - 1 = 4 - 1 = 3 \text{ branches}$$

and each cotree contains

$$L = B - (N - 1) = 5 - 3 = 2 \text{ links.}$$

Applying the rules outlined earlier, the circuit has only one tree and one cotree, which are drawn in Figure 2.19(c) (the cotree is shown dotted).

The voltage V_A is a control variable and is shown in the figure, and we must assign another variable, V_B, to the remaining branch. The rules indicate that we need $(N-1) = 3$ equations to solve the circuit, but this value is reduced by one because of the independent voltage source in the tree branch. The equations can be deduced as follows.

Taking the left-hand node of the top arm of the tree, the current entering the node is $V_A/5$ and the current leaving it is $V_B/20$. That is

$$\frac{V_A}{5} = \frac{V_B}{20} \quad \text{or} \quad V_B = 4V_A$$

Looking next at the centre node of the top arm, a current of $V_B/20$ enters it from the left, a current of $V_A/10$ leaves to the right and, since the voltage at the top of the 4 ohm resistor is $(10 + V_A)$ with respect to the bottom node, a current of $(10 + V_A)/4$ leaves downwards through the 4-ohm branch. The equation for this node is therefore

$$\frac{V_B}{20} = \frac{V_A}{10} + \frac{10 + V_A}{4}$$

Solving these equations gives $V_A = -16.667$ V and $V_B = -66.667$ V.

Example 2.10

Construct a tree for the network in Figure 2.20(a). Write a set of equations in terms of the link currents, and calculate the value of I.

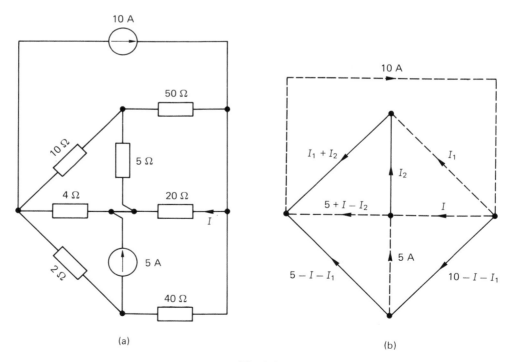

(a)

(b)

Fig 2.20

Solution 2.10

The network has 5 principal nodes and 9 branches, so that each tree has $(5-1) = 4$ branches, and each cotree has $(9-4) = 5$ links. Since the circuit does not contain voltage sources, we must select a tree containing only resistors. A tree (shown in full line) and its cotree (dotted lines) are shown in Figure 2.20(b); since the unknown quantity (I) is a current, it is omitted from the tree.

Basically, this method of solution needs $[B - (N-1)] = 9 - 4 = 5$ equations, but since the circuit contains two independent current sources, we need only three equations. Accordingly, Figure 2.20(b) is marked with appropriate currents.

Next, one cotree link at a time is inserted into the tree, and KVL is applied to the resulting loop in the tree. Inserting the link carrying I_1 gives the loop equation

$$50I_1 + 10(I_1 + I_2) - 2(5 - I - I_1) - 40(10 - I - I_1) = 0$$

or

$$42I + 102I_1 + 10I_2 = 410$$

Inserting the link carrying current I gives

$$20I + 5I_2 + 10(I_1 + I_2) - 2(5 - I - I_1) - 40(10 - I - I_1) = 0$$

or

$$62I + 52I_1 + 15I_2 = 410$$

and inserting the link carrying $(5 + I - I_2)$ gives

$$4(5 + I - I_2) - 10(I_1 + I_2) - 5I_2 = 0$$

or

$$4I - 10I_1 - 19I_2 = -20$$

The matrix form of the equations is

$$\begin{bmatrix} 410 \\ 410 \\ -20 \end{bmatrix} = \begin{bmatrix} 42 & 102 & 10 \\ 62 & 52 & 15 \\ 4 & -10 & -19 \end{bmatrix} \begin{bmatrix} I \\ I_1 \\ I_2 \end{bmatrix}$$

Hence,

$$I = \begin{vmatrix} 410 & 102 & 10 \\ 410 & 52 & 15 \\ -20 & -10 & -19 \end{vmatrix} \Bigg/ \begin{vmatrix} 42 & 102 & 10 \\ 62 & 52 & 15 \\ 4 & -10 & -19 \end{vmatrix} = \frac{389\,800}{82\,800} = 4.708 \text{ A}$$

Example 2.11

Calculate the output resistance of the network in Figure 2.21(a).

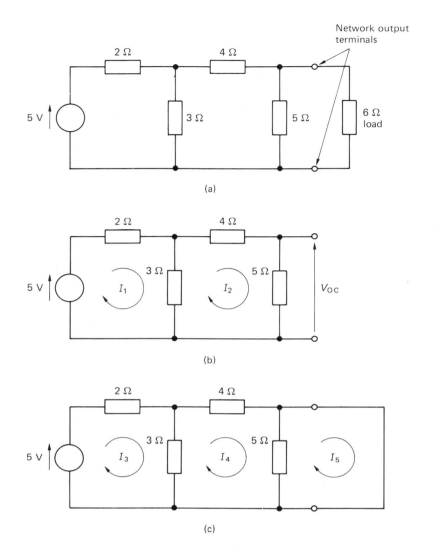

(a)

(b)

(c)

Fig 2.21

Solution 2.11

The 6 ohm resistance is the 'load' connected to the network. This resistance is removed, and the open-circuit voltage between these terminals and the short-circuit current between the terminals of the network are calculated as follows.

Open-circuit voltage

When the load is disconnected, the circuit is as shown in Figure 2.21(b). Applying mesh analysis, the circuit equations are

$$5 = 5I_1 - 3I_2$$
$$0 = -3I_1 + 12I_2$$

Hence,

$$I_2 = \left| \begin{matrix} 5 & 5 \\ -3 & 0 \end{matrix} \right| \Big/ \left| \begin{matrix} 5 & -3 \\ -3 & 12 \end{matrix} \right| = 0.294 \text{ A}$$

Hence,

$$V_{OC} = 5I_2 = 1.47 \text{ V}$$

Short-circuit current

When the load is replaced by a short-circuit, the circuit is as shown in Figure 2.21(c). The corresponding matrix form of the mesh current equations is

$$\begin{bmatrix} 5 \\ 0 \\ 0 \end{bmatrix} = \begin{bmatrix} 5 & -3 & 0 \\ -3 & 12 & -5 \\ 0 & -5 & 5 \end{bmatrix} \begin{bmatrix} I_3 \\ I_4 \\ I_5 \end{bmatrix}$$

Solving for I_5 by Cramer's rule gives

$$I_5 = I_{SC} = 0.577 \text{ A}$$

Output resistance

The output resistance of the circuit is given by

$$R_{OUT} = V_{OC}/I_{SC} = 1.47/0.577 = 2.55 \text{ ohm}$$

2.3 Unworked Problems

Problem 2.1

If the 10 V source in Worked Example 2.1 is replaced by a 10 A current source, and the 20 V source is replaced by a 20 A source, determine the value of I_2 in Figure 2.9. Note that the 10 A source acts in the direction of I_1, in Figure 2.9, and the 20 A source opposes I_3.
[$I_2 = 5.83$ A circulating in an anticlockwise direction]

Problem 2.2

If the voltage source and the current source in Worked Example 2.3 (see Figure 2.11) are interchanged (so that $I_1 = 5$ A, and the 10 V source opposes I_1), calculate the value of I_2 and I_3.
[$I_2 = 1.55$ A (clockwise); $I_3 = 2.47$ A (clockwise)]

Problem 2.3

If the 10 V voltage source and the $2v_4$ dependent current source in Worked Example 2.4 (see Figure 2.13) are interchanged (so that $I_1 = 2v_4$, and the 10 V source assists I_3), determine the value of I_1, I_2, and I_3.
[$I_1 = 1.744$ A (anticlockwise); $I_2 = 0.255$ A (clockwise); $I_3 = 0.036$ A (clockwise)]

Problem 2.4

If the 2 A source in Worked Example 2.5 (see Figure 2.15) is replaced by the combination of a 2 V source in series with a 1 ohm resistor, and the 3 A source is replaced by the combination of a 3 V source in series with a 2 ohm resistor (the 2 V source tending to drive a current in a clockwise direction around its mesh, and the 3 V source tending to drive a current in an anticlockwise direction around its mesh), determine the current in each of the three meshes in the circuit.
[$I_1 = 0.58$ A (clockwise); $I_2 = 0.13$ A (anticlockwise); $I_3 = 0.52$ A (anticlockwise)]

Problem 2.5

If the direction of the two current sources in Worked Example 2.6 are interchanged (i.e., the 2 A source drives current towards node 1, and the $5v_{13}$ A source drives current towards node 3), determine the voltage of nodes 1, 2 and 3 relative to node 0 in Figure 2.16.
[$V_1 = 0.522$ V; $V_2 = -0.772$ V; $V_3 = 0.304$ V]

Problem 2.6

When the 10 V source and the 2 A source in Worked Example 2.7 are interchanged (i.e., in Figure 2.17, $V_1 = +10$ V, and the 2 A source drives current towards V_3), determine the voltage at nodes 2 and 3, and also the current flowing in the 10 V source.
[$V_2 = 7.2$ V; $V_3 = 6.8$ V; 17.6 A]

Problem 2.7

Write down the mesh current equations for the circuit in Figure 2.22, hence determine the value if the voltage source V_1. What value of ideal current source would be required to replace the voltage source V_1 in order to produce a current of 1 A in the 10 ohm resistor?
[$V_1 = 22$ V; $I = 5.75$ A]

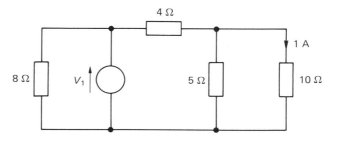

Fig 2.22

Problem 2.8

Write down the mesh current equations for the circuit in Figure 2.23, and deduce an expression for the input resistance of the network. What is the value of the input resistance when the load resistance $R = 20$ ohm.

$$\left[\frac{100 + 6R}{11 + 0.5R}; 10.48 \text{ ohm} \right]$$

Problem 2.9

Evaluate the output resistance of the circuit in Figure 2.23.
[$R_{\text{OUT}} = 16.67$ ohm]

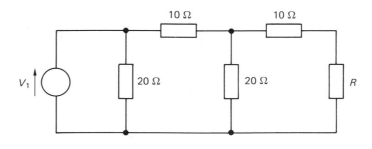

Fig 2.23

Problem 2.10

(a) How many trees can be constructed for the circuit in Figure 2.24 which satisfy the conditions laid down in section (h) of the Fact Sheet for this chapter?
(b) Draw a suitable tree and write a set of tree-branch equations which enable V_R to be calculated. What is the value of V_R?
[(a) 1; (b) 17.88 V]

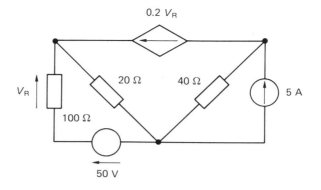

Fig 2.24

Problem 2.11

How many links are in the circuit in Figure 2.24? Construct a cotree; write a set of equations in terms of the link currents, and solve them for the current in the 20 ohm resistor. What is the value of this current?
[3; 3.39 A]

Problem 2.12

Calculate the voltage between the two principal nodes in Figure 2.25.

(Staffordshire Polytechnic)

[1.5 V]

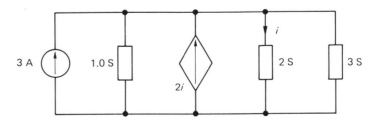

Fig 2.25

Problem 2.13

Write down, but do not solve, the mesh equations to solve for the currents I_1, I_2 and I_3 in Figure 2.26.

(Staffordshire Polytechnic)

$[8 = 8I_1 - I_2 - 5I_3; -3 = -I_1 + 6I_2 - 2I_3; -5 = -5I_1 - 2I_2 + 17I_3]$

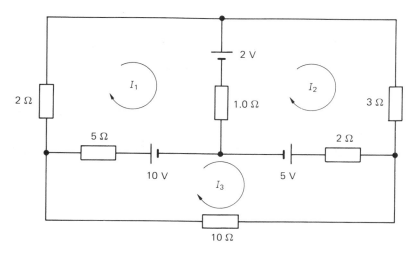

Fig 2.26

Problem 2.14

Calculate the mesh currents in Problem 2.13.
$[I_1 = 0.91\ \text{A};\ I_2 = -0.372\ \text{A};\ I_3 = -0.07\ \text{A}]$

Problem 2.15

(a) Write down, but do not solve, the three equations for the mesh currents I_1, I_2 and I_3 in Figure 2.27. **(b)** Write down, but do not solve, the two node voltage equations for V_1 and V_2 in Figure 2.27. **(c)** Using Thévenin's theorem, calculate the current in the 3 ohm resistor in Figure 2.27.

(Staffordshire Polytechnic)

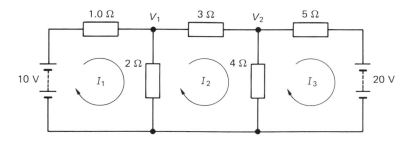

Fig 2.27

$[$**(a)** $10 = 3I_1 - 2I_2;\ 0 = -2I_1 + 9I_2 - 4I_3;\ -20 = -4I_2 + 9I_3;$
(b) $10 = 1.833V_1 - 0.333V_2;\ 4 = -0.333V_1 + 0.783V_2;$
(c) 0.377 A flowing from the right$]$

Problem 2.16

(a) Solve the mesh equations in Problem 2.15(a) for I_1, I_2 and I_3. **(b)** Solve the node equations in Problem 2.15(b) for V_1 and V_2.
$[$**(a)** $I_1 = 3.08\ \text{A};\ I_2 = -0.377\ \text{A};\ I_3 = -2.39\ \text{A};$
(b) $V_1 = 6.92\ \text{V};\ V_2 = 8.05\ \text{V}]$

3 Waveforms and Fourier Analysis

3.1 Fact Sheet

(a) Introduction

This chapter deals with *periodic alternating waveforms* or repetitive waveforms in which $f(t) = f(t + nT)$, where n is an integer and T is the periodic time of the waveform (see Figure 3.1 for examples).

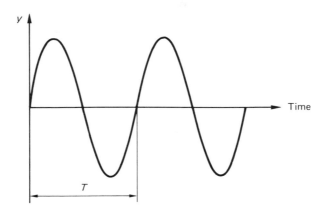

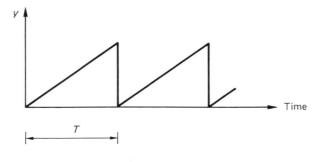

Fig 3.1

The *frequency* of the waveform is the number of cycles completed per second, and is given by

$$\text{frequency, } f = 1/T \text{ hertz (Hz)}$$

where T is in seconds, and the *angular frequency*, ω, of the wave is

$$\omega = 2\pi f \text{ rad/s}$$

(b)   Average Value or Mean Value of a Wave

For a periodic function $y(t)$ with a period of T, the mathematical expression for the average value, Y_{AV}, is

$$Y_{AV} = \frac{1}{T} \int_0^T y(t)\, dt$$

In the case of electrical circuits, the average value of a number of forcing function waveforms is zero, e.g., sine and cosine waves. In these cases, we make an exception to the strict mathematical rule, and compute the average value over one half-cycle of the wave. On this basis, the mean value of the functions $y \sin \omega t$ and $y \cos \omega t$ is

$$Y_{AV} = 2Y_M/\pi = 0.637 Y_M$$

where Y_M is the maximum value of the waveform. Also, the mean value of a square waveform, having a positive peak of $+Y_M$ and a negative peak of $-Y_M$, is Y_M. The 'electrical' mean value is sometimes known as the *rectified mean value* of the wave.

(c)   Root-mean-square (r.m.s.) Value or Effective Value

When an alternating current $i(t)$ with a periodic time of T flows in a resistor, the average power consumed is P watt. The *effective value* of the current which would produce this power if it passed through the resistor for the whole cycle is the r.m.s. current, I, and is given by

$$I = \sqrt{\left(\frac{1}{T} \int_0^T i^2(t)\, dt\right)}$$

There is a similar expression for the calculation of the r.m.s. value of a voltage wave.

(d)   Form Factor and Peak Factor of an Alternating Wave

The *form factor* gives some information about the form or shape of the wave, and is defined as

$$\text{form factor, } k_F = \frac{\text{r.m.s. value}}{\text{rectified mean value}}$$

For sine and cosine waves, the form factor is 1.111.

The *peak factor* or *crest factor* is defined as

$$\text{peak factor, } k_P = \frac{\text{peak value}}{\text{r.m.s. value}}$$

For sine and cosine waves, the peak factor is 1.414.

(e)   R.M.S. Value of a Complex Periodic Wave

A complex periodic wave has the general equation

$$y(t) = A_0 + (a_1\cos \omega t + a_2\cos 2\omega t + \ldots + a_N\cos N\omega t + \ldots)$$
$$+ (b_1\sin \omega t + b_2\sin 2\omega t + \ldots + b_N\sin N\omega t + \ldots)$$

where A_0 is the 'd.c.' component of the waveform, a_1 is the maximum value of $a_1\cos \omega t$, b_1 is the maximum value of $b_1\cos \omega t$, etc, and N is an integer. The series may, alternatively, be given in one of the following trigonometric forms

$$f(t) = A_0 + \sum_{N=1}^{\infty} c_N \cos (N\omega t - \theta_N)$$

$$f(t) = A_0 + \sum_{N=1}^{\infty} c_N \sin (N\omega t + \phi_N)$$

where $c_N = \surd(a_N + b_N)$, $\theta_N = \tan (b_N/a_N)$, and $\phi_N = \tan (a_N/b_N)$
   The r.m.s. value, Y, is

$$Y = \surd(A_0^2 + \tfrac{1}{2}(a_1^2 + a_2^2 + \ldots + a_N^2 + \ldots) + \tfrac{1}{2}(b_1^2 + b_2^2 + \ldots + b_N^2 + \ldots))$$
$$= \surd(A_0^2 + (A_1^2 + A_2^2 + \ldots + A_N^2 + \ldots) + (B_1^2 + B_2^2 + \ldots + B_N^2 + \ldots))$$

where

$$A_N = a_N/\surd 2 = \text{effective value of } a_N\cos \omega N t$$

and

$$B_N = b_N/\surd 2 = \text{effective value of } b_N\sin \omega N t$$

Also, if a complex wave has an r.m.s. value of Y, and the corresponding r.m.s. values of the harmonics are $Y_1, Y_2 \ldots Y_N$, then

$$Y = \surd(Y_1^2 + Y_2^2 + \ldots + Y_N^2)$$

(f)   Power Supplied by a Complex Wave

The average power supplied is the sum of the average powers supplied by each component of the wave. For the Nth harmonic, the power supplied is

$$P_N = V_N I_N\cos \phi_N$$

where V_N and I_N are r.m.s. values. The average power supplied per cycle of the complex wave is

$$P = V_1 I_1\cos \phi_1 + V_2 I_2\cos \phi_2 + \ldots + V_N I_N\cos \phi_N + \ldots$$

(g) Power Factor of a Complex Wave

This section is included here for completeness, and readers wishing to know more about power factor should consult Chapter 8. If V_N and I_N are the r.m.s. values of the current and voltage of the Nth harmonic of the complex wave, and V and I are the r.m.s. values of the voltage and current for the complex wave, then

$$\text{overall power factor} = \text{total power}/VI$$

$$= (V_1 I_1 \cos \phi_1 + V_2 I_2 \cos \phi_2 + \ldots + V_N I_N \cos \phi_N + \ldots)/VI$$

(h) Trigonometric Fourier Analysis

A periodic waveform for which $f(t) = f(t + T)$, where T is the periodic time of the wave, can be represented by a Fourier series provided that, within the period T

1. if the wave is discontinuous, it has a finite number of discontinuities,

2. it has a finite average value, and

3. it has a finite number of positive and negative maxima.

If these *Dirichlet conditions* are met (as is usually the case in electrical engineering practice), the wave can be represented by the trigonometric form of the Fourier series as follows.

$$f(t) = A_0 + \sum_{N=1}^{\infty} (a_N \cos N\omega t + b_N \sin N\omega t)$$

where

$$A_0 = \frac{1}{T} \int_{-T/2}^{T/2} f(t)\ \mathrm{d}t$$

$$a_N = \frac{2}{T} \int_{-T/2}^{T/2} f(t)\ \cos N\omega t\ \mathrm{d}t$$

$$b_N = \frac{2}{T} \int_{-T/2}^{T/2} f(t)\ \sin N\omega t\ \mathrm{d}t$$

and

$$\omega = 2\pi/T \text{ rad/s}$$

Note that the limits of integration can be any convenient interval covering the range T, i.e., 0 to T, $-T/4$ to $3T/4$, etc. Also, if $\omega t = \theta$, the integrations are carried out over any convenient range of 2π, i.e., $-\pi/2$ to $\pi/2$, etc.

(i) Waveform Symmetry

Some waveforms exhibit symmetry about a particular point or axis, and a knowledge of this symmetry may result in a reduced number of calculations being done when the Fourier coefficients are evaluated. (If more than one form of symmetry exists, there will be more than one factor missing from the series.)

Even Functions (see Figure 3.2(a))

These exhibit *symmetry about the y axis.* If $f(t) = f(-t)$, there are no sine terms in the series, i.e.,

$$f(t) = A_0 + a_1\cos \omega t + a_2\cos 2\omega t + \ldots$$

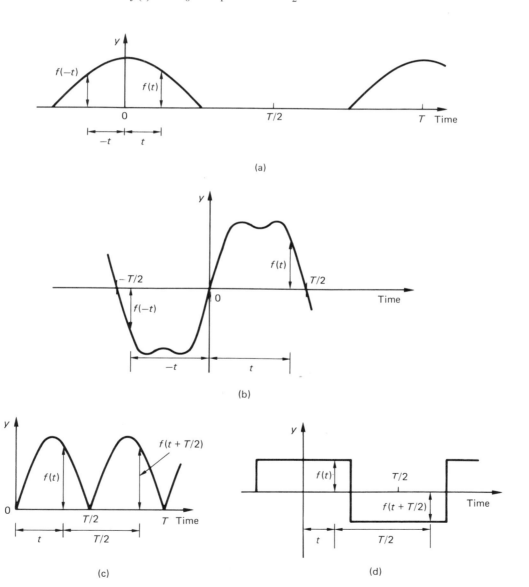

Fig 3.2

A_0 may exist, a_N exists, $b_N = 0$. The sum of two or more even functions is an even function (even if a constant is added).

Odd Functions (see Figure 3.2(b))

These exhibit *symmetry about the origin*. If $f(t) = -f(-t)$, the series has no cosine terms, i.e.,

$$f(t) = b_1 \sin \omega t + b_2 \sin 2\omega t + \ldots$$

$A_0 = 0$, $a_N = 0$, b_N exists. The sum of two or more odd functions is an odd function. The addition of a constant makes the function no longer an odd function (see Worked Example 3.11). The product of two odd functions is an even function.

Half Wave Repetition (see Figure 3.2(c))

If $f(t) = f(t + T/2)$, no odd terms exist in the series. A_0 may exist, and only even terms exist in a_N and b_N.

Half Wave Inversion (see Figure 3.2(d))

If $f(t) = -f(t + T/2)$, the series does not contain even terms. $A_0 = 0$, and only odd terms exist in a_N and b_N.

(j)   Line Spectrum

The *line spectrum* of a waveform is a plot of the modulus of the harmonic amplitudes in a complex wave to a base of the order of the harmonic (or to a base of the frequency). The majority of waveforms in electrical and electronic engineering have rapidly converging values, so that only the first few terms in the Fourier series are generally significant. The line spectra for the first few terms of the square wave in Figure 3.3(a) are shown in Figure 3.3(b).

Where necessary, the amplitude and phase spectra of the wave can be shows separately (see Worked Example 3.10).

(k)   Harmonic Analysis

Where the shape of a waveform is known, but it has no simple mathematical expression, the values of the Fourier series coefficients which describe the wave can be estimated from a knowledge of the value of equally-spaced ordinates of the wave.

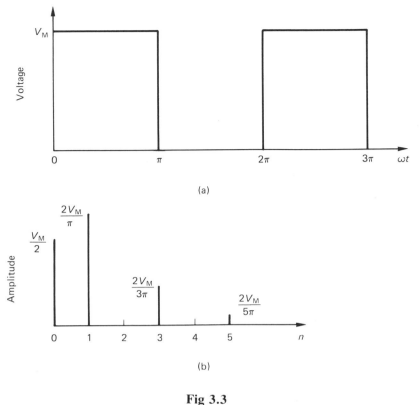

Fig 3.3

The values of the coefficients are estimated as follows.

A_0 = average value of the complex wave over one cycle

a_N = 2 × average value of $f(t)$ cos $N\omega t$ over one cycle

b_N = 2 × average value of $f(t)$ sin $N\omega t$ over one cycle

Care should be taken in selecting not only the number of ordinates, but also in the physical positioning of the ordinates. For example, if the ordinates are places 20° apart, there exists the possibility that the ordinates may be placed at the nodes of the ninth harmonic; in this case, there will be no indication of the existence of the ninth harmonic (if present) when the calculation is complete. The value of the highest harmonic calculated by this method should, of course, be limited by the number of ordinates used.

(l)   Selective Resonance

A complex wave contains many frequencies, and if the circuit contains both inductance and capacitance, the circuit may *resonate selectively* (see Chapter 6 for details of resonance) with one of the frequencies. Depending on the form of resonance, it may result in a very large current at the resonant frequency, and/or in a very large voltage across the inductors and capacitors in the circuit.

3.2 Worked Examples

Example 3.1

Calculate the average value and r.m.s. value of the waveform in Figure 3.4.

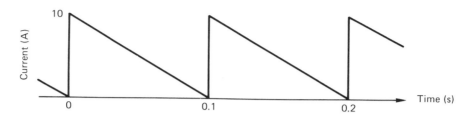

Fig 3.4

Solution 3.1

For the interval $0 < t < 0.1$

$$i = 10 - 100t \text{ A}$$

and

$$I_{AV} = \frac{1}{T} \int_0^T i \, \mathrm{d}t = \frac{1}{0.1} \int_0^{0.1} (10 - 100t) \, \mathrm{d}t$$

$$= 10(1 - 0.5) = 5 \text{ A}$$

Also

$$I_{RMS}^2 = \frac{1}{T} \int_0^T i^2 \, \mathrm{d}t = \frac{1}{0.1} \int_0^{0.1} (10 - 100t)^2 \, \mathrm{d}t$$

$$= 100 \int_0^{0.1} (1 - 20t + 100t^2) \, \mathrm{d}t$$

$$= 100 \left[t - 20 \frac{t^2}{2} + 100 \frac{t^3}{3} \right]_0^{0.1} = 33.33$$

Hence, $I_{RMS} = \sqrt{33.33} = 5.77 \text{ A}$

Example 3.2

Determine the form factor and the peak factor of the waveform in Figure 3.4.

Solution 3.2

$$\text{form factor, } k_F = \frac{\text{r.m.s. value}}{\text{mean value}} = \frac{5.77}{5} = 1.154$$

$$\text{peak factor, } k_P = \frac{\text{peak value}}{\text{r.m.s. value}} = \frac{10}{5.77} = 1.733$$

Example 3.3

During the interval $0 < t < 10$, the waveform in Figure 3.5 follows the equation $v = 20(1 - e^{-t/2})$ V. Calculate the mean value, the effective value, the form factor, and the peak factor of the wave.

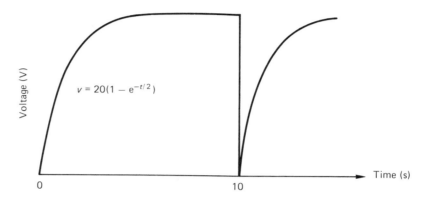

Fig 3.5

Solution 3.3

$$V_{AV} = \frac{1}{T} \int_0^T v \, dt = \frac{1}{10} \int_0^{10} 20(1 - e^{-t/2}) \, dt = \frac{20}{10} \int_0^{10} (1 - e^{-t/2}) \, dt$$

$$= 2 \left[t + 2e^{-t/2} \right]_0^{10} = 16.027 \text{ V}$$

and

$$V_{RMS}^2 = \frac{1}{T} \int_0^T v^2 \, dt = \frac{1}{10} \int_0^{10} 20^2 (1 - e^{-t/2})^2 \, dt$$

$$= \frac{400}{10} \int_0^{10} (1 - 4e^{-t/2} + e^{-t}) \, dt$$

$$= 40 \left[t + 4e^{-t/2} - e^{-t} \right]_0^{10} = 280.8$$

Hence, $V_{RMS} = 16.77$ V
and

$$\text{form factor} = \frac{\text{r.m.s. value}}{\text{mean value}} = \frac{16.77}{16.027} = 1.046$$

$$\text{peak value} = 20(1 - e^{-5}) = 19.87 \text{ V}$$

$$\text{peak factor} = \frac{\text{peak value}}{\text{r.m.s. value}} = \frac{19.87}{16.77} = 1.185$$

Example 3.4

The clipped sine wave in Figure 3.6 is produced by an electronic circuit. Calculate the mean value and the r.m.s. value of the wave.

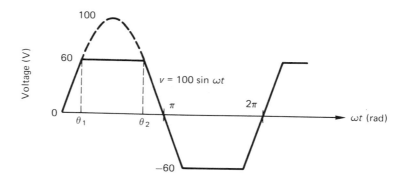

Fig 3.6

Solution 3.4

The value of θ_1 is calculated as follows

$$60 = 100 \sin \theta_1$$

Hence,

$$\theta_1 = \sin^{-1}(60/100) = 0.6435 \text{ rad}$$

and

$$\theta_2 = \pi - \theta_1 = 2.4981 \text{ rad}$$

Since the complete wave has a zero mathematical average value, the electrical mean value is calculated from the first half cycle as follows.

$$
V_{AV} = \frac{1}{\pi}\left\{ \int_0^{\theta_1} V_M \sin \omega t \, \mathrm{d}(\omega t) + \int_{\theta_1}^{\theta_2} 0.6 \, V_M \, \mathrm{d}(\omega t) + \int_{\theta_2}^{\pi} V_M \sin \omega t \, \mathrm{d}(\omega t) \right\}
$$

$$
= \frac{V_M}{\pi}\left\{ \left[-\cos \omega t \right]_0^{\theta_1} + \left[0.6\omega t \right]_{\theta_1}^{\theta_2} + \left[-\cos \omega t \right]_{\theta_2}^{\pi} \right\}
$$

$$
= 48.16 \text{ V}
$$

The r.m.s. value of the wave can also be computed over the first half cycle as follows.

$$
V_{R.M.S.}^2 = \frac{1}{\pi}\left\{ \int_0^{\theta_1} (V_M \sin \omega t)^2 \, \mathrm{d}(\omega t) + \int_{\theta_1}^{\theta_2} (0.6 V_M)^2 \, \mathrm{d}(\omega t) + \int_{\theta_2}^{\pi} (V_M \sin \omega t)^2 \, \mathrm{d}(\omega t) \right\}
$$

$$
= \frac{V_M}{\pi}\left\{ \int_0^{\theta_1} \sin^2 \omega t \, \mathrm{d}(\omega t) + \int_{\theta_1}^{\theta_2} 0.36 \, \mathrm{d}(\omega t) + \int_{\theta_2}^{\pi} \sin^2 \omega t \, \mathrm{d}(\omega t) \right\} = 2640
$$

Hence,

$$V_{R.M.S.} = 51.38 \text{ V}$$

Example 3.5

A complex current, of r.m.s. value 10A, has 25 per cent third harmonic content, and 10 per cent fifth harmonic content. Determine the r.m.s. value of the fundamental frequency component, and of the third and fifth harmonic components of the wave.

Solution 3.5

The magnitude of the r.m.s. current is

$$I = \sqrt{(I_1^2 + I_3^2 + I_5^2)}$$

where I_1, I_3 and I_5 are the respective r.m.s. values of the fundamental, the third harmonic, and the fifth harmonic components.

Also $I_3 = 0.25I_1$, and $I_5 = 0.1I_1$. Hence

$$10 = \sqrt{[I_1^2 + (0.25I_1)^2 + (0.1I_1)^2]} = 1.036I_1$$

Therefore,

$$I_1 = 10/1.036 = 9.65 \text{ A}$$
$$I_3 = 0.25I_1 = 2.41 \text{ A}$$
$$I_5 = 0.1I_1 = 0.965 \text{ A}$$

Example 3.6

A current of

$$i = 2.58 \sin (\omega t + 1.25) + 0.765 \sin (3\omega t + 0.3) \text{ A}$$

flows in an inductive circuit when the voltage

$$v = 200 \sin \omega t + 20 \sin 3\omega t \text{ V}$$

is applied to it. Calculate the power supplied by each of the harmonic components of the wave, the total power consumed, and the overall power factor of the circuit.

Solution 3.6

The r.m.s. components of the current are

$$I_1 = 2.58/\sqrt{2} = 1.824 \text{ A and } I_3 = 0.765/\sqrt{2} = 0.541 \text{ A}$$

and for the voltage wave are

$$V_1 = 200/\sqrt{2} = 141.42 \text{ V and } V_3 = 20/\sqrt{2} = 14.14 \text{ V}$$

The power supplied by the fundamental frequency component is

$$V_1 I_1 \cos 1.25 \text{ rad} = 141.42 \times 1.824 \times 0.3153 = 81.33 \text{ W}$$

and the power supplied by the third harmonic is

$$V_3 I_3 \cos 0.3 \text{ rad} = 14.14 \times 0.541 \times 0.9553 = 7.305 \text{ W}$$

Total power $= 81.33 + 7.305 = 88.64$ W
Now, the r.m.s. current in the circuit is

$$I = \sqrt{[(2.58^2 + 0.765^2)/2]} = 1.903 \text{ A}$$

and

$$V = \sqrt{[(200^2 + 20^2)/2]} = 142.13 \text{ V}$$

$$\text{overall power factor} = \frac{\text{total power}}{VI} = \frac{88.64}{1.903 \times 142.13}$$

$$= 0.33$$

Example 3.7

For the waveform in Figure 3.7, evaluate the Fourier components A_0, a_1, b_1 and b_3.

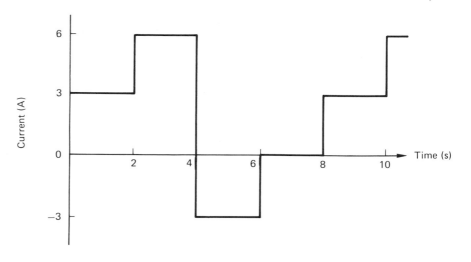

Fig 3.7

Solution 3.7

This is a relatively simple problem which illustrates the method of evaluating specific components in the series.

The periodic time of the wave is $T = 8$ s. The 'd.c.' or mean component, A_0, is calculated as follows.

Note that in the case of simple shapes, the area under the graph can be determined by inspection.

$$A_0 = \frac{1}{T} \int_0^T f(t) \, dt = \frac{1}{T} \int_0^T \text{area under the curve}$$

$$= \frac{1}{8} \left[\int_0^2 3 \, dt + \int_2^4 6 \, dt + \int_4^6 (-3) \, dt + \int_6^8 0 \, dt \right]$$

$$= \frac{1}{8} \left[(3 \times 2) + (6 \times 2) + (-3 \times 2) + 0 \right] = 1.5 \text{ A}$$

$$a_1 = \frac{2}{T} \int_0^T f(t) \cos \omega t \, dt \quad \text{where } \omega = \frac{2\pi}{T} = \frac{2\pi}{8} = \frac{\pi}{4} \text{ rad/s}$$

$$= \frac{2}{8} \left[\int_0^2 3 \cos \frac{\pi t}{4} \, dt + \int_2^4 6 \cos \frac{\pi t}{4} \, dt + \int_4^6 -3 \cos \frac{\pi t}{4} \, dt \right]$$

$$= \frac{12}{4\pi} \left[\sin \frac{2\pi}{4} + 2 \left(\sin \pi - \sin \frac{\pi}{2} \right) - \left(\sin \frac{3\pi}{2} - \sin \pi \right) \right] = 0$$

$$b_1 = = \frac{2}{T} \int_0^T f(t) \sin \omega t \, dt$$

$$= \frac{1}{4} \left[\int_0^2 3 \sin \frac{\pi t}{4} \, dt + \int_2^4 6 \sin \frac{\pi t}{4} \, dt + \int_4^6 (-3) \sin \frac{\pi t}{4} \, dt \right]$$

$$= \frac{-12}{4\pi} \left[-1 + 2 \left(\cos \pi - \cos \frac{\pi}{2} \right) - \left(\cos \frac{3\pi}{2} - \cos \pi \right) \right] = 3.82 \text{ A}$$

$$b_3 = \frac{2}{T} \int_0^T f(t) \sin 3\omega t \, dt$$

$$= \frac{1}{4} \left[\int_0^2 3 \sin \frac{3\pi t}{4} \, dt + \int_2^4 6 \sin \frac{3\pi t}{4} \, dt + \int_4^6 (-3) \sin \frac{3\pi t}{4} \, dt \right]$$

$$= \frac{-1}{\pi} \left[-1 + 2 \left(\cos 3\pi - \cos \frac{3\pi}{2} \right) - \left(\cos \frac{9\pi}{2} - \cos 3\pi \right) \right] = 1.27 \text{ A}$$

Example 3.8

Deduce the Fourier series for the waveform in Figure 3.7.

Solution 3.8

In this example, we will determine the general solution of the Fourier series for the wave in Figure 3.7 (see Worked Example 3.7 for the calculation of specific components). The value of A_0 is calculated in the way outlined in Worked Example 3.7, so that $A_0 = 1.5$ A.

Now

$$a_N = \frac{2}{T} \int_0^T f(t) \cos N\omega t \; dt \quad \text{where } \omega = \frac{2\pi}{T} = \frac{\pi}{4} \text{ rad/s}$$

$$= \frac{2}{8} \left\{ \int_0^2 3 \cos \frac{N\pi t}{4} \, dt + \int_2^4 6 \cos \frac{N\pi t}{4} \, dt + \int_4^6 (-3) \cos \frac{N\pi t}{4} \, dt \right\}$$

$$= \frac{1}{4} \left\{ \frac{12}{N\pi} \left[\sin \frac{N\pi t}{4} \right]_0^2 + \frac{24}{N\pi} \left[\sin \frac{N\pi t}{4} \right]_2^4 - \frac{12}{N\pi} \left[\sin \frac{N\pi t}{4} \right]_4^6 \right\}$$

$$= \frac{3}{N\pi} \left\{ \sin \frac{N\pi}{2} - 2 \sin \frac{N\pi}{2} - \sin \frac{3N\pi}{2} \right\} = 0 \text{ for all } N$$

and

$$b_N = \frac{2}{T} \int_0^T f(t) \sin N\omega t \; dt$$

$$= \frac{1}{4} \left\{ \int_0^2 3 \sin \frac{N\pi t}{4} \, dt + \int_2^4 6 \sin \frac{N\pi t}{4} \, dt + \int_4^6 (-3) \sin \frac{N\pi t}{4} \, dt \right\}$$

$$= \frac{-1}{4} \left\{ \frac{12}{N\pi} \left[\cos \frac{N\pi t}{4} \right]_0^2 + \frac{24}{N\pi} \left[\cos \frac{N\pi t}{4} \right]_2^4 - \frac{12}{N\pi} \left[\cos \frac{N\pi t}{4} \right]_4^6 \right\}$$

$$= \frac{-3}{N\pi} \left\{ -1 + 2 \cos N\pi + \cos N\pi \right\}$$

That is

$$b_N = \frac{12}{N\pi} \text{ for } N \text{ odd}$$

and

$$b_N = \frac{-6}{N\pi} \text{ for } N \text{ even}$$

Hence, the Fourier series for the waveform in Figure 3.7 is

$$i = 1.5 + 3.82 \sin \omega t - 0.96 \sin 2\omega t + 1.27 \sin 3\omega t - 0.48 \sin 4\omega t + \ldots \text{ A}$$

Note that the amount of work involved in the analysis can sometimes be reduced (as is the case here) by removing the d.c. term from the wave and studying the symmetry of the a.c. component of the wave. In this case, this is done by drawing a new x-axis through $y = A_0 = 1.5$; the remaining a.c. wave is seen to be symmetrical about the origin for which $a_N = 0$.

Example 3.9

Deduce the Fourier series for the half-wave rectified sinewave in Figure 3.8, and draw the line spectra for the wave.

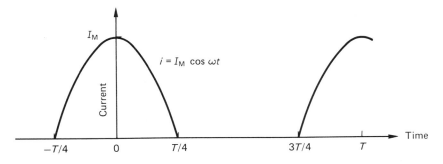

Fig 3.8

Solution 3.9

An inspection of the wave shows that it is an even function (see section (i) in the Fact Sheet of this chapter), so that its Fourier series does not contain sine terms and, for this reason, we need not attempt to calculate b_N (the reader will find it a useful exercise to verify the truth of this statement).

Now, $\omega T = 2\pi$, hence

$$\omega t = 2\pi t/T$$

$$A_0 = \frac{1}{T}\int_{-T/2}^{T/2} f(t)\ dt$$

However, the function is finite only in the period $-T/4$ to $T/4$, so that it need only be integrated over this period as follows.

$$A_0 = \frac{1}{T}\int_{-T/4}^{T/4} I_M \cos \frac{2\pi t}{T}\ dt = \frac{I_M}{2\pi}\left[\sin \frac{2\pi t}{T}\right]_{-T/4}^{T/4} = \frac{I_M}{\pi}$$

and

$$a_N = \frac{2}{T}\int_{-T/4}^{T/4} f(t)\ \cos N\omega t\ dt$$

$$= \frac{2}{T}\int_{-T/4}^{T/4} I_M \cos \frac{2\pi t}{T}\ \cos \frac{N2\pi t}{T}\ dt$$

$$= \frac{I_M}{T}\int_{-T/4}^{T/4\mathrm{T}} \left\{\cos \frac{(N+1)2\pi t}{T} + \cos \frac{(N-1)2\pi t}{T}\right\}\ dt$$

$$= \frac{I_M}{2\pi}\left[\left\{\frac{1}{(N+1)}\sin \frac{(N+1)\pi}{2} + \frac{1}{(N-1)}\sin \frac{(N-1)\pi}{2}\right\}\right.$$

$$\left. -\left\{\frac{1}{(N+1)}\sin \frac{(N+1)(-\pi)}{2} + \frac{1}{(N-1)}\sin \frac{(N-1)(-\pi)}{2}\right\}\right]$$

For odd values of N, $a_N = 0$, with the exception of a_1, which is indeterminant.

The latter is evaluated as follows.

$$a_1 = \frac{2}{T} \int_{-T/4}^{T/4} I_M \cos \frac{2\pi t}{T} \cos \frac{2\pi t}{T} \, dt = \frac{2I_M}{T} \int_{-T/4}^{T/4} \cos^2 \frac{2\pi t}{T} \, dt = \frac{I_M}{2}$$

Hence a Fourier series which describes the wave is

$$f(t) = \frac{I_M}{\pi} \left(1 + \frac{\pi}{2} \cos \omega t + \frac{2}{3} \cos 2\omega t - \frac{2}{15} \cos 4\omega t + \frac{2}{35} \cos 6\omega t - \dots \right)$$

The resulting magnitude line spectrum is shown in Figure 3.9.

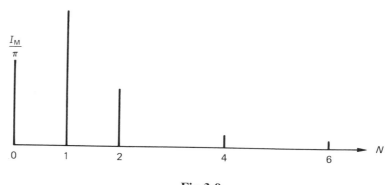

Fig 3.9

Example 3.10

The trigonometric Fourier series for a periodic function of time is

$$f(t) = 25 - 20.26 \cos 200\pi t - 2.25 \cos 300\pi t + 31.83 \sin 100\pi t$$
$$- 15.92 \cos 200\pi t + 10.6 \sin 300\pi t$$

and $\omega = 100\pi$ rad/s. Determine the periodic time T, the average value of the waveform, and the r.m.s. value of the wave. Draw the magnitude and phase line spectra of the wave.

Solution 3.10

Since $\omega T = 2\pi$, then $\omega t = 2\pi t/T$. For the fundamental frequency,

$$\omega = \frac{2\pi}{T} = 100\pi \text{ rad/s, or } T = 0.02 \text{ s} \left(f = \frac{1}{0.02} = 50 \text{ Hz} \right).$$

An examination of the Fourier series shows that the average value is

$$\text{average value} = A_0 = 25$$

and

$$\text{r.m.s. value} = \sqrt{[25^2 + (20.26^2 + 2.25^2 + 31.83^2 + 15.92^2 + 10.6^2)/2]}$$
$$= 39.02$$

Since the second and third harmonics have both sine and cosine terms, it is necessary to compute the effective magnitude and phase shift of each of them as follows.

$$\text{magnitude} = \sqrt{(a_N^2 + b_N^2)}$$

$$\text{phase shift} = \tan^{-1}(-a_N/b_N)$$

that is

$$\text{magnitude of 2nd harmonic} = \sqrt{(20.26^2 + 15.92^2)} = 25.77$$

$$\text{phase shift of 2nd harmonic} = \tan^{-1}(15.92/(-20.26))$$

$$= 141.84°$$

$$\text{magnitude of 3rd harmonic} = \sqrt{(2.25^2 + 10.6^2)} = 10.84$$

$$\text{phase shift of 3rd harmonic} = \tan^{-1}(-10.6/(-2.25))$$

$$= -102°$$

The magnitude and phase spectra of the wave are drawn in Figure 3.10.

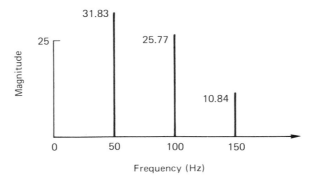

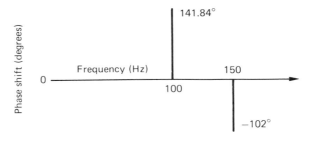

Fig 3.10

Example 3.11

For the waveforms in Figure 3.11, state which type (if any) of symmetry exists.

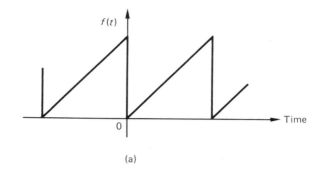

(a)

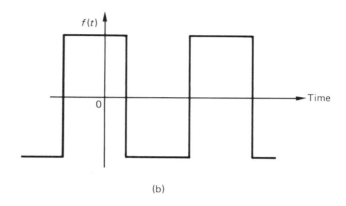

(b)

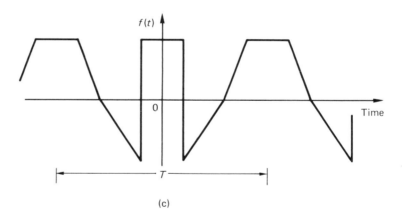

(c)

Fig 3.11

Solution 3.11

The reader should refer to section (i) of the Fact Sheet in this chapter when studying the following answers.

Waveform (a): None of the standard forms of symmetry exists. A_0 is finite.

Waveform (b): Half-wave inversion: $A_0 = 0$, and odd terms in a_N and b_N exist.

Waveform (c): Even function. A_0 is finite, a_N exists, $b_N = 0$.

Example 3.12

The following waveform results were obtained from tests on an electrical machine.

$\theta°$	0	30	60	90	120	150	180	210	240	270	300	330
$f(t)$	−130	−440	−320	−100	−90	−140	−60	60	140	320	510	360

Using harmonic analysis, estimate the value of the coefficients in the trigonometric Fourier series up to and including the third harmonic which describes the waveform.

Solution 3.12

The solution can be obtained in tabular form (see Table 3.1) and, in so doing, the problem is reduced to a series of semi-mechanical operations, minimizing the risk of error; the calculations are based on the method outlined in section (k) of the Fact Sheet for this chapter.

Table 3.1

$\theta°$	$f(t)$	$f(t) \sin\theta$	$f(t) \cos\theta$	$f(t) \sin2\theta$	$f(t) \cos2\theta$	$f(t) \sin3\theta$	$f(t) \cos 3\theta$
0	−130	0	−130	0	−130	0	−130
30	−440	−220	−381	−381	−220	−440	0
60	−320	−277	−160	−277	160	0	320
90	−100	−100	0	0	100	100	0
120	−90	−77.9	45	77.9	45	0	−90
150	−140	−70	121.2	121.2	−70	−140	0
180	−60	0	60	0	−60	0	60
210	60	−30	−52	52	30	−60	0
240	140	−121.3	−70	121.3	−70	0	140
270	320	−320	0	0	−320	320	0
300	510	−441.7	255	−441.7	−255	0	−510
330	360	−180	311.8	−311.8	180	−360	0
Sum	110	−1837.9	0	−1039.1	−610	−580	−210

In the following, we calculate the mean value, together with the first three cosine and sine coefficients in the series. From Table 3.1:

$$A_0 = \text{mean value of } \Sigma f(t) = 110/12 = 9.17$$

$$a_1 = 2 \times \text{mean value of } \Sigma f(t) \cos\theta = 2 \times 0/12 = 0$$

$$a_2 = 2 \times \text{mean value of } \Sigma f(t) \cos 2\theta = 2 \times (-610)/12 = -101.7$$

$$a_3 = 2 \times \text{mean value of } \Sigma f(t) \cos 3\theta = 2 \times (-210)/12 = -35$$

$$b_1 = 2 \times \text{mean value of } \Sigma f(t) \sin \theta = 2 \times (-1837.9)/12 = -306.3$$

$$b_2 = 2 \times \text{mean value of } \Sigma f(t) \sin 2\theta = 2 \times (-1039.1)/12 = -173.2$$

$$b_3 = 2 \times \text{mean value of } \Sigma f(t) \sin 3\theta = 2 \times (-580)/12 = -96.7$$

Hence, the first few terms in the series are

$$f(t) = 9.17 - 101.7 \cos 2\theta - 35 \cos 3\theta \ldots$$
$$- 306.3 \sin \theta - 173.2 \sin 2\theta - 97.6 \sin 3\theta \ldots$$

Whilst the magnitude of the coefficients of the series appear to be diminishing as the order of the harmonics increases, care should be taken with this type of analysis, because some of the high-order harmonics may, in fact, be quite large.

3.3 Unworked Problems

Problem 3.1

Determine (a) the form factor, (b) the peak factor for (i) a half-wave rectified sine wave, (ii) a full-wave rectified sine wave.
[(a) (i) 1.57, (ii) 2.0; (b) (i) 1.11, (ii) 1.414]

Problem 3.2

For the following waveforms determine (a) the maximum value, (b) the r.m.s. value; (i) $50 \cos \omega t$, (ii) $20 \cos \omega t - 30 \sin \omega t$, (iii) $(M-N) \cos (\omega t + \pi/8)$
[(a) (i) 50, (ii) 36.06, (iii) $M-N$; (b) (i) 35.36, (ii) 25.5, (iii) $(M-N)/\sqrt{2}$]

Problem 3.3

The first half cycle of the m.m.f. waveform in an electrical machine increases uniformly from 0 at 0° to a maximum of F at α radians. It remains constant at a value of F from α to $(\pi - \alpha)$ radians, when it decreases uniformly to zero at π radians. For (a) $\alpha = \pi/6$ radian, and (b) $\alpha = \pi/2$ radian, calculate (i) the mean and (ii) the r.m.s. value of the waveform. In each case, draw the waveform of m.m.f.
[(a) (i) $5F/6$; (ii) $F\sqrt{(7/9)}$; (b) (i) $F/2$, (ii) $F/\sqrt{3}$]

Problem 3.4

The current in a circuit containing a resistance and an inductance is

$$i = 10 \sin (\omega t - 0.7) + \sin (3\omega t - 0.15) + 0.25 \sin (5\omega t + 1.3) \text{ A}$$

where $\omega = 350$ rad/s. If the voltage applied to the circuit is

$$v = 282.8 \sin (\omega t + 0.085) + 63.25 \sin (3\omega t + 1.1) + 25.5 \sin (5\omega t + 2.674) \text{ V}$$

calculate **(a)** the r.m.s. value of the voltage and the current, **(b)** the power supplied to the circuit, and **(c)** the power factor of the circuit.
[**(a)** 205.7 V, 10.05 A; **(b)** 1010.6 W; **(c)** 0.49 lagging]

Problem 3.5

An a.c. circuit contains a 1000 ohm resistor in series with a 1.0 H inductor. If the supply voltage is

$$v = 200 \sin 500t + 100 \sin 1500t + 50 \sin 2500t \text{ V}$$

deduce an expression for the current in the circuit, and calculate the power dissipated in the circuit.

Note: the reader will need an understanding of basic a.c. circuit theory before attempting this question.
[$i = 0.179 \sin (500t - 0.464) + 0.055 \sin (1500t - 0.983) + 0.0186 \sin (2500t - 1.19)$ A; 35.41 W]

Problem 3.6

If the 1000 ohm resistor and the 1.0 H inductor in Problem 3.5 are connected in parallel with one another, and the combination is connected in series with a capacitor of 15 microfarad capacitance to a supply of

$$v = 10 \sin 500t + 20 \sin (1500t + 40°) \text{ V}$$

deduce an expression for the voltage across the capacitor, and calculate the power consumed by the circuit. Calculate also the percentage fifth harmonic content of the resultant current.

Note: the reader needs to have an understanding of a.c. circuit theory before attempting this problem.
[$i = 0.05 \sin 500t + 0.026 \sin (1500t - 14.63°)$ A; 0.972 W; 52%]

Problem 3.7

State if any form of symmetry exists in the waveform in Figure 3.12. Deduce the trigonometric Fourier series which describes the waveform. Draw the line frequency spectrum for the wave.

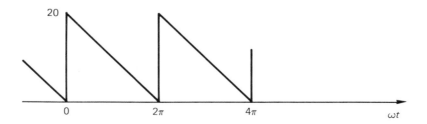

Fig 3.12

[None of the standard forms of symmetry exist;

$$f(\omega t) = 10 + \frac{20}{\pi}\sin \omega t + \frac{20}{2\pi}\sin 2\omega t + \ldots$$

$$= 10 + \frac{20}{\pi}\sum_{N=1}^{\infty}\frac{\sin N\omega t}{N}]$$

Problem 3.8

The discrete amplitude and phase spectra of a complex signal are respectively shown in Figure 3.13(a) and (b). Determine for this wave (a) the trigonometric form of the Fourier series for the wave, (b) the value of the coefficients A_0, a_1 to a_3, and b_1 to b_3 for the wave, and the mean value of the wave.
[$f(t) = 20 + 30\sin(\omega t - 11°) + 4\sin(2\omega t - 30°) + 3\sin(3\omega t - 45°)$;
$A_0 = 20$, $a_1 = -1.73$, $b_1 = 37.2$, $a_2 = -1.73$, $b_2 = 3$, $a_3 = -2.12$, $b_3 = 2.12$;
mean value = 20]

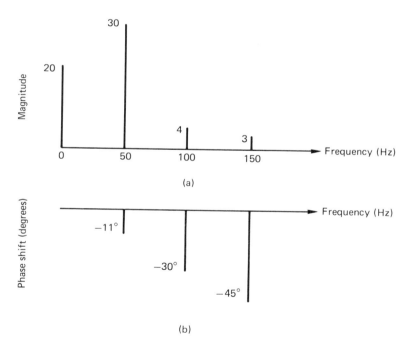

Fig 3.13

Problem 3.9

The following measurements were obtained from a complex voltage waveform, the second half-cycle having the same instantaneous values but of opposite sign.

θ (deg)	0	20	40	60	80	100	120	140	160
v (V)	-174	206	560	684	590	416	346	386	380

Determine the complex expression for the waveform up to and including the third harmonic. Express the amplitude of the third harmonic as a percentage of the fundamental.

$[v = - \cos \omega t + 598 \sin \omega t - 172 \cos 3\omega t + 101 \sin 3\omega t$ V
$= 598.01 \sin \omega t + 199.5 \sin (3\omega t - 59.6°)$ V; 33.36 %]

Problem 3.10

Investigate the symmetry of the waveforms in Figure 3.14, and state which type of symmetry exists in each case. Deduce the trigonometric Fourier series for the waveform in Figure 3.14(b).

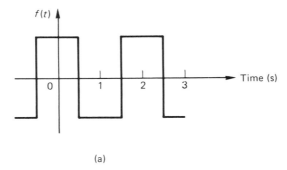

(a)

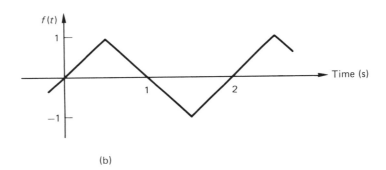

(b)

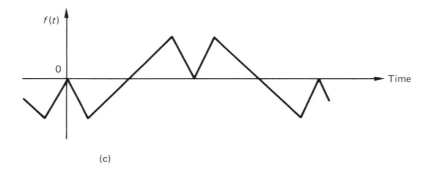

(c)

Fig 3.14

[diagram

	(a)	(b)	(c)
Even function	YES	NO	YES
Odd function	NO	YES	NO
Half-wave repetition	NO	NO	NO
Half-wave inversion	YES	YES	YES

$$f(t) = \frac{8}{\pi^2} \left(\sin \pi t - \frac{1}{3^2} \sin 3\pi t + \frac{1}{5^2} \sin 5\pi t - \ldots \right)]$$

Problem 3.11

Figure 3.15 shows a waveform with a periodic time of 0.1 second. **(a)** State if the function is odd, even, or neither, and give reasons for your answer. **(b)** Determine the amplitude of the fundamental and third harmonic of the waveform, and state the frequency of each. **(c)** Determine the magnitude of the d.c. component of the waveform.

(Liverpool Polytechnic)

[**(a)** neither; **(b)** 0.637, 0.212, 10 Hz, 30 Hz; **(c)** 1 V]

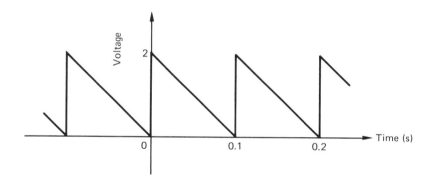

Fig 3.15

Problem 3.12

A voltage waveform supplied to a d.c. motor by a power electronics drive source consists of a series of positive rectangular pulses of magnitude E and duration T_d, the periodic time of the pulses being T. If the mark-space duty ratio of the wave is $D = T_d/T$, determine the form factor of the waveform in terms of D.

(Liverpool Polytechnic)

[form factor $= 1/\sqrt{D}$]

Problem 3.13

Calculate the mean value of the voltage waveform in Figure 3.16.

(Staffordshire Polytechnic)
[Hint: use the area of the graph divided by the period; 1.5 V]

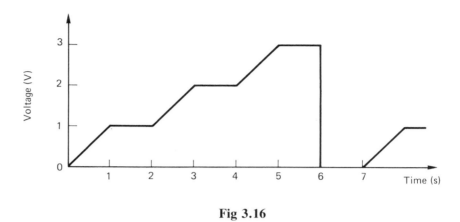

Fig 3.16

4 Reactance, Susceptance, Impedance and Admittance

4.1 Fact Sheet

(a) Reactance and Susceptance of a Pure Inductor

When a resistanceless inductor is connected to a sinusoidal supply, the current which flows produces a magnetic flux. This, in turn, induces an e.m.f. in the inductor which opposes the flow of current, and restricts the current in the inductor. The r.m.s. magnitude of the current, I, in the inductor is

$$I = E/X_L \text{ A}$$

where E is the r.m.s. value of the supply voltage, and X_L is the *inductive reactance* of the inductor. The value of X_L is calculated from

$$X_L = \omega L = 2\pi f L \text{ ohm}$$

where ω is the supply frequency in rad/s, and f is the supply frequency in Hz.
Alternatively, the relationship may be written as

$$I = EB_L \text{ A}$$

where B_L is the *inductive susceptance* of the inductor, and

$$B_L = 1/\omega L = 1/2\pi f L \text{ S}$$

(b) Reactance and Susceptance of a Capacitor

When a capacitor is connected to an alternating supply, the alternations of voltage cause an alternating charging current to flow in the circuit. If the circuit contains only a capacitor, the magnitude of the current in the capacitor is

$$I = E/X_C \text{ A}$$

where X_C is the *capacitive reactance* of the capacitor; X_C is calculated from

$$X_C = 1/\omega C = 1/2\pi f C \text{ ohm}$$

Alternatively, the relationship can be written in the form

$$I = EB_C \text{ A}$$

where B_C is the *capacitive susceptance* of the capacitor, and

$$B_C = \omega C = 2\pi f C \text{ S}$$

(d) Impedance and Admittance

The *impedance* of an element, a branch, or a complete circuit is its effective opposition to the flow of alternating current, and is given by

$$\text{impedance, } \mathbf{Z} = \mathbf{E}/\mathbf{I} \text{ ohm}$$

where $\mathbf{E}$ is the r.m.s. voltage applied to the element, branch, or circuit, and $\mathbf{I}$ is the r.m.s. current which flows in it. Letters printed in **bold typeface** are complex values, which are described in detail not only in sections (g) to (i) of this Fact Sheet, but also later in the book and in Appendix 1.

The *admittance* of an element, branch, or circuit is the reciprocal of its impedance, and

$$\text{admittance, } \mathbf{Y} = 1/\mathbf{Z} \text{ S}$$

$$\mathbf{I} = \mathbf{EY} \text{ A}$$

A detailed treatment of complex impedance and admittance is given later in this chapter.

(e) Phase Angle

A sinusoidal forcing function is a function of time but, when analysing a.c. circuits, it is more convenient to deal with a number which represents the sinusoid as though it is not a function of time. The phasor is a simple transform which allows us to do this.

To illustrate the phasor concept, consider the sinusoidal voltage waveform in Figure 4.1(b) which is traced out by the vertical projection of the tip of the line of length V_M (Figure 4.1(a)), which is rotating in an anticlockwise direction at a speed of ω rad/s. When the line has been rotating for t_1 seconds, it reaches an angle ωt_1 radians, and the instantaneous value (the vertical component of the line) of the current is $v = V_M \sin \omega t_1$ V.

The *phasor*, V, in Figure 4.1(c) represents both the *r.m.s. value and the phase angle* of the voltage at a particular point in time; it is important to note that the length of the phasor is scaled to represent the r.m.s. value (V) of the waveform, and *it does not represent* the maximum value of the wave. In the case of Figure 4.1(c), we chose to 'freeze' the phasor at time t_1; however, we could have

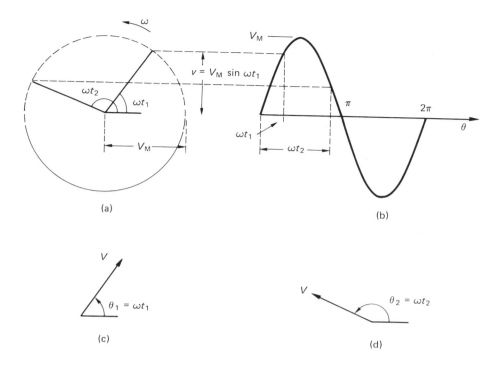

Fig 4.1

selected some other time, such as t_2, merely by allowing the line V_M to rotate a little further. The phasor corresponding to time t_2 is illustrated in Figure 4.1(d). The reader should note that in Figure 4.1(c) and (d) the phasor has the same length. That is to say, a phasor diagram is not unique to the circuit, and there are a multiplicity of phasor diagrams which can be used to represent the state of the circuit, but at different points in time.

The equation for the instantaneous value of voltage can be expressed in the form

$$v = V_M \sin (\omega t + \phi) \text{ V}$$

e.g.

$$v = 7.07 \sin (100t + 45°) \text{ V}$$

The reader should note that whilst ω, in the above case, is 100 rad/s, the angle ϕ is expressed in degrees (this is often the case in electrical engineering, but you should note that angle ϕ could also be in radians!). The above expression is a time-varying quantity, and can be expressed as the *imaginary* (Im) part of a complex quantity, that is

$$v = \text{Im}(V_M e^{j(\omega t + \phi)})$$

We represent this voltage as a *polar complex quantity* simply by dropping Im, and simplifying it as follows

$$V = V\angle\phi$$

where V is the r.m.s. value (i.e., the *modulus* or *magnitude*) of the voltage waveform, and ϕ is its *phase angle*. Thus, the complex voltage V represents both the r.m.s. value and the phase angle of the phasor.

The reader should observe that v is a *time-domain representation* of the voltage, and V is a *frequency domain representation*.

(f) Phasor Diagrams

Consider the waveform diagrams of voltage and current in Figure 4.2. The *phase angle displacement* or *phase difference* between the two waves is the angular difference (either in degrees or radians) between the corresponding point on the two waves. The phase angle between the two waves in Figure 4.2(a) is ϕ. The phasor diagram corresponding to angle B on the waveform diagram is shown in Figure 4.2(b), and the phasor diagram corresponding to angle C is in Figure 4.2(c). If, in these diagrams, the r.m.s. voltage was 100 V, and the current was 50 A, we could write

$$\text{If} \quad V = 100\angle 0° \text{ V} \quad \text{then } I = 50\angle -45° \text{ A}$$

$$\text{or if } V = 100\angle 90° \text{ V} \quad \text{then } I = 50\angle 45° \text{ A, etc.}$$

In most cases, it is convenient to show one of the phasors in the *reference direction*; Figure 4.2(b) illustrates this for the case where V is in the reference direction.

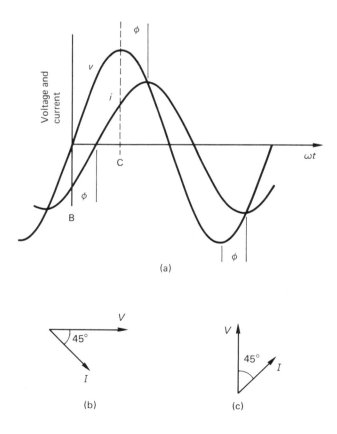

(a)

(b)

(c)

Fig 4.2

88

(g) Complex Inductive Reactance and Susceptance

If a pure inductor is connected to a sinusoidal supply, the current through the inductor lags behind the voltage across it by 90° (see Figure 4.3). That is if $V_L = V\angle 0°$ then $I = I\angle -90°$ and the complex inductive reactance, X_L, is

$$\frac{V_L}{I} = \frac{V\angle 0°}{I\angle -90°} = X_L\angle 90° = \omega L\angle 90° = j\omega L \text{ ohm}$$

and the complex inductive susceptance, B_L, is

$$\frac{1}{X_L\angle 90°} = \frac{1}{\omega L\angle 90°} = \frac{-j}{X_L} = \frac{-j}{\omega L} \text{ S}$$

Note that the complex inductive susceptance has a negative mathematical sign.

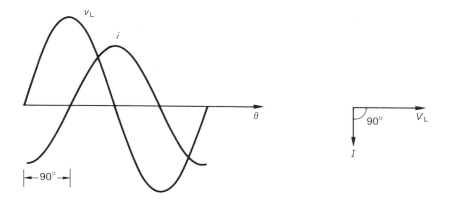

Fig 4.3

(h) Complex Capacitive Reactance and Susceptance

When a capacitor is connected to a sinusoidal supply, the current through the capacitor leads the voltage across it by 90° (see Figure 4.4). That is if $V_C = V\angle 0°$ then $I = I\angle 90°$, and the complex capacitive reactance, X_C, is

$$\frac{V_C}{I} = \frac{V\angle 0°}{I\angle 90°} = X_C\angle -90° = \frac{1}{\omega C\angle 90°} = \frac{1\angle -90°}{\omega C} = \frac{1}{j\omega C} = \frac{-j}{\omega C} \text{ ohm}$$

and the complex capacitive susceptance is

$$1/X_C\angle -90° = \omega C\angle 90° = j\omega C \text{ S}$$

(i) Complex Impedance and Admittance

The *complex impedance* of an element, branch, or circuit, in ohms, is given by Ohm's law as

$$Z = E/I \text{ ohm}$$

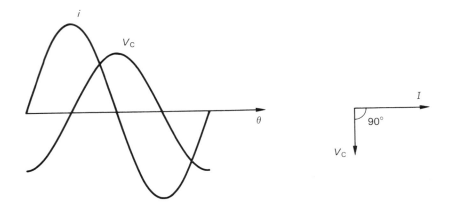

Fig 4.4

The impedance of an a.c. circuit is a complex number, but *is not a phasor*. Since the value is complex, it has a real part (the *resistance*) and an imaginary part (the *reactance*). That is it can be expressed in *rectangular complex form* as

$$Z = R \pm jX \text{ ohm}$$

Similarly, the admittance of an a.c. circuit is a complex number which is not a phasor. It has a real part (the *conductance*) and an imaginary part (the *susceptance*). That is

$$Y = G \pm jB \text{ S}$$

4.2   Worked Examples

Example 4.1

Calculate the reactance and susceptance of an inductor of 0.1 H inductance at a frequency of **(a)** 100 Hz, **(b)** 1 kHz. What is the effect on the value of the reactance if the inductance is doubled?

Solution 4.1

(a) $X_L = 2\pi fL = 2\pi \times 100 \times 0.1 = 62.83 \text{ ohm}$

and $B_L = 1/X_L = 0.0159 \text{ S}$

(b) $X_L = 2\pi fL = 2\pi \times 1000 \times 0.1 = 628.3 \text{ ohm}$

and $B_L = 1/X_L = 0.00159 \text{ S}$

The above calculations show that a tenfold increase in frequency results in a corresponding increase in inductive reactance (and a corresponding reduction in inductive susceptance).

Also, since $X_L = 2\pi f L$, then at constant frequency $X_L \propto L$. Hence, at a given frequency, the reactance is doubled (and the susceptance halved) if the inductance is doubled.

Example 4.2

A capacitor has a reactance of 80 ohm at a frequency of 200 Hz, and another has the same reactance at 2 kHz. Calculate the capacitance of the capacitor in each case.

Solution 4.2

Now $X_c = 1/2\pi f C$ or $C = 1/2\pi f X_c$, so that

(a) $\qquad C = 1/(2\pi \times 200 \times 80) = 9.95 \times 10^{-6}$ F or 9.95 μF

(b) $\qquad C = 1/(2\pi \times 2000 \times 80) = 0.995 \times 10^{-6}$ F or 0.995 μF

Example 4.3

An electrical circuit is connected to a 100 V, 50 Hz supply, and the current in the circuit is 2.5 A. Calculate the modulus of the impedance and admittance of the circuit. If the circuit comprises **(a)** a pure inductor, **(b)** a pure capacitor, calculate the value of the circuit element.

Solution 5.3

The modulus of the impedance is

$$Z = V/I = 100/2.5 = 40 \text{ ohm}$$

and that of the admittance is

$$Y = 1/Z = 1/40 = 0.025 \text{ S}$$

If the element in the circuit is either a pure inductor, or a pure capacitor, the circuit impedance is equal to the reactance of the element.

(a) In the case of a pure inductor

$$X_L = 40 = 2\pi f L$$

or

$$L = X_L/2\pi f = 40/(2\pi \times 50) = 0.127 \text{ H}$$

(b) In the case of a pure capacitor

$$X_c = 1/2\pi fC$$

or

$$C = 1/2\pi fX_c = 1/(2\pi \times 50 \times 40) = 79.6 \times 10^{-6} \text{ F or } 79.6 \text{ μF}$$

Example 4.4

Draw the phasor diagram corresponding to each of the waveforms in Figure 4.5, and state the phase relationship between the voltage and current in each case. Also state an expression for the voltage and current waves expressed as a function of time, and give each as a polar complex quantity. Calculate the impedance of the circuit associated with each waveform.

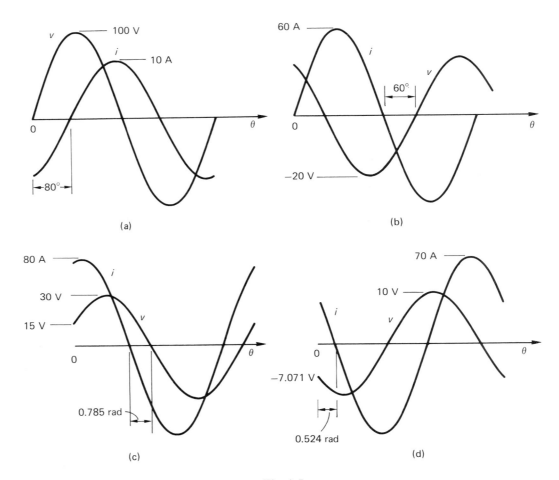

Fig 4.5

Solution 4.4

The phasor diagram associated with each waveform is shown in Figure 4.6, and are described below.

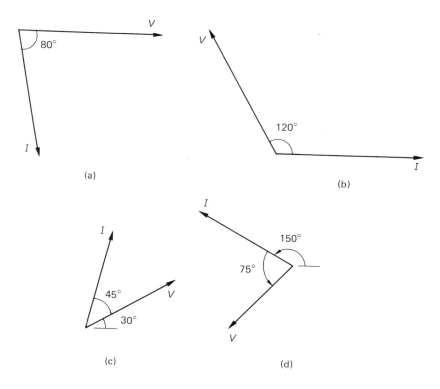

Fig 4.6

(a) In this case (see part (a) of Figure 4.5 and 4.6), the sinewave of voltage commences at $\theta = 0$, and the current passes through zero and increases in a positive direction, reaching zero some 80° later; that is, I lags behind V by 80°. The corresponding phasor diagram at time $t = 0$ is shown in Figure 4.6(a). Expressions which describe the voltage and current are

$$v = 100 \sin \omega t \text{ A}$$

$$i = 10 \sin (\omega t - 80°) \text{ A}$$

In polar complex form, the voltage and current are

$$V = \frac{100}{\sqrt{2}} \angle 0° = 70.71 \angle 0° \text{ V}$$

and

$$I = \frac{10}{\sqrt{2}} \angle -80° = 7.071 \angle -80° \text{ A}$$

In this case, the magnitude of the impedance is

$$Z = \frac{V_M}{I_M} = \frac{100}{10} = 10 \text{ ohm}$$

Alternatively, using r.m.s. values

$$Z = \frac{V}{I} = \frac{70.71}{7.071} = 10 \text{ ohm}$$

(b) The waveform and corresponding phasor diagram are shown in Figure 4.6(b). In this case, the voltage waveform leads the current waveform by 120° (or, alternatively, the current leads the voltage waveform by 240°, or the current lags behind the voltage by 120°). Expressions which describe the voltage and current are

$$v = 20 \sin (\omega t + 120°) \text{ V}$$

and

$$i = 60 \sin \omega t \text{ A}$$

and the polar complex values are

$$V = \frac{20}{\sqrt{2}} \angle 120° = 14.142 \angle 120° \text{ V}$$

and

$$I = \frac{60}{\sqrt{2}} \angle 0° = 42.43 \angle 0° \text{ A}$$

and the modulus of the impedance of the circuit is

$$Z = \frac{V_M}{I_M} = \frac{20}{60} = 0.3333 \text{ ohm}$$

(c) In this case, the phase angle difference between the voltage and current is 0.785 rad or 45°, with the current leading the voltage. Using the data in Figure 4.5(c), the angle of the voltage phasor at $\theta = 0$ is $\sin^{-1} (15/30) = 30°$, hence the voltage and current can be expressed as a function of time as follows.

$$v = 30 \sin (\omega t + 30°) \text{ V}$$

and

$$i = 80 \sin (\omega t + 75°) \text{ A}$$

and the polar complex expressions may be written in the form

$$V = \frac{30}{\sqrt{2}} \angle 30° = 21.21 \angle 30° \text{ V}$$

and

$$I = \frac{80}{\sqrt{2}} \angle 75° = 56.57/75° \text{ A}$$

The modulus of the circuit impedance is

$$Z = \frac{V_M}{I_M} = \frac{30}{80} = 0.375 \text{ ohm}$$

(d) In this case, when $\theta = 0$, the voltage phasor has already rotated through an angle of $180° + \sin^{-1}(-0.7071/(-10)) = 225°$. Also, since the current waveform reaches zero at an angle of 0.524 rad or 30°, it has rotated through an angle of $180° - 30° = 150°$ by $t = 0$. That is,

$$v = 10 \sin (\omega t + 225°) \text{ V}$$

and

$$i = 70 \sin (\omega t + 150°) \text{ A}$$

Hence, the voltage leads the current by $225° - 150° = 75°$, and the voltage may be expressed in the form

$$V = \frac{10}{\sqrt{2}} \angle 225° = 7.071 \angle 225° \text{ V}$$

or in the form $V = 7.071 \angle -135°$ V, and

$$I = \frac{70}{\sqrt{2}} \angle 150° = 49.5 \angle 150° \text{ A}$$

and the modulus of the circuit impedance is

$$Z = \frac{V_M}{I_M} = \frac{10}{70} = 0.143 \text{ ohm}$$

Example 4.5

A circuit of impedance $(10 + j15)$ ohm is energized by a voltage $v = 141.2 \sin (2000t + 45°)$ V. Calculate the current in the circuit expressed **(a)** in polar complex form and **(b)** as a function of time.

Solution 4.5

The supply voltage expressed in polar complex form is

$$V = \frac{141.2}{\sqrt{2}} \angle 45° = 100 \angle 45° \text{ V}$$

and the impedance in rectangular form is $Z = 10 + j15$ ohm, which is converted into its complex polar form (see appendix 1 for details) to give

$$Z = 18.03 \angle 56.31° \text{ ohm}$$

(a) The current in the circuit is given in complex polar form by (see Appendix 1 for details of complex number division)

$$I = \frac{V}{Z} = \frac{100 \angle 45°}{18.03 \angle 56.31°} = 5.55 \angle -11.31° = 5.44 - j1.1 \text{ A}$$

(b) From part (a) of the solution, the current waveform passes through zero at an angle of 11.31° after $\omega t = 0$, and the maximum current is $I_M = \sqrt{2} \times 5.55 = 7.85$ A, hence $i = 7.85 \sin (\omega t - 11.31°)$ A.

Example 4.6

The current flowing in a circuit is (4 + j12) A when the applied voltage is $180\angle 55°$ V. Determine both polar and rectangular complex expressions for the impedance of the circuit, and state the type of elements in the circuit.

Solution 4.6

The current is converted into its polar form using the techniques outlined in Appendix 1.

$$I = 4 + j12 = 12.65\angle 71.57° \text{ A}$$

From Ohm's law, the circuit impedance is

$$Z = \frac{V}{I} = \frac{180\angle 55°}{12.65\angle 71.57°} = 14.23\angle -16.57° = 13.64 - j4.06 \text{ ohm}$$

The rectangular complex form of expression for the impedance shows that the circuit contains a resistive element of 13.64 ohm and, since the expression contains a '$-j$' term, it also contains a capacitor of reactance 4.06 ohm.

Example 4.7

A voltage of $10\angle 30°$ V is applied to a series circuit comprising a resistor of 15 ohm resistance and an inductor of 95 ohm reactance. Determine a complex expression for the impedance of the circuit and one for the admittance of the circuit. Calculate also the current in the circuit.

Solution 4.7

The impedance of the circuit is

$$Z = R + jX_L = 15 + j95 = 96.18\angle 81.03° \text{ ohm}$$

and

$$Y = \frac{1}{Z} = \frac{1}{96.18\angle 81.03°} = 0.0104\angle -81.03° = 0.0016 - j0.0103 \text{ S}$$

The current in the circuit is

$$I = \frac{V_s}{Z} = \frac{10\angle 30°}{96.18\angle 81.03°} = 0.104\angle -51.03° \text{ A}$$

4.3 Unworked Problems

Problem 4.1

Calculate the admittance Y, the conductance G, and the susceptance B of a series circuit consisting of a resistor of 10 ohm resistance in series with a 0.1 H inductor. The supply frequency is 50 Hz.
[Y = 0.0303 S; G = 0.0092 S; B = −0.029 S]

Problem 4.2

A 250 V, 50 Hz alternating voltage produces a current of 2 A in a coil. When 100 V d.c. is applied to the coil, the current is also 2 A. Calculate the resistance and inductance of the coil, and its inductive reactance at a frequency of 100 Hz.
[50 ohm; 0.365 H; 229 ohm]

Problem 4.3

Five 80 microfarad capacitors are connected (a) in series, (b) in parallel to a 250 V, 50 Hz supply. Calculate, for each combination, complex expressions for (i) the impedance, (ii) the current.
[(a) (i) 198.9∠−90° ohm, (ii) 7.96∠90° ohm; (b) (i) 1.26∠90° A, (ii) 31.4°∠90° A]

Problem 4.4

A circuit of admittance (0.1 + j0.02) S is energized by a voltage of 20∠−20° V. Determine complex expressions for the circuit current.
[2.04∠−8.69° = 2 − j0.3 A]

Problem 4.5

The voltage applied to a circuit is given by $V_s = V_1 + V_2$. If $V_1 = 200∠50°$ V and $V_2 = 100∠−10°$ V, draw the waveform and phasor diagrams for V_s, V_1 and V_2. By calculation and from the phasor diagram determine V_s.
[173.2∠80° V]

Problem 4.6

A parallel circuit has three branches. If the total current flowing into the parallel circuit is 10∠30° mA, a current of 3∠80° mA flows in one branch, and 4∠−50° mA in another branch, what current flows in the third branch? Draw the phasor diagram showing the currents. If the supply voltage is 10∠30° V, what is the impedance of the third branch?
[7.6∠42.5° mA; 1322∠−12.5° ohm]

Problem 4.7

The impedance of a parallel circuit is given by the expression

$$Z = \frac{Z_1 Z_2}{Z_1 + Z_2}. \text{ If } Z_1 = 10\angle 85° \text{ ohm, and } Z_2 = 5 - j6 \text{ ohm}$$

Calculate (a) the impedance of the circuit, (b) the current drawn by the parallel circuit, and (c) the current in each branch of the circuit. The voltage applied to the circuit is $(10 + j2)$ V.
[(a) $11.03\angle 0.8°$ ohm;   (b) $0.925\angle 10.52°$ A;   (c) $I_1 = 1.02\angle -73.69°$ A, $I_2 = 1.31\angle 61.51°$ A]

Problem 4.8

If the current through a 100-microfarad capacitor is $i = 40 \sin (500t + 60°)$ mA, deduce an expression for the instantaneous voltage across the capacitor. Sketch the waveforms of i and v.

(Staffordshire Polytechnic)

$[v = 0.8 \sin (500t - 30°) \text{ V}]$

Problem 4.9

The current through a coil is given by $i = 5 \sin 314t$ mA. If the self-inductance of the coil is 2 H, calculate the r.m.s. voltage across the coil when the coil resistance is (a) negligible, (b) 628 ohm.

(Staffordshire Polytechnic)

[(a) 2.22 V; (b) 3.14 V]

5 A.C. Series and Parallel Circuits

5.1 Fact Sheet

(a) Series Circuits

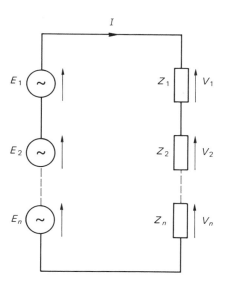

Fig 5.1

Applying KVL to Figure 5.1 yields

$$E_1 + E_2 + \ldots + E_N = IZ_1 + IZ_2 + \ldots + IZ_N$$
$$= I(Z_1 + Z_2 + \ldots + Z_N)$$
$$= IZ_E$$

where Z_E is the *effective impedance* of the circuit and is

$$Z_E = Z_1 + Z_2 + \ldots + Z_N$$
$$= (R_1 + jX_1) + (R_2 + jX_2) + \ldots + (R_N + jX_N)$$
$$= (R_1 + R_2 + \ldots + R_N) + j(X_1 + X_2 + \ldots + X_N)$$
$$= Z_E \angle \phi$$

where Z_E is the modulus of the effective impedance, and ϕ is the phase angle between I and the total e.m.f. E.

If $Z_E = R + jX$, the circuit has a *net inductive reactance* ($X_L > X_C$), and I lags behind E (or, alternatively, E leads I); if $Z_E = R - jX$, the circuit has a *net capacitive reactance* ($X_L < X_C$), and I leads E (or, alternatively, E lags behind I) – see Figure 5.2. *In no case can the phase angle of the circuit element exceed 90°.*

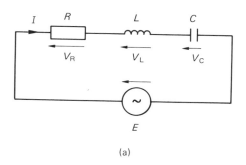

(a)

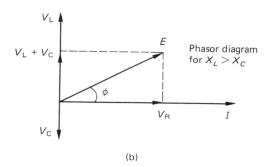

(b)

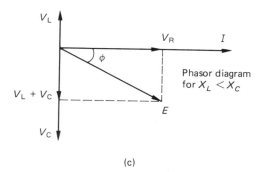

(c)

Fig 5.2

In Figure 5.2, and for our own convenience, the current has been taken for the reference phasor. However, simply by rotating the complete diagram through an appropriate angle, any phasor can be selected to be in the reference direction.

Also the effective admittance of an a.c. circuit is given by

$$Y_E = \frac{1}{Z_E}$$

When dealing with a.c. circuits, all values are complex (unless otherwise stated).

(b) Z to Y and Y to Z Conversion

The general relationship between Z and Y is

$$Y = 1/Z$$

If $Z = R + jX$

then $Y = \dfrac{1}{R + jX} = \dfrac{R - jX}{(R + jX)(R - jX)} = \dfrac{R - jX}{R^2 + X^2}$

$$= \frac{R}{R^2 + X^2} - j\frac{X}{R^2 + X^2} = G - jB$$

where

$$G = \frac{R}{R^2 + X^2} \quad \text{and} \quad B = \frac{X}{R^2 + X^2}$$

and if

$$Y = G + jB$$

then

$$Z = \frac{1}{G + jB} = \frac{G - jB}{(G + jB)(G - jB)} = \frac{G - jB}{G^2 + B^2} = R - jX$$

where

$$R = \frac{G}{G^2 + B^2} \quad \text{and} \quad X = \frac{B}{G^2 + B^2}$$

Note that it is generally easier to convert an impedance value to an admittance value (or vice versa) using the polar component value than it is to do so using the rectangular component value.

(c) Potential Division in a Series Circuit

If E is the algebraic sum of the e.m.f.s in a series circuit, then the potential drop, V_N, across the Nth element is

$$V_N = IZ_N = \frac{EZ_N}{Z_E}$$

Note:

$$\frac{V_N}{E} = \frac{Z_N}{Z_E}$$

(d) Parallel Circuits

In a parallel circuit, the same voltage appears across each branch of the circuit so that, in Figure 5.3

$$E = I_1 Z_1 = I_2 Z_2 = \ldots = I_N Z_N$$

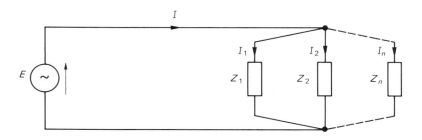

Fig 5.3

KCL states that the total current flowing towards a node is equal to the algebraic sum of the currents flowing away from the node, that is

$$I = I_1 + I_2 + \ldots + I_N = \frac{E}{Z_1} + \frac{E}{Z_2} + \ldots + \frac{E}{Z_N}$$

$$= E \left\{ \frac{1}{Z_1} + \frac{1}{Z_2} + \ldots + \frac{1}{Z_N} \right\} = \frac{E}{Z_E}$$

where Z_E is the *equivalent impedance* of the parallel circuit.
  Hence

$$\frac{1}{Z_E} = \frac{1}{Z_1} + \frac{1}{Z_2} + \ldots + \frac{1}{Z_N} = Y_E$$

where Y_E is the *equivalent admittance* of the parallel circuit.
  Also

$$I = EY_E$$

and

$$Y_E = Y_1 + Y_2 + \ldots + Y_N$$

that is, the equivalent admittance of a parallel circuit is the sum of the individual admittances in the circuit, and

$$Y_E = G_E + jB_E$$

$$= (G_1 + jB_1) + (G_2 + jB_2) + \ldots + (G_N + jB_N)$$

where G_E is the effective conductance of the parallel circuit, and B_E is the effective susceptance.

If B has a positive value, the circuit has a *net capacitive susceptance* $(B_C > B_L)$, and I leads E (or E lags behind I). If B has a negative value, the circuit has a *net inductive susceptance* $(B_C < B_L)$, and I lags E (or E leads I).

(e)   Division of Current in a Parallel Circuit

The current I_N in the Nth branch of Figure 5.3 is

$$I_N = \frac{E}{Z_N} = \frac{IZ_E}{Z_N}$$

or, alternatively

$$I_N = EY_N = \frac{IY_N}{Y_E}$$

Note:

$$\frac{I_N}{I} = \frac{Y_N}{Y_E}$$

(f)   A Two-branch Parallel Circuit

This is a special case in which

$$\frac{1}{Z_E} = \frac{1}{Z_1} + \frac{1}{Z_2}$$

or

$$Z_E = \frac{Z_1 Z_2}{Z_1 + Z_2}$$

Using the equations developed in part (e)

$$I_1 = \frac{IZ_2}{Z_1 + Z_2} \quad \text{and} \quad I_2 = \frac{IZ_1}{Z_1 + Z_2}$$

5.2   Worked Examples

Example 5.1

A current of $(10 + j6)$ A flows in a series circuit of impedance $(2 + j3)$ ohm. Calculate the voltage across the resistive and reactive elements in the circuit, and determine polar and rectangular complex expressions for the applied voltage. Calculate the phase angle between the current and the applied voltage.

Solution 5.1

$$E = IZ = (10 + j6)(2 + j3)$$

$$= 11.662\angle 30.96° \times 3.606\angle 56.31° = 42.053\angle 87.27° \text{ V}$$

$$= 2 + j42 \text{ V}$$

Hence $V_R = 2$ V and $V_x = 42$ V. Since the reactance is positive, the circuit is inductive, and the current lags behind the voltage by $87.27° - 30.96° = 56.31°$.

Example 5.2

In Figure 5.4, calculate the equivalent impedance of the circuit, the current, and the p.d. across each element in the circuit. Draw the phasor diagram showing the current and voltages in the circuit.

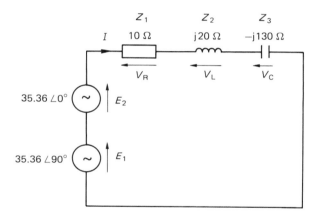

Fig 5.4

Solution 5.2

The equivalent impedance of the circuit is

$$Z_E = Z_1 + Z_2 + Z_3 = 10 + j20 - j30 = 10 - j10$$

$$= 14.142\angle -45° \text{ ohm}$$

and the net e.m.f. applied is

$$E = E_1 + E_2 = 35.36\angle 0° + 35.36\angle 90°$$

$$= 35.36 + j35.36 = 50\angle 45° \text{ V}$$

From Ohm's law

$$I = \frac{E}{Z_E} = \frac{50\angle 45°}{14.142\angle -45°} = 3.536\angle 90° = 0 + j3.536 \text{ A}$$

and

$$V_R = IZ_1 = 3.536\angle 90° \times 10 = 35.36\angle 90° = j35.36 \text{ V}$$

$$V_L = IZ_2 = 3.536\angle 90° \times 20\angle 90° = 70.72\angle 180° = -70.72 \text{ V}$$

$$V_C = IZ_3 = 3.536\angle 90° \times 30\angle -90° = 106.08\angle 0° = 106.08 \text{ V}$$

Note: $E = V_R + V_L + V_C = 35.36 + j35.36 = E_1 + E_2$

Since the impedance of the circuit is predominantly capacitive, the current leads the voltage (by 45° in this case), as shown in the phasor diagram in Figure 5.5.

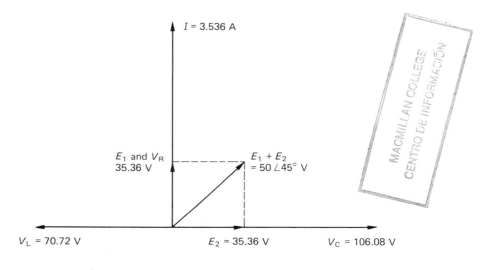

Fig 5.5

Note that V_R is in phase with I, V_L leads I by 90°, and V_C lags behind I by 90°.

Example 5.3

A capacitor of 100 microfarad capacitance is connected in series with a coil of resistance 5 ohm and inductance 0.12 H (see Figure 5.6). The current in the circuit is 64.85 A. If the current lags behind the supply voltage by 49.6°, and the frequency is 50 Hz, calculate the r.m.s. value of the voltage across the coil and across the capacitor. What is the value of the supply voltage?

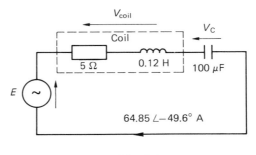

Fig 5.6

Solution 5.3

$$\mathbf{Z}_{coil} = 5 + j(2\pi \times 50 \times 0.12) = 5 + j37.7$$
$$= 38.03\angle 82.45° \text{ ohm}$$

Using $\mathbf{E}$ as the reference phasor

$$\mathbf{V}_{coil} = \mathbf{IZ}_{coil} = 64.85\angle -49.6° \times 38.03\angle 82.45°$$
$$= 2466.25\angle 32.85° = 2071.9 + j1337.8 \text{ V}$$
$$\mathbf{Z}_C = -jX_C = -j/(2\pi \times 50 \times 100 \times 10^{-6})$$
$$= -j31.83 = 31.83\angle -90° \text{ ohm}$$

hence

$$\mathbf{V}_c = \mathbf{IZ}_c = 64.85\angle -49.6° \times 31.83\angle -90°$$
$$= 2064.18\angle -139.6° = -1571.9 - j1337.8 \text{ V}$$

therefore

$$\mathbf{E} = \mathbf{V}_{coil} + \mathbf{V}_c$$
$$= (2071.9 + j1337.8) + (-1571.9 - j1337.8)$$
$$= 500 + j0 = 500\angle 0° \text{ V}$$

Note that the supply voltage is significantly less than either the voltage across the coil or across the capacitor. The reason for this is explained in Chapter 6.

Example 5.4

The series-connected circuit in Figure 5.7 contains impedances of $(3 + j6)$, $(4 + j0)$, and $(8 - j2)$ ohm. If the supply voltage is $110\angle 45°$ V, compute the circuit impedance, the current and its phase angle, and the voltage across each element in the circuit.

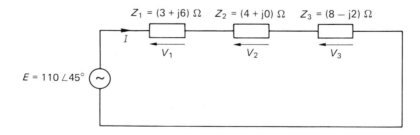

Fig 5.7

Solution 5.4

$$\mathbf{Z}_E = \mathbf{Z}_1 + \mathbf{Z}_2 + \mathbf{Z}_3 = (3 + j6) + (4 + j0) + (8 - j2)$$
$$= 15 + j4 = 15.22\angle 14.93° \text{ ohm}$$

Using the equations in section (c) of the Fact Sheet of this chapter, we can evaluate the potential across each element, but first we need to know the polar expression for each impedance as follows.

$$Z_1 = 3 + j6 = 6.708\angle 63.43° \text{ ohm}$$

$$Z_2 = 4 + j0 = 4\angle 0° \text{ ohm}$$

$$Z_3 = 8 - j2 = 8.246\angle -14.04° \text{ ohm}$$

Hence,

$$I = \frac{E}{Z_E} = \frac{110\angle 45°}{15.52\angle 14.93°} = 7.09\angle 30.07° \text{ A}$$

and the current lags behind the supply voltage by

$$45° - 30.07° = 14.93°$$

and

$$V_1 = IZ_1 = 7.09\angle 30.07° \times 6.708\angle 63.43° = 47.55\angle 93.5° \text{ V}$$

$$V_2 = IZ_2 = 7.09\angle 30.07° \times 4\angle 0° = 28.36\angle 30.07° \text{ V}$$

$$V_3 = IZ_3 = 7.09\angle 30.07° \times 8.246\angle -14.04° = 58.46\angle 16.03° \text{ V}$$

Example 5.5

A coil and a pure resistor are connected in series to a 200 V a.c. supply; the current drawn from the supply is 20.3 A, lagging by 24° behind the voltage. If the voltage across the coil is 114.9 V, determine the resistance of the resistor and the voltage across it, and the resistance and reactance of the coil.

Solution 5.5

The effective impedance of the circuit is

$$Z_E = \frac{E}{I} = \frac{200\angle 0°}{20.3\angle -24°} = 9.85\angle 24° = 9 + j4 \text{ ohm}$$

Referring to the phasor diagram in Figure 5.8, the reader will note that

$$\frac{V_{coil}}{\sin 24°} = \frac{E}{\sin a}$$

or

$$\text{angle } a = \sin^{-1}(\sin 24° \times 200/114.9) = 135.1°$$

Hence,

$$\text{angle } b = 180° - (135.1° + 24°) = 20.9°$$

Since V_R is the voltage across the pure resistor, then

$$\frac{V_R}{\sin b} = \frac{V_{coil}}{\sin 24°}$$

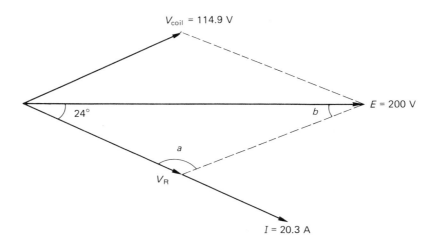

Fig 5.8

Therefore,

$$V_R = 114.9 \times \sin 20.9°/\sin 24° = 100.8 \text{ V}$$

and

$$R = \frac{V_R}{I} = \frac{100.8}{20.3} = 4.96 \text{ ohm}$$

Also, since $\mathbf{Z}_E = \mathbf{Z}_{coil} + R$, then

$$\mathbf{Z}_{coil} = \mathbf{Z}_E - R = (9 + j4) - 4.96 = 4.04 + j4 \text{ ohm}$$

Hence,

$$\text{resistance of coil} = 4.04 \text{ ohm}$$

$$\text{reactance of coil} = 4 \text{ ohm}$$

Example 5.6

For the two-branch parallel circuit in Figure 5.9, calculate the impedance and admittance of each branch, the effective impedance and admittance of the

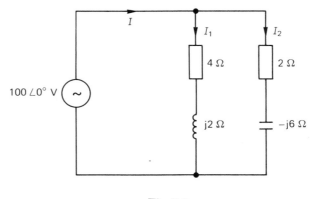

Fig 5.9

circuit, the current in each branch, the total current, and the phase angle of the supply current with respect to the supply voltage. Draw the phasor diagram for the circuit.

Solution 5.6

For the left-hand branch in Figure 5.9.

$$\mathbf{Z}_1 = 4 + j2 = 4.472\angle 26.57° \text{ ohm}$$

$$\mathbf{Z}_2 = 2 - j6 = 6.325\angle -71.57° \text{ ohm}$$

that is

$$\mathbf{Y}_1 = 1/\mathbf{Z}_1 = 0.224\angle -26.57° = 0.2 - j0.1 \text{ S}$$

and

$$\mathbf{Y}_2 = 1/\mathbf{Z}_2 = 0.158\angle 71.57° = 0.05 + j0.15 \text{ S}$$

The effective impedance of the circuit is

$$\mathbf{Z}_E = \frac{\mathbf{Z}_1\mathbf{Z}_2}{\mathbf{Z}_1 + \mathbf{Z}_2} = \frac{4.472\angle 26.57° \times 6.325\angle -71.57°}{(4 + j2) + (2 - j6)}$$

$$= \frac{28.285\angle -45°}{7.211\angle -33.69°} = 3.922\angle -11.31° = 3.846 - j0.769 \text{ ohm}$$

and

$$\mathbf{Y}_E = \mathbf{Y}_1 + \mathbf{Y}_2 = (0.2 - j0.1) + (0.05 + j0.15)$$

$$= 0.25 + j0.05 = 0.255\angle 11.31° \text{ S}$$

Note:

$$\mathbf{Y}_E = \frac{1}{\mathbf{Z}_E} = \frac{1}{3.922\angle -11.31°} = 0.255\angle 11.31° \text{ S}$$

The current drawn by the left-hand branch is

$$\mathbf{I}_1 = \frac{\mathbf{E}}{\mathbf{Z}_1} = \frac{100\angle 0°}{4.472\angle 26.57°} = 22.36\angle -26.57° = 20 - j10 \text{ A}$$

and

$$\mathbf{I}_2 = \frac{\mathbf{E}}{\mathbf{Z}_2} = \frac{100\angle 0°}{6.325\angle -71.57°} = 15.81\angle 71.57° = 5 + j15 \text{ A}$$

Hence,

$$\mathbf{I} = \mathbf{I}_1 + \mathbf{I}_2 = (20 - j10) + (5 + j15) = 25 + j5$$

$$= 25.5\angle 11.31° \text{ A}$$

That is, the current I leads the supply voltage by 11.31°, as shown in the phasor diagram in Figure 5.10.

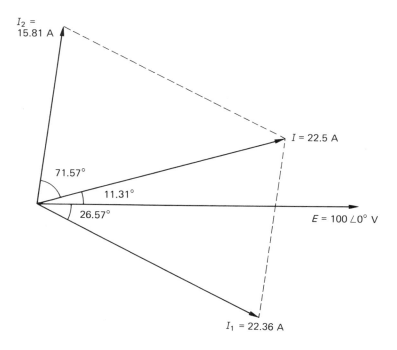

Fig 5.10

Example 5.7

Three admittances are connected in parallel with one another. The admittance of Y_1 is $0.1\angle-45°$ S, and that of Y_2 is $0.2\angle-60°$ S. If the current in Y_1 is $20\angle-35°$ A, and the total current drawn by the circuit is $128.94\angle3.51°$ A, calculate the current in Y_3, the admittance of Y_3, and the supply voltage.

Solution 5.7

The circuit is shown in Figure 5.11, and the supply voltage is

$$E = \frac{I_1}{Y_1} = \frac{20\angle-35°}{0.1\angle-45°} = 200\angle10° \text{ V}$$

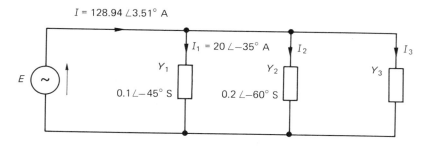

Fig 5.11

and the current drawn by Y_2 is

$$I_2 = EY_2 = 200\angle 10° \times 0.2\angle -60° = 40\angle -50° = 25.71 - \text{j}30.64 \text{ A}$$

Now $I_1 = 20\angle -35° = 16.38 - \text{j}11.47$ A and
$I = 128.9\angle 3.51° = 128.7 + \text{j}7.89$ A.
Hence,

$$\begin{aligned} I_3 &= I - (I_1 + I_2) \\ &= (128.7 + \text{j}7.89) - [(16.38 - \text{j}11.47) + (25.71 - \text{j}30.64)] \\ &= 86.81 + \text{j}50 = 100\angle 30° \text{ A} \end{aligned}$$

Therefore,

$$Y_3 = \frac{I_3}{E} = \frac{100\angle 30°}{200\angle 10°} = 0.5\angle 20° = 0.47 + \text{j}0.17 \text{ S}$$

Example 5.8

Calculate the current in each branch in the circuit in Figure 5.12.

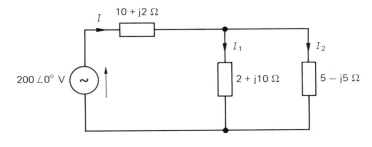

Fig 5.12

Solution 5.8

The impedance of the circuit is

$$\begin{aligned} Z_E &= (10 + \text{j}2) + \frac{(2 + \text{j}10)(5 - \text{j}5)}{(2 + \text{j}10) + (5 - \text{j}5)} \\ &= 18.38 + \text{j}1.73 = 18.46\angle 5.38° \text{ ohm} \end{aligned}$$

The current drawn by the circuit is

$$I = \frac{E}{Z_E} = \frac{200\angle 0°}{18.46\angle 5.38°} = 10.83\angle -5.38° \text{ A}$$

For the parallel circuit alone

$$Z_1 + Z_2 = (2 + \text{j}10) + (5 - \text{j}5) = 7 + \text{j}5 = 8.6\angle 35.54° \text{ ohm}$$

also

$$Z_1 = 2 + j10 = 10.2\angle78.69° \text{ ohm}$$

$$Z_2 = 5 - j5 = 7.071\angle-45° \text{ ohm}$$

The current in each branch of the parallel circuit is calculated as follows

$$I_1 = \frac{IZ_2}{(Z_1 + Z_2)} = \frac{10.83\angle-5.38° \times 7.071\angle-45°}{8.6\angle35.54°} = 8.905\angle-85.92° \text{ A}$$

$$I_2 = \frac{IZ_1}{(Z_1 + Z_2)} = \frac{10.83\angle-5.38° \times 10.2\angle78.69°}{8.6\angle35.54°} = 12.85\angle37.77° \text{ A}$$

Example 5.9

Convert the series circuit in Figure 5.13(a) into its equivalent parallel circuit (Figure 5.13(b)). Verify that the two are equivalent by calculating the current drawn by both circuits when 100 V is applied to each of them.

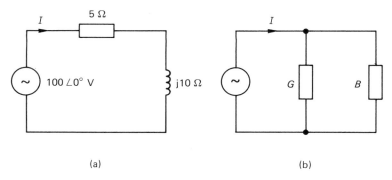

(a)   (b)

Fig 5.13

Solution 5.9

For the series circuit in Figure 5.13(a)

$$Z = 5 + j10 = 11.18\angle63.43° \text{ ohm}$$

The equivalent admittance is

$$Y = 1/Z = 1/11.18\angle63.43° = 0.0895\angle-63.43° = 0.04 - j0.08 \text{ S}$$

The equivalent parallel circuit therefore consists of a conductance of 0.04 S in parallel with an inductive susceptance of 0.08 S.

The current drawn by the series circuit is

$$I = \frac{E}{Z} = \frac{100\angle0°}{11.18\angle63.43°} = 8.95\angle-63.43° \text{ A}$$

and for the parallel circuit is

$$I = EY = 100\angle0° \times 0.0895\angle-63.43° = 8.95\angle-63.43° \text{ A}$$

Example 5.10

For Figure 5.14, calculate the effective impedance of the circuit, the total current, and the current in each element. Calculate also the voltage across each parallel circuit.

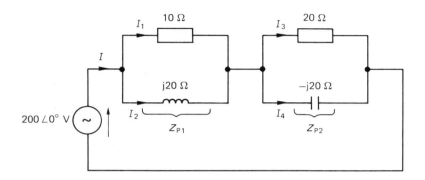

Fig 5.14

Solution 5.10

$$Z_{pl} = \frac{10 \times j20}{10 + j20} = 8 + j4 = 8.944\angle 26.56° \text{ ohm}$$

$$Z_{p2} = \frac{20 \times (-j20)}{20 - j20} = 10 - j10 = 14.142\angle -45° \text{ ohm}$$

For the complete circuit

$$Z_E = Z_{pl} + Z_{p2} = (8 + j4) + (10 - j10) = 18 - j6$$
$$= 18.97\angle -18.43° \text{ ohm}$$

The total current drawn by the circuit is

$$I = \frac{E}{Z_E} = \frac{200\angle 0°}{18.97\angle -18.43°} = 10.54\angle 18.43° = 10 + j3.33 \text{ A}$$

Applying the rule for current division in a parallel circuit

$$I_1 = I \times \frac{j20}{10 + j20} = 9.427\angle 45° = 6.666 + j6.666 \text{ A}$$

$$I_2 = I \times \frac{10}{10 + j20} = 4.714\angle -45° = 3.333 - j3.333 \text{ A}$$

$$I_3 = I \times \frac{-j20}{20 - j20} = 7.453\angle -26.57° = 6.666 - j3.333 \text{ A}$$

$$I_4 = I \times \frac{20}{20 - j20} = 7.453\angle 63.43° = 3.333 + j6.666 \text{ A}$$

113

Note:

$$I = I_1 + I_2 = I_3 + I_4 = 10 + j3.33 \text{ A}$$

Using the rule for potential division in a series circuit, the voltage V_{pt} across the first parallel circuit is

$$V_{p1} = IZ_{p1} = 10.54\angle 18.43° \times 8.944\angle 26.56°$$

$$= 94.27\angle 44.99° = 66.67 + j66.65 \text{ V}$$

and the voltage V_{p2} across the second parallel circuit is

$$V_{p2} = IZ_{p2} = 10.54\angle 18.43° \times 14.142\angle -45°$$

$$= 149.06\angle -25.57° = 133.32 - j66.67 \text{ V}$$

Note:

$$E = V_{p1} + V_{p2} = 199.98 - j0.02 \text{ V}$$

5.3 Unworked Problems

Problem 5.1

An impedance of $(10 + j5.77)$ ohm has a potential drop of $240\angle 120°$ V across it. Calculate the current in the circuit.
$[I = 20.78\angle 90° = j20.78 \text{ A}]$

Problem 5.2

Impedances of $10\angle 45°$, $20\angle -30°$, and $60\angle 10.2°$ ohm are connected in series. Calculate the effective impedance of the circuit, the current which flows in the circuit when 200 V is applied to it, and the potential drop across each impedance.
$[Z_E = 83.8\angle 5.27° \text{ ohm}; I = 2.387\angle -5.27° \text{ A}; V_1 = 23.87\angle 39.73° \text{ V};$
$V_2 = 47.74\angle -35.27° \text{ V}; V_3 = 143.22\angle 4.93° \text{ V}]$

Problem 5.3

If, in a circuit similar to that in Problem 5.2, the p.d. across Z_2 is $(3 - j4)$ V, calculate the current in the circuit, the p.d. across the other two impedances, and the supply voltage.
$[I = 0.25\angle -23.13° \text{ A}; V_1 = 2.5\angle 21.87° \text{ V}; V_2 = 15\angle -12.93° \text{ V};$
$E = 20.95\angle -17.86° \text{ V}]$

Problem 5.4

A current of $(5 + j6)$ A flows in a circuit of impedance $10\angle 30°$ ohm. Determine the voltage applied to the circuit. Draw the phasor diagram for the circuit.
$[E = 78.1\angle 80.19° = 13.31 + j76.96 \text{ V}]$

Problem 5.5

A pure inductance of 0.1 H is connected (a) in series (b) in parallel with a 500 ohm resistor, and both circuits are supplied by a 10 V, 1 kHz supply. Calculate (i) the impedance and admittance of each circuit, (ii) the current drawn by each circuit. Draw the phasor diagram for each circuit.
[(i) (a) $Z = 803\angle 51.49°$ ohm; $Y = 0.00125\angle -51.49°$ S; (i) (b) $Z = 391.2\angle 38.52°$ ohm; $Y = 0.00257\angle -38.52°$ S; (ii) (a) $0.0125\angle -51.49°$ A; (b) $0.0256\angle -38.52°$ A]

Problem 5.6

A voltage of 100 V d.c. produces a current of 10 A in a coil. When an alternating voltage of 100 V, 50 Hz, is applied to the coil, the r.m.s. current in the coil is 20 A. Calculate the resistance and inductance of the coil, and also the impedance at 50 Hz. Draw the phasor diagram of the circuit at 50 Hz.
[$R = 5$ ohm; $L = 27.57$ mH; $Z = 10\angle 60°$ ohm]

Problem 5.7

Calculate, for Figure 5.15, the capacitance and the reactance of the capacitor, the impedance of the circuit, the p.d. across the resistor and across the capacitor, and the phase angle of the current with respect to the supply voltage.
[$X_C = 229.1$ ohm; $C = 13.89$ microfarad; $Z = 250\angle -66.42°$ ohm; $V_R = 100\angle 66.42°$ V; $V_C = 229.1\angle -23.58°$ V; I leads E by 66.42°]

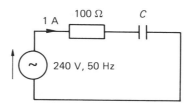

Fig 5.15

Problem 5.8

A resistance of 30 ohm is connected in series with a 100 ohm inductive reactance and a capacitive reactance of 60 ohm, the supply voltage being 200 V. Determine the circuit impedance, the current in the circuit, the phase angle between I and V, and the voltage across each element in the circuit. Draw the phasor diagram for the circuit.
[$Z = 50\angle 53.13°$; $I = 4\angle -53.13°$; I lags V by 53.13°; $V_R = 120\angle -53.13°$ V; $V_L = 400\angle 36.87°$ V; $V_C = 240\angle -143.13°$ V]

Problem 5.9

For the circuit in Figure 5.16, calculate Z_A and Z_B, the effective impedance of the circuit, the voltage across Z_A and across Z_B, and the phase angle between the voltage across Z_A and that across Z_B.
[$Z_A = 22.36\angle 63.44°$ ohm; $Z_B = 22.36\angle -26.56°$ ohm; $Z_E = 31.62\angle 18.44°$ ohm; $I = 10\angle -18.44°$ A; $V_A = 223.6\angle 45°$ V; $V_B = 223.6\angle -45°$ V; V_A leads V_B by 90°]

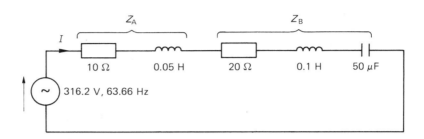

Fig 5.16

Problem 5.10

A series circuit contains a resistor of 5 ohm, a capacitor of reactance 3 ohm, and an impedance. If the supply voltage is $102\angle 0°$ V, and the p.d. across the resistor is $50\angle -11.31°$ V, determine the value of the components in the impedance. Draw the phasor diagram for the circuit.
[The impedance comprises a resistance of 5 ohm in series with an inductor of reactance 5 ohm]

Problem 5.11

Determine the impedance and admittance of the circuit which has the phasor diagram in Figure 5.17.
[$Z = 0.845 + j1.813$ ohm; $Y = 0.211 - j0.453$ S]

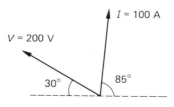

Fig 5.17

Problem 5.12

Draw the phasor diagram for the circuit in Figure 5.18. For the circuit, determine the value of R and L; calculate also I, the phase angle between I and the supply voltage E, and the value of Z_E.
[R = 30 ohm; L = 0.0955 H; I = 2 + j0 A; $\angle 36.87°$ lagging; Z_E = 50$\angle 36.87°$ ohm]

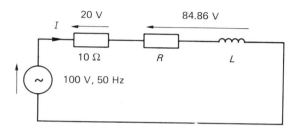

Fig 5.18

Problem 5.13

Calculate, for Figure 5.19, the complex admittance and impedance of the parallel circuit which produces the phasor diagram shown.
[Y_E = 0.2$\angle 65°$ S; Z_E = 5$\angle -65°$ ohm]

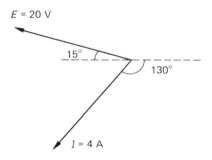

Fig 5.19

Problem 5.14

In a three-branch parallel circuit, the currents are $I_1 = 10\angle -170°$ A, $I_2 = 5\angle 260°$ A, and $I_3 = 20\angle -80°$ A. Calculate the total current drawn from the supply.
[I = 27.33$\angle 254.63°$ A]

Problem 5.15

For the two-branch parallel circuit in Figure 5.20, calculate a polar expression for the impedance of each branch of the circuit, the impedance and admittance of the complete circuit, the current in each branch, and the total current.
[$Z_1 = 32.02\angle -51.34°$ ohm; $Z_2 = 12.81\angle 38.66°$ ohm; $Z_E = 11.89\angle 16.86°$ ohm; $Y_E = 0.0841\angle -16.86°$ S; $I_1 = 3.123\angle 51.34°$ A; $I_2 = 7.806\angle -38.66°$ A; $I = 8.41\angle -16.86°$ A]

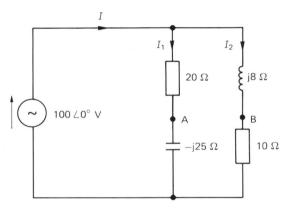

Fig 5.20

Problem 5.16

Referring to Figure 5.20, determine the value of V_{AB}.
[$V_{AB} = 163.92\angle -128.66°$ V; Note: $V_{BA} = 163.92\angle 51.34°$ V]

Problem 5.17

In a three-branch parallel circuit, $I_1 = 10\angle 45°$ A, $I_2 = 10\angle -60°$, and the total current drawn from the supply is $25\angle -10°$ A. Calculate the value of I_3.
[$I_3 = 12.85\angle -12.37°$ A]

Problem 5.18

Referring to Problem 5.17, if the supply voltage is $10\angle 10°$ V, determine the impedance and admittance of the complete circuit, and of each branch of the parallel circuit.
[$Z_E = 0.4\angle 10°$ ohm; $Y_E = 2.5\angle -10°$ S; $Z_1 = 1\angle -45°$ ohm; $Z_2 = 1\angle 60°$ ohm; $Z_3 = 0.778\angle 12.37°$ ohm; $Y_1 = 1\angle 45°$ S; $Y_2 = 1\angle -60°$ S; $Y_3 = 1.285\angle -12.37°$ S]

118

Problem 5.19

If, in Figure 5.21, the voltage across the 10 ohm resistor is 10 V, calculate the current in the 20 ohm resistor, the total current, and the p.d. across the circuit. Draw the phasor diagram for the circuit.
[Hint: Assume the voltage across the 10 ohm resistor to be in the reference directionl; $I_{20} = 0.686\angle-30.95°$ A; $I = 1.627\angle-12.52°$ A; $E = 141.4\angle-45°$ V]

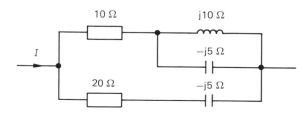

Fig 5.21

Problem 5.20

If, in the circuit in Figure 5.21, the current in the j10 ohm inductive reactance is 5 A, calculate the value of I.
[Hint: Assume the current in the inductive reactance is in the reference direction; $I = 2.92\angle167.47°$ A]

Problem 5.21

A current of $4\angle20°$ A flows into a two-branch parallel circuit containing a 12 ohm resistor in one branch and a j18 ohm inductive reactance in the second branch. Calculate the current in the inductive reactance.

(Liverpool Polytechnic)

$[2.22\angle-36.31°$ A]

Problem 5.22

For the circuit in Figure 5.22, the supply voltage is $10\angle0°$ V, the frequency is 1 kHz, $R = 10$ ohm, $X_L = 30$ ohm, $X_C = 53$ ohm. Calculate **(a)** the impedance of the coil (in polar form), **(b)** the complex values of I_1, I_2 and I, **(c)** the self-inductance of the coil, **(d)** the capacitance of the capacitor, **(e)** the power dissipated in the coil, **(f)** the power factor of the coil. Also, **(g)** draw the phasor diagram of the circuit. To what value should the frequency of the supply be changed in order to cause the current, I, to be in phase with the supply voltage? (Note: see also Chapter 6) Draw the phasor diagram of the circuit for the latter condition.

(Staffordshire Polytechnic)

119

[(**a**) 31.62∠71.57° ohm; (**b**) $I_1 = 0.316∠-71.57°$ A, $I_2 = 0.189∠90°$ A, $I = 0.149∠-48°$ A; (**c**) 4.77 mH; (**d**) 3 microfarad; (**e**) 1 W; (**f**) 0.316 lagging; (**h**) 1 288 Hz]

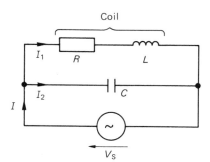

Fig 5.22

Problem 5.23

For the circuit in Figure 5.23, $V_s = 260$ V, $f = 50$ Hz, $R = 10$ ohm, $X_L = 26$ ohm, $X_C = 50$ ohm. Calculate (**a**) the complex impedance of the circuit, (**b**) the complex current in the circuit. (**c**) What is the phase angle of the circuit? State whether the current lags behind or leads the voltage. Calculate (**d**) the power factor of the circuit, (**e**) the self-inductance of the circuit, and (**f**) the capacitance of the capacitor. (**g**) Draw a diagram showing the supply voltage and the voltage across the capacitor. (**h**) What value should the frequency be in order that the current is in phase with the supply voltage? (Note: see also chapter 6) (**i**) At the frequency calculated in part (**h**), determine the power dissipated in the circuit. For the condition in part (**h**), sketch the waveform of the voltage across L, clearly labelling its amplitude and periodic time.

(Staffordshire Polytechnic)

[(**a**) (10 − j24) ohm; (**b**) 3.85 + j9.23 A; (**c**) 67.38° leading; (**d**) 0.385 leading; (**e**) 82.8 mH; (**f**) 63.66 microfarad; (**g**) the maximum voltage across the capacitor is 707.1 V, lagging the supply voltage by 90°; (**h**) 69.32 Hz; (**i**) 6.76 kW; in part (**h**), the voltage across the inductor has a maximum value of 1326 V, and leads the supply voltage by 90°.]

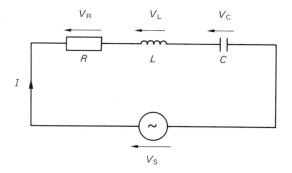

Fig 5.23

6 Resonance

6.1 Fact Sheet

(a) Introduction

Resonance is said to occur in an electrical circuit when a small value of driving alternating voltage or current produces a larger amplitude oscillation in the circuit.

(b) Series Resonance

The series RLC circuit in Figure 6.1 has an impedance of

$$Z = R + j(\omega L - 1/\omega C)$$

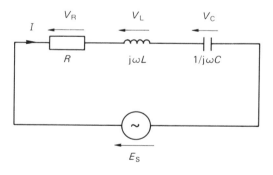

Fig 6.1

The circuit resonates when $Z = R + j0$, or when $\omega L = 1/\omega C$. This occurs at the *resonant frequency*, ω_0, where

$$\omega_0 = 1/\sqrt{(LC)} \text{ rad/s}$$

or

$$f_0 = \omega_0/2\pi = 1/(2\pi\sqrt{(LC)}) \text{ Hz}$$

The response of the circuit to changing frequency (at constant r.m.s. supply voltage) is shown in Figure 6.2. At frequencies below ω_0, X_C is greater than X_L;

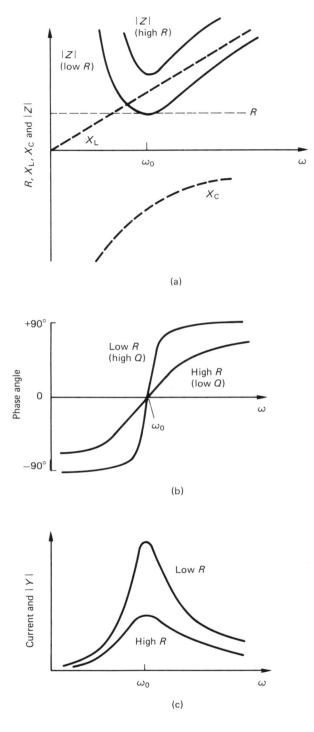

(a)

(b)

(c)

Fig 6.2

at these frequencies the circuit has a high impedance and the supply current leads the supply voltage by angles up to 90° (see Figure 6.2(b)). At frequencies above ω_0, X_L is greater than X_C; once again the circuit impedance is high, and the supply current lags behind the supply voltage by angles up to 90°.

When the supply frequency is equal to the resonant frequency, the circuit impedance is at its minimum, and

$$|Z| = R$$

At this frequency, the current is in phase with the supply voltage. Also, since the impedance is at its minimum at this frequency, the current drawn by the circuit is a maximum (see Figure 6.2(c)). Moreover, the higher the resistance of the circuit, the lower the value of the current at resonance. In electrical power circuits, where the circuit resistance is inherently low, series resonance can cause a dangerously high value of current to flow (with associated high voltages across L and C).

A typical phasor diagram for a series resonant circuit containing ideal elements is shown in Figure 6.3.

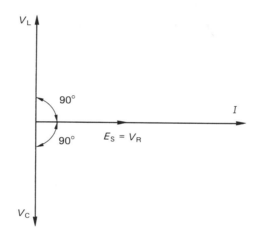

Fig 6.3

(c)   Quality Factor or Q-factor of a Series Circuit

The Q-factor of a coil, capacitor or circuit is defined as

$$Q = \frac{2\pi \times \text{maximum energy stored}}{\text{energy dissipated per cycle}}$$

It can be shown that the Q-factor of a series circuit at resonance is

$$Q_0 = \omega_0 L/R$$

$$= \frac{1}{R}\sqrt{\frac{L}{C}}$$

(d)   Cut-off (Half-power) Frequencies and Bandwidth of Series Resonant Circuit

As the name implies, the power input to a series circuit at a *half-power frequency* is one half of the maximum input power (the latter being the power at the resonant frequency). In general, there are two half-power frequencies known as the *upper* and *lower* half-power frequencies (they are also known as the *half-power points* or *cut-off points*). The lower and upper cut-off frequencies are shown as ω_L and ω_H in Figure 6.4. The frequency separation between the two half-power frequencies is known as the *bandwidth* (BW) of the circuit — see Figure 6.4 — and is expressed either in rad/s or in Hz.

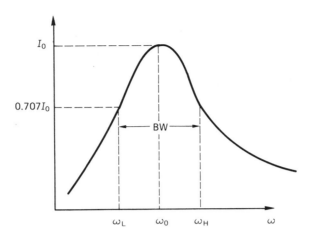

Fig 6.4

The Q-factor of the circuit at resonance is given by the expression (see also the Worked Example 6.1)

$$Q_0 = \frac{\omega_0}{\text{BW}} = \frac{\omega_0}{\omega_H - \omega_L} = \frac{f_0}{f_H - f_L}$$

and it can be shown that the resonant frequency is the geometric mean of the two half-power frequencies as follows.

$$\omega_0 = \surd(\omega_H\omega_L) \quad \text{or} \quad f_0 = \surd(f_Hf_L)$$

(e) Parallel Resonance of a Pure GLC Circuit

The admittance of the parallel circuit containing ideal components in Figure 6.5 is

$$Y = G + j(B_C - B_L)$$

where $B_C = \omega C$ and $B_L = 1/\omega L$. At the resonant frequency, ω_0, $(B_C - B_L) = 0$, and $Y = G + j0$; also $\omega_0 = 1/\surd(LC)$.

The response of the circuit with a constant r.m.s. supply voltage with a changing frequency is shown in Figure 6.6. At frequencies below the resonant frequency, $B_L > B_C$, and the circuit is predominantly capacitive. At frequencies above the resonant frequency, the reverse is true. At resonance, $B_L = B_C$, and the net admittance is equal to G; at this frequency, the supply current and voltage are in phase with one another.

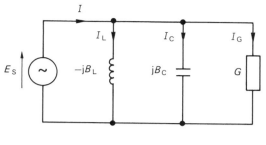

Fig 6.5

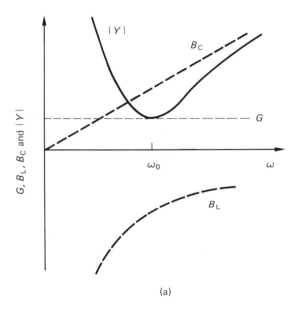

(a)

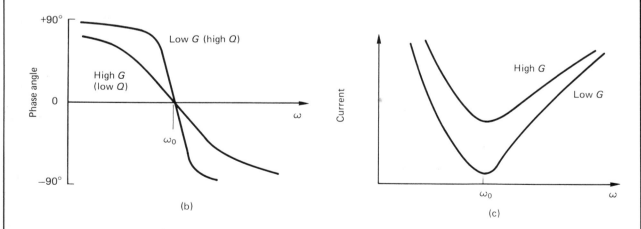

(b)   (c)

Fig 6.6

The phasor diagram for an idealized parallel circuit at resonance is shown in Figure 6.7.

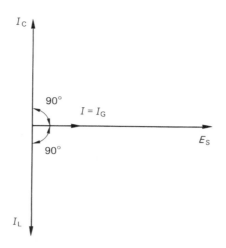

Fig 6.7

(f) Parallel Resonance of a Practical Circuit

A practical parallel circuit includes some resistance in the inductive branch, and may include resistance in series with the capacitor, as shown in Figure 6.8(a). and its phasor diagram is shown in Figure 6.8(b).

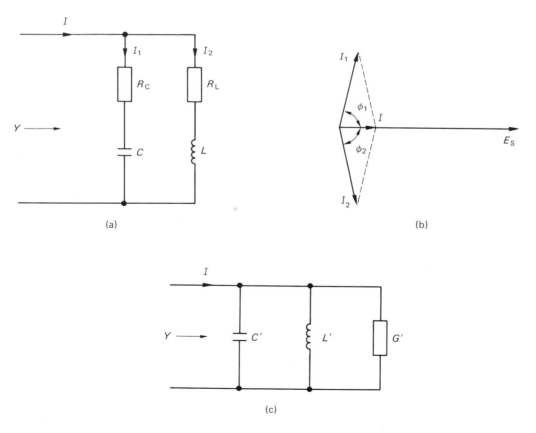

Fig 6.8

Using the method of converting impedance to admittance outlined in Chapter 5, the practical circuit in Figure 6.8(a) can be converted to the circuit in Figure 6.8(c), which is generally similar to the pure GLC circuit discussed in section (e) of this Fact Sheet. We can therefore use the results deduced in that section here.

It was shown in section (b) of the Fact Sheet in Chapter 5 that a series impedance $(R + jX)$ could be converted into a parallel circuit comprising a conductance $R/(R^2 + X^2)$ and a susceptance $-jX/(R^2 + X^2)$. This means that, at the resonant frequency, the capacitive branch of Figure 6.8(a) can be converted into the following parallel-connected components:

$$G'_c = \frac{R_c}{R_C^2 + 1/(\omega_0 C)^2} \quad \text{and} \quad C' = \frac{1/(\omega_0^2 C)}{R_C^2 + 1/(\omega_0 C)^2}$$

and the inductive branch becomes

$$G'_L = \frac{R_L}{R_L^2 + (\omega_0 L)^2} \quad \text{and} \quad L' = \frac{R_L^2 + (\omega_0 L)^2}{\omega_0^2 L}$$

It was shown in section (e) of this Fact Sheet that the resonant frequency of a circuit of the type in Figure 6.8(b) is

$$\omega_0 = \frac{1}{\sqrt{(L'C')}} = \frac{1}{\sqrt{(LC)}} \sqrt{\left(\frac{R_L^2 - L/C}{R_C^2 - L/C}\right)} \text{ rad/s}$$

The circuit can be resonant only when ω_0 has a real positive value. This occurs under either of two conditions, namely

1. when $R_L^2 > L/C$ AND $R_C^2 > L/C$
2. when $R_L^2 < L/C$ AND $R_C^2 < L/C$.

When $R_L^2 = R_C^2 = L/C$, the circuit is resonant (i.e., resistive) at all frequencies (see the Worked Example 6.6).

The effective conductance, G', of the circuit in Figure 6.8(a) at resonance is

$$G' = G'_C + G'_L = \frac{R_C}{R_C^2 + (1/\omega_0 C)^2} + \frac{R_L}{R_L^2 + (\omega_0 L)^2}$$

The special case where $R_C = 0$ and $R_L^2 \ll (\omega_0 L)^2$ is often quoted in text books; in this case, $G' = CR_L/L$; in this case, the *dynamic impedance* at resonance is $R_D = L/CR_L$. Under these conditions, the resonant frequency is

$$\omega_0 = \frac{1}{\sqrt{(LC)}} \sqrt{\left(\frac{L - CR_L^2}{L}\right)} \text{ rad/s}$$

(g) *Q*-factor of a Parallel Circuit at Resonance

At resonance, energy is continually interchanged between the inductance and capacitance, so that the circuit stores a constant amount of energy.

Pure GLC parallel circuit (see Figure 6.5)

In a pure GLC parallel circuit at resonance, the maximum energy stored in the inductor is $LI_{MAX}^2/2$ and, a little while later, the maximum energy stored in the capacitor is $CV_{MAX}^2/2$. Inserting these values in the equation for Q-factor (section (c) of this Fact Sheet) gives, for the resonant parallel circuit

$$Q_0 = \frac{1}{G\omega_0 L} = \omega_0 \frac{C}{G}$$

where G, L and C are the respective conductance, inductance and capacitance of the idealized parallel circuit.

Practical parallel circuit containing resistance (see Figure 6.8)

In the case of the practical circuit in Figure 6.8, the Q-factor is obtained by using the above equations, but by letting $G = G'$, $L = L'$, and $C = C'$ (see also section (f) of this Fact Sheet).

(h)   Cut-off Frequencies and Bandwidth of a Parallel Circuit

The cut-off frequencies (see also section (d) of this Fact Sheet) of a parallel circuit are defined as the frequencies at which the magnitude of the input admittance is $\sqrt{2}$ times greater than it is at resonance. These occur at frequencies ω_H and ω_L, where $\omega_H > \omega_L$; the bandwidth (BW) is given by $(\omega_H - \omega_L)$. The relationship between ω_0, ω_H, and ω_L is as given in section (d) of this Fact Sheet.

6.2   Worked Examples

Example 6.1

If, in Figure 6.9, $R = 10$ ohm, $L = 0.01$ H, $C = 0.01$ microfarad, $V_s = 10$ mV, calculate the resonant frequency of the circuit, the Q-factor at resonance, the bandwidth, the upper and lower cut-off frequencies, and the current in the circuit at resonance.

Determine also the voltage across each element in the circuit at resonance, and draw the phasor diagram at resonance. Calculate the current in the circuit at 90 per cent of the resonant frequency.

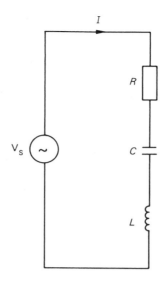

Fig 6.9

Solution 6.1

The resonant frequency is

$$\omega_0 = 1/\sqrt{(LC)} = 1/\sqrt{(0.01 \times (0.01 \times 10^{-6}))}$$
$$= 100\ 000 \text{ rad/s or } 15\ 915 \text{ Hz}$$

and the Q-factor at resonance is

$$Q_0 = \frac{1}{R}\sqrt{\left(\frac{L}{C}\right)} = \frac{1}{10}\sqrt{\frac{0.01}{0.01 \times 10^{-6}}} = 100$$

The bandwidth of the resonant circuit is

$$\text{BW} = \frac{\omega_0}{Q_0} = \frac{100\ 000}{100} = 1000 \text{ rad/s or } 159.2 \text{ Hz}$$

and

$$\text{lower cutoff frequency, } \omega_L = 100\ 000 - \frac{\text{BW}}{2}$$
$$= 99\ 500 \text{ rad/s or } 15\ 836 \text{ Hz}$$

and

$$\text{upper cutoff frequency, } \omega_H = 1000 + \frac{\text{BW}}{2}$$
$$= 100\ 500 \text{ rad/s or } 15\ 995 \text{ Hz}$$

The current at resonance is

$$\boldsymbol{I} = V/R = 10 \times 10^{-3}/10 = 10^{-3} \text{ A or } 1 \text{ mA}$$

At resonance, the voltage across the inductance is

$$V_L = IZ_L = 0.001\angle 0° \times \omega_0 L\angle 90°$$

$$= 0.001\angle 0° \times (100\ 000 \times 0.01)\angle 90° = 1\angle 90° = \text{j}1\ \text{V}$$

and the voltage across the capacitor is

$$V_c = IZ_c = 0.001\angle 0° \times (1/(\omega_0 C\angle 90°))$$

$$= \frac{0.001\angle 0°}{100\ 000 \times 0.01 \times 10^{-6}\angle 90°} = 1\angle -90° = -\text{j}1\ \text{V}$$

and the voltage across R at resonance is

$$V_R = IR = 0.001\angle 0° \times 10 = 0.01\angle 0°\ \text{V}$$

The phasor diagram for the circuit (not to scale) is shown in Figure 6.10.

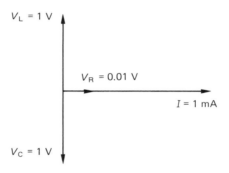

Fig 6.10

At 90 per cent of the resonant frequency, the frequency is 90 000 rad/s, and the circuit impedance is

$$Z = 10 + \text{j}\left[(90\ 000 \times 0.01) - \frac{1}{90\ 000 \times 0.01 \times 10^{-6}}\right]$$

$$= 10 - \text{j}211.1 = 211.3\angle -87.29°\ \text{ohms}$$

and the current at 90 000 rad/s is

$$I = \frac{10 \times 10^{-3}\angle 0°}{211.3\angle -87.29°} = 0.047 \times 10^{-3}\angle 87.29°\ \text{A}$$

Example 6.2

If, in Figure 6.9, $L = 0.05$ H, $V_S = 1$ V, and the power consumed at resonance is 0.1 W, calculate the value of R and C if the bandwidth of the circuit is 200 rad/s, and the r.m.s. voltage across L at resonance is 70.71 V. Determine also the resonant frequency of the circuit.

Solution 6.2

Since the capacitor and inductor are pure elements then, at resonance, the supply voltage appears across R, hence

$$R = V_S^2/\text{power} = 1^2/0.1 = 10 \text{ ohm}$$

The current in the circuit at resonance is

$$I = V_S/R = 1/10 = 0.1 \text{ A}$$

and the voltage across the inductor at resonance is

$$V_L = I\omega_0 L$$

Hence,

$$\omega_0 = V_L/IL = 70.71/(0.1 \times 0.05) = 14\ 142 \text{ rad/s}$$

Now

$$Q_0 = \frac{\omega_0}{\text{BW}} = \frac{14\ 142}{200} = 70.71$$

but

$$Q_0 = 1/\omega_0 CR$$

Therefore,

$$C = 1/\omega_0 Q_0 R = 1/(14\ 142 \times 70.71 \times 10)$$
$$= 10^{-7} \text{ F or } 0.1 \text{ microfarad}$$

Example 6.3

For the circuit in Figure 6.11, calculate the resonant frequency, the Q-factor at resonance, and the current drawn by the circuit. Draw the phasor diagram for the circuit at resonance.

Solution 6.3

The voltage across the circuit is

$$1 + j0 = 10(I + 2V_L) + j0.01\omega I + \frac{I}{j0.01 \times 10^{-6}\omega}V$$

where $V_L = j0.01\omega I$

Hence,

$$1 + j0 = I\left[10 + j\left(0.21\omega - \frac{1}{0.01 \times 10^{-6}\omega}\right)\right]V$$

At resonance, $\omega = \omega_0$, and the current drawn from the supply is in phase with the supply voltage, that is

$$0.21\omega_0 - \frac{1}{0.01 \times 10^{-6}\omega_0} = 0$$

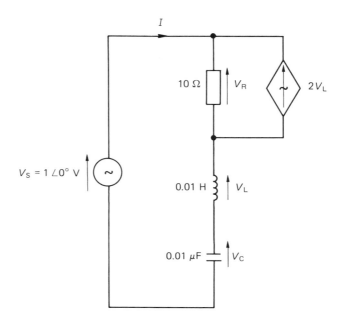

Fig 6.11

or

$$\omega_0 = 21\ 821 \text{ rad/s or } 3\ 473 \text{ Hz}$$

Also, since the current and supply voltage are in phase with one another, and the voltage across the circuit is

$$1 + j0 = 10I \text{ V}$$

that is, the impedance at resonance is $(10 + j0)$ ohm, and the current at resonance is

$$I = (1 + j0)/(10 + j0) = 0.1 + j0 \text{ A}$$

Also, it appears possible to say that

$$Q_0 = \frac{\omega_0 L}{R} = \frac{21\ 821 \times 0.01}{10} = 21.8$$

At this point, the reader will have noted that the values used in the basic RLC circuit in Figure 6.11 are the same as those used in Worked Example 6.1. However, the voltage-dependent source has had the effect of reducing the resonant frequency of the circuit and, apparently, reducing the Q-factor at resonance. Whilst the former is true, the latter (as will be seen from later figures) is not as clear cut as it seems because we have used the voltage across the inductor to calculate Q. Had we used the voltage across the capacitor to calculate Q, we would have reached quite a different conclusion! The reader will find it an interesting exercise to analyse in detail the effect of the voltage dependent source on the circuit.

The reactance of the inductor and of the capacitor are

$$X_L = \omega_0 L = 21\ 821 \times 0.01 = 218.21 \text{ ohm}$$

$$X_C = 1/\omega_0 C = 1/(21\ 821 \times 0.01 \times 10^{-6}) = 4583 \text{ ohm}$$

(the reader should note that at resonance, in this case, $X_L \neq X_C$).

The voltage across the inductor at resonance is

$$V_L = I \times jX_L = 0.1 \times j218.21 = j21.821 \text{ V}$$

and that across the capacitor is

$$V_C = I(-jX_C) = 0.1 \times (-j4583) = -j458.3 \text{ V}$$

The voltage across the resistor is calculated as follows

$$V_R = V_S - (V_L + V_C) = (1 + j0) - (j21.821 + (-j458.3))$$
$$= 1 + j436.48 = 436.5\angle 89.87° \text{ V}$$

Note: the magnitude of the current in the resistor is $436.5/10 = 43.65$ A compared with 0.1 A in the main circuit!

The phasor diagram for the circuit (not to scale) is shown in Figure 6.12.

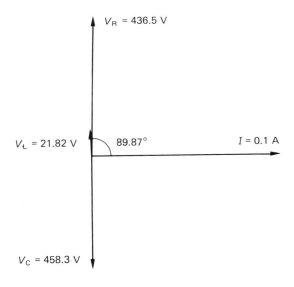

Fig 6.12

Example 6.4

The circuit in Figure 6.13 represents a coil in parallel with a pure capacitor. Calculate the resonant frequency of the circuit, the dynamic impedance of the circuit, the Q-factor at resonance, and draw the phasor diagram for the circuit at resonance.

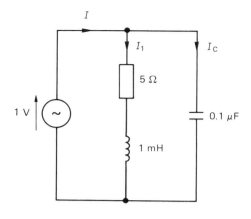

Fig 6.13

Solution 6.4

From the work in section (f) of the Fact Sheet in this chapter

$$\omega_0 = \frac{1}{\sqrt{(LC)}} \sqrt{\left(\frac{L - CR_L^2}{L}\right)}$$

$$= \frac{1}{\sqrt{(10^{-3} \times 0.1 \times 10^{-6})}} \sqrt{\left(\frac{10^{-3} - (0.1 \times 10^{-6} \times 5^2)}{10^{-3}}\right)}$$

$$= 99\ 870 \text{ rad/s or } 15\ 895 \text{ Hz}$$

The impedance of the circuit at resonance is

$$R_D = L/CR_L = 10^{-3}/(0.1 \times 10^{-6} \times 5) = 2000 \text{ ohm}$$

and the Q-factor at resonance is

$$Q_0 = \omega_0 C R_D = 99\ 870 \times 0.1 \times 10^{-6} \times 2000 = 19.97$$

or, alternatively, the Q-factor can be calculated from the current magnification produced at resonance by the circuit as follows.

The magnitude of current drawn by the parallel circuit is

$$I = V/R_D = 1/2000 = 0.0005 \text{ A}$$

and the magnitude of the current in the capacitor at resonance is

$$I_C = V/X_C = 1/(1/\omega_0 C) = \omega_0 C = 99870 \times 0.1 \times 10^{-6}$$

$$= 0.009987 \text{ A}$$

and

$$Q_0 = I_C/I \text{ at resonance}$$

$$= 0.009987/0.0005 = 19.97$$

In order to draw the phasor diagram, we need first to calculate (at resonance) the current in the coil as follows

$$Z_1 = R_L + j\omega_0 L = 5 + j(99\ 870 \times 1 \times 10^{-3}) = 5 + j99.87$$

$$= 100\angle 87.13° \text{ ohm}$$

and the current in the coil is

$$I_1 = V_S/Z_1 = 1\angle 0°/100\angle 87.13° = 0.01\angle -87.13° \text{ A}$$

The corresponding phasor diagram is shown in Figure 6.14.

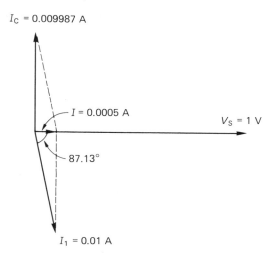

Fig 6.14

Example 6.5

If, in Figure 6.15, $R_1 = 5$ ohm, $R_2 = 10$ ohm, $L = 2$ mH, and $C = 1.0$ microfarad, calculate the resonant frequency, the impedance at resonance, the Q-factor at resonance, and the bandwidth of the circuit.

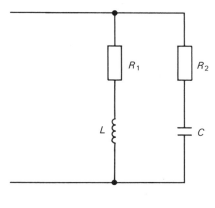

Fig 6.15

Solution 6.5

Using the equations developed in section (f) of the Fact Sheet in this chapter, the circuit can be converted into the form in Figure 6.8(c), in which the resonant frequency is

$$\omega_0 = \frac{1}{\sqrt{(LC)}} \sqrt{\left(\frac{R_L^2 - L/C}{R_C^2 - L/C}\right)}$$

$$= \frac{1}{\sqrt{(2 \times 10^{-3} \times 1 \times 10^{-6})}} \sqrt{\left(\frac{5^2 - (2 \times 10^{-3}/10^{-6})}{(10^2 - (2 \times 10^{-3}/10^{-6})}\right)}$$

$$= 22\ 798 \text{ rad/s or } 3\ 628.4 \text{ Hz}$$

and

$$G_L' = \frac{R_1}{R_1^2 + (\omega_0 L)^2} = \frac{5}{5^2 + (22\ 798 \times 2 \times 10^{-3})^2} = 0.00238 \text{ S}$$

$$G_c' = \frac{R_2}{R_2^2 + (1/\omega_0 C)^2} = \frac{10}{10^2 + 1/(22\ 798 \times 10^{-6})^2} = 0.00494 \text{ S}$$

Hence $G' = G_C' + G_L' = 0.00732$ S and the dynamic impedance of the circuit at resonance is $R_D = 1/G' = 136.6$ ohms.

Referring to Figure 6.8(c)

$$C' = \frac{1/\omega_0^2 C}{R_2^2 + 1/(\omega_0 C)^2} = \frac{0.0019}{100 + 1924} = 0.939 \times 10^{-6} \text{ F}$$

and

$$Q_0 = \omega_0 C' R_D = 22\ 798 \times 0.939 \times 10^{-6} \times 136.6 = 2.92$$

Hence,

$$\text{BW} = \frac{\omega_0}{Q_0} = \frac{22\ 798}{2.92} = 7808 \text{ rad/s or } 1243 \text{ Hz}$$

Example 6.6

Show that the impedance of the circuit in Figure 6.15 is equal to R, and is independent of the frequency if $R = R_1 = R_2 = L/C$.

Solution 6.6

The effective impedance of the circuit at any frequency ω is

$$Z_E = \frac{Z_1 Z_2}{Z_1 + Z_2} = \frac{(R - j/\omega C)(R + j\omega L)}{R - j/\omega C + R + j\omega L}$$

$$= R \frac{[2R + j(\omega L - 1/\omega C)]}{[2R + j(\omega L - 1/\omega C)]} = R$$

That is, the circuit impedance is purely resistive at all frequencies.

Example 6.7

In Worked Example 6.5, what are the limiting values of R_1 and R_2 for which the circuit can be resonant?

Solution 6.7

The equation for the resonant frequency of the circuit is

$$\omega_0 = \frac{1}{\sqrt{(LC)}} \sqrt{\left(\frac{R_1^2 - L/C}{R_2^2 - L/C}\right)}$$

and in the circuit of Worked Example 6.5

$$L/C = 2 \times 10^{-3}/1 \times 10^{-6} = 2000$$

Since the value of ω_0 must be positive, one of the limits to resonance is when the value of the numerator approaches zero, when the resonant frequency also approaches zero. This occurs when

$$R_1 = \sqrt{2000} = 44.72 \text{ ohm}$$

The second limit occurs when the value of the denominator approaches zero, when the resonant frequency of the circuit approaches infinity. That is, when

$$R_2 = \sqrt{2000} = 44.72 \text{ ohm}$$

The reader should also see the solution to Worked Example 6.6.

Example 6.8

Determine the effective inductance at resonance of the circuit in Figure 6.16. Calculate also the resonant frequency of the circuit and the Q-factor at resonance.

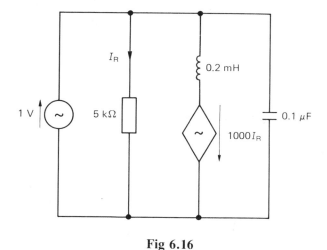

Fig 6.16

Solution 6.8

The dependent voltage source in the inductive branch will have the effect of altering the net inductance of the circuit. The following steps are used to determine the effective inductance of the branch at resonance. The current in the inductive branch at resonance is

$$\frac{\text{voltage across the branch}}{\text{impedance of the inductor}} = \frac{1 + 1000I_R}{j\omega_0 L}$$

$$= \frac{1 + (1000 \times 1/5000)}{j\omega_0 \times 0.2 \times 10^{-3}} = \frac{6000}{j\omega_0} = \frac{V_S}{Z_L}$$

where Z_L is the effective impedance of the inductive branch, and $V_S = 1\angle 0°$ V. Hence

$$Z_L = \frac{j\omega_0 V_S}{6000} = j\omega_0 \times \frac{1\angle 0°}{6000} = j\omega_0 \times 0.1667 \times 10^{-3} \text{ ohm}$$

That is, the effective inductance is 0.1667 mH. The value of the components in the other branches are unaltered by the dependent voltage source, and the circuit may therefore be thought of as a 3-branch parallel circuit containing the following elements:

Branch 1: contains $R' = 5000$ ohm

Branch 2: contains $L' = 0.1667$ mH

Branch 3: contains $C' = 0.1$ microfarad

The resonant frequency is

$$\omega_0 = 1/\sqrt{(L'C')} = 1/\sqrt{(0.1667 \times 10^{-3} \times 0.1 \times 10^{-6})}$$

$$= 244\ 925 \text{ rad/s or } 38\ 981 \text{ Hz}$$

and the Q-factor at resonance is

$$Q_0 = \omega_0 C' R' = 244\ 925 \times 0.1 \times 10^{-6} \times 5000 = 122.5$$

As with Worked Example 6.3, the reader will find it a useful exercise to analyse the effect of the dependent voltage source on the resonant frequency.

6.3 Unworked Problems

Problem 6.1

If the lower cutoff frequency of a series resonant circuit is 50 000 rad/s, and the Q-factor at resonance is 80, calculate the bandwidth and resonant frequency of the circuit.
[628.9 rad/s; 50 312 rad/s]

Problem 6.2

A coil of inductance 1.0 mH and resistance 4 ohm is connected in series with a capacitor. What value of capacitance makes the circuit resonate at a frequency of (a) 1 kHz and (b) 50 kHz? If the r.m.s. voltage applied to the circuit is 10 V,

what is the current in the circuit at (i) the resonant frequency and (ii) 1.1 times
the resonant frequency when resonance occurs at 1 kHz?
[(a) 25.33 microfarad, (i) 2.5 A, (ii) $2.4\angle -16.7°$ A; (b) 0.0101 microfarad, (i)
2.5 A, (ii) $0.17\angle -86.13°$ A]

Problem 6.3

A series circuit comprising a coil and a variable capacitor is energized by a
1.0 MHz source. When the capacitance is 700 pF the current and the supply
voltage are in phase with one another, and when its value is 800 pF the phase
angle between the two is 45°. Determine the value of the resistance and the
inductance of the coil, and also the Q-factor of the circuit at resonance.
[28.39 ohm; 0.036 mH; 8]

Problem 6.4

A coil of inductance 1.2 H and resistance 10 ohm is connected in series with a
capacitor, the circuit being connected to a constant voltage a.c. source of
variable frequency. If the maximum current is 0.5 A at 200 Hz, determine the
supply frequency when the current is 0.25 A.
[198.85 Hz or 201.15 Hz]

Problem 6.5

A coil of resistance 20 ohm and inductance 0.2 H is connected in series with a
capacitor. When a sinusoidal supply of constant voltage is connected to the
circuit, the current is a maximum at a frequency of 1.0 kHz. What value of
capacitance must be connected in parallel with the circuit in order to make the
new parallel circuit resonate at 2 kHz? What is the Q-factor of the circuit in each
case, and what current is drawn from the supply?
[0.042 microfarad; $Q_{SERIES} = 62.8$, $Q_{PARALLEL} = 94$; $I_{SERIES} = 10$ A;
$I_{PARALLEL} = 1.129$ mA]

Problem 6.6

A parallel circuit having a coil of resistance 10 ohm and inductance 10 microhen-
ry in one branch, and a capacitor of capacitance 1 nF in the other branch, is
supplied by a 10 V variable frequency source. Calculate the current drawn by the
circuit at (a) the resonant frequency, (b) 0.9 of the resonant frequency.
[1.584 MHz; (a) 0.01 A; (b) $0.024\angle -59.2°$ A]

Problem 6.7

A coil of resistance 20 ohm and inductance 0.1 H is connected in parallel with a
capacitor of 0.1 microfarad capacitance. Determine the resonant frequency of

the circuit, and the dynamic impedance at resonance. Calculate the phase angle of the circuit at twice the resonant frequency.
[1591 Hz; 50 kΩ; 89.81°]

Problem 6.8

A series circuit consisting of a capacitor and a coil whose inductance is 0.1 H and resistance is 20 ohm, is energized by the voltage

$$v = 50 \sin \omega t + 10 \sin (3\omega t + 10°) + 5 \sin (5\omega t - 45°) \text{ V}$$

where $\omega = 500$ rad/s. Determine the capacitance of the capacitor which produces resonance with the third harmonic frequency, and deduce an expression for the current in the circuit. Calculate the r.m.s. current in the circuit at this frequency.
[4.44 microfarad; $0.125 \sin (\omega t + 87.13°) + 0.5 \sin (3\omega t + 10°) + 0.031 \sin (5\omega t - 127.87°)$ A; 0.365 A]

Problem 6.9

Calculate, for the circuit in Figure 6.17, the value of R for resonance. Convert the circuit into the equivalent pure GLC parallel circuit shown in Figure 6.8(c).
[8.165 ohm; $G' = 0.069$ S; $X'_L = 16.67$ ohm; $X'_C = 16.67$ ohm]

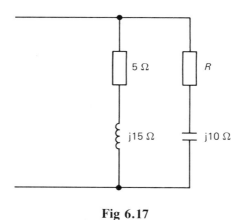

Fig 6.17

Problem 6.10

(a) Sketch graphs showing how (i) X_L, (ii) X_C, (iii) Z each vary with frequency for a series RLC circuit which exhibits resonance at frequency f_0. Use the same axes for all three graphs. (b) Prove that the bandwidth between the two half-power frequencies of a series resonant circuit is given by

$$\text{bandwidth} = \text{resonant frequency}/Q\text{-factor}$$

given that the Q-factor $= \omega_0 L/R$ at resonance. (c) Sketch graphs of V_R, V_L, V_c and I to a base of frequency for a series resonant circuit (Q-factor > 10)

(Staffordshire Polytechnic)

Problem 6.11

A coil of resistance R and self-inductance L is connected in parallel with a capacitor C to a constant-voltage, variable-frequency sinusoidal supply. (a) Draw the phasor diagram for the circuit at resonance. (b) If $R = 100$ ohm, $L = 10$ mH, and $C = 0.005$ microfarad, calculate for the circuit the resonant frequency, its Q-factor, and the bandwidth of the circuit.

(Staffordshire Polytechnic)

[(b) 22 452 Hz; 14.1; 1 592 Hz]

7 Frequency Response

7.1 Fact Sheet

For the two-port network shown in Figure 7.1, with a sinusoidal input voltage, the voltage gain of the network is

$$G(j\omega) = \frac{V_o}{V_1}$$

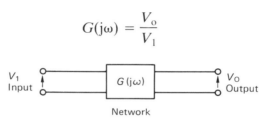

Fig 7.1

For the specific network of Figure 7.2, Z_1 and Z_2 are impedances. By potential divider action,

$$\frac{V_o}{V_1} = \frac{Z_2}{Z_1 + Z_2}$$

This equation assumes that the output is not loaded, i.e., the supply current I passes only through Z_1 and Z_2. V_1 is a sinusoidal input voltage which remains constant for all I.

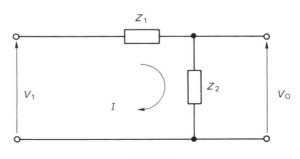

Fig 7.2

(a) Simple Lag Circuit

Refer to Figure 7.3 where $Z_1 = R$ and $Z_2 = 1/j\omega C$

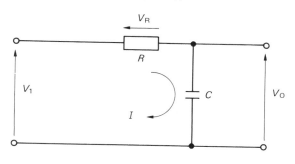

Fig 7.3

Then,

$$G_{LAG} = \frac{V_o}{V_1} = \frac{\dfrac{1}{j\omega C}}{R + \dfrac{1}{j\omega C}} = \frac{1}{1 + j\omega T} \tag{7.1}$$

where $T = RC$, the circuit time constant. Expressing the voltage gain in polar form,

$$G_{LAG} = \frac{1}{\sqrt{(1 + \omega^2 T^2)}} \underline{/-\tan^{-1} \omega t} \tag{7.2}$$

$$= G\angle\phi$$

Equation 7.2 shows that the magnitude of the gain is unity for zero frequency, and tends to zero as the frequency becomes very large.

The phasor diagram (Figure 7.4) shows that V_o lags V_1 by angle ϕ, where ϕ varies from 0 (at zero frequency) to $-90°$ (infinite frequency). The locus of G_{LAG} as ω varies from 0 to infinity, is a semicircle, centre $(\frac{1}{2}, 0)$ and radius $\frac{1}{2}$; see Figure 7.5. This is the basis of the Nyquist diagram used in closed-loop control systems to study stability.

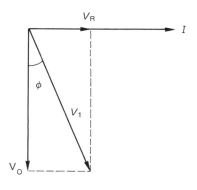

Fig 7.4

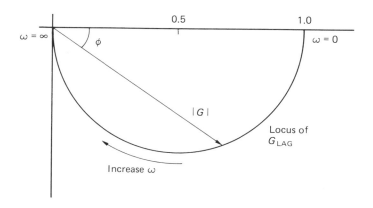

Fig 7.5

(b) Simple Lead Circuit

Refer to Figure 7.6, where

$$Z_1 = \frac{1}{j\omega C} \quad \text{and} \quad Z_2 = R$$

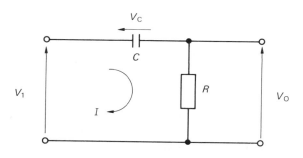

Fig 7.6

Then,

$$G_{LEAD} = \frac{V_o}{V_1} = \frac{R}{\dfrac{1}{j\omega C} + R} = \frac{j\omega T}{1 + j\omega T} \tag{7.3}$$

In polar form,

$$G_{LEAD} = \frac{\omega T}{\sqrt{(1 + \omega^2 T^2)}} \underline{/90° - \tan^{-1}\omega T} \tag{7.4}$$

$$= |G|\underline{/\phi}$$

The phasor diagram (Figure 7.7) shows that V_o leads V_1 by angle ϕ, where ϕ varies from 90° (zero frequency) to 0 (infinite frequency). The locus of G_{LEAD}, as

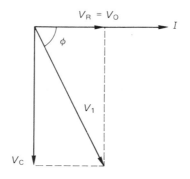

Fig 7.7

ω varies from 0 to infinity, is also a semicircle, centre $(\frac{1}{2}, 0)$ and radius $\frac{1}{2}$ but now ϕ is a leading angle; see Figure 7.8.

When $\omega T = 1$, the gain of each circuit in Figures 7.5 and 7.8 is $1/\sqrt{2}$ and the phase shift is 45°. This represents the half power point in the circuits and is a significant point in the Bode diagram, which is considered later.

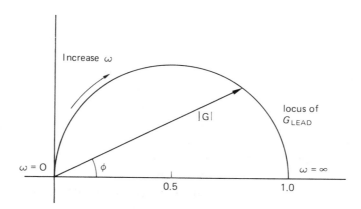

Fig 7.8

(c)   Gain-Frequency Response

The voltage gain of the network shown in Figure 7.1 may be expressed in logarithmic units (decibels or dB) so that the overall gain of complex functions may be determined by adding together the dB gains of the terms forming the function.

Definition:

$$\text{gain} = 20\log \left| \frac{V_o}{V_1} \right| = 20\log |G| \text{ dB}$$

For the simple lag network, using Equation 7.2,

$$\text{gain} = 20\log \frac{1}{\sqrt{(1 + \omega^2 T^2)}} \text{ dB}$$

$$= -20\log\sqrt{(1 + \omega^2 T^2)} \text{ dB} \qquad (7.5)$$

(d) Repeated Terms

The complex gain function of the product of for example three terms, is given by:

$$\text{gain} = |G_1| \underline{/\phi_1} \times |G_2| \underline{/\phi_2} \times |G_3| \underline{/\phi_3}$$

The overall gain expressed in dB units is

$$\text{gain} = 20\log|G_1| + 20\log|G_2| + 20\log|G_3| \text{ dB}$$

and the overall phase shift is given by

$$\text{phase shift} = \phi_1 + \phi_2 + \phi_3$$

(e) Linear Asymptotes

The gain-frequency graph may be linearised if the following observations are made: (a) at low frequencies, $\omega T \ll 1$, and gain = 0 dB; (b) at high frequencies, $\omega T \gg 1$, when gain = $-20\log\omega T$ dB.

Also, in the high frequency range, if the frequency were doubled from say ω_H to $2\omega_H$, i.e., one octave, then the gain would change from $G_1 = -20\log\omega_H T$ to $G_2 = -20\log 2\omega_H T = -20\log\omega_H T - 20\log 2$ dB. So, $G_2 = G_1 - 6$ dB. Hence, if a logarithmic scale is used for the frequency axis of the graph, the high frequency gain will be represented by a straight line whose slope is -6 dB/octave. Repeating this analysis for a frequency increase by a factor of 10 (one decade), shows that the gain falls by 20 dB, so the slope is -20 dB/decade.

These low- and high-frequency asymptotes, (a) and (b) respectively, are illustrated in Figure 7.9. The intersection of the two asymptotes occurs when (a)

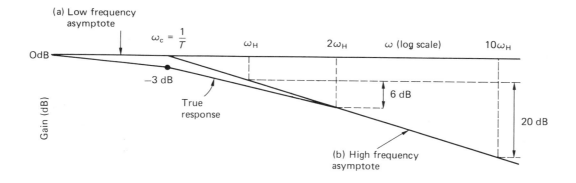

Fig 7.9

146

and (b) are equated, i.e., when $0 = -20\log\omega_C T$. This occurs when $\omega_C T = 1$, where ω_C is called the *corner frequency* or *roll-off frequency*.

Substituting this value in the actual gain equation, Equation 7.5 shows that the gain at ω_C is -3 dB, which is also the bandwidth of the network.

(f) Phase-frequency Response

A graph of phase shift against frequency (also using a logarithmic scale to achieve symmetry) for the simple lag network is obtained using Equation 7.2, which gives,

$$\text{phase shift}, \phi = -\tan^{-1}\omega T$$

This is a curve but may be represented approximately by five straight line segments as shown in Figure 7.10.

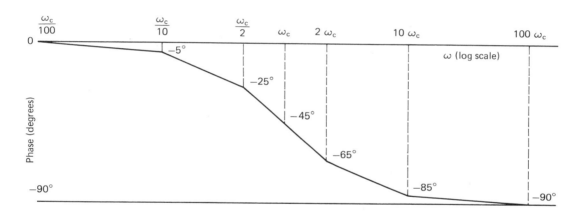

Fig 7.10

(g) Bode diagram

This is the gain-frequency graph and the phase-frequency graph plotted with a logarithmic frequency axis (rad/s or Hz), usually on one sheet of log-linear graph paper.

(h) Generalised Bode diagram

1. For the function

$$G(j\omega) = (j\omega T)^n \tag{7.6}$$

where n is a positive or negative integer, the diagram or plot is shown in Figure 7.11(a) and (b).

147

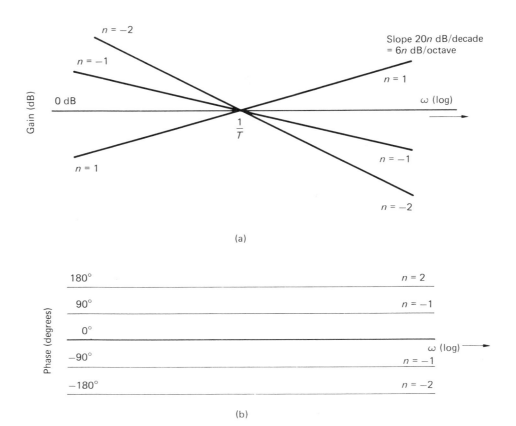

(a)

(b)

Fig 7.11

2. For the function

$$G(j\omega) = (1 + j\omega T)^n \tag{7.7}$$

the diagram is shown in Figure 7.12(a) and (b). Note that the true gain response differs from the linear asymptotes by $3n$ dB at the corner frequency and by n dB at one octave above and below this, as shown in the detail of Figure 7.13(a). The linearised graph is shown in Figure 7.13(b).

3. For the quadratic gain function

$$G(j\omega) = \frac{1}{1 + 2d(j\omega T) + (j\omega T)^2} \tag{7.8}$$

where d is the damping ratio.

Re-writing this as

$$G(j\omega) = \frac{1}{(1 - \omega^2 T^2) + j2d\omega T}$$

it may then be expressed in polar form as

$$\text{gain} = \frac{1}{\sqrt{[(1 - \omega^2 T^2)^2 + 4d^2\omega^2 T^2]}} \bigg/ \tan^{-1} \frac{2d\omega T}{1 - \omega^2 T^2}$$

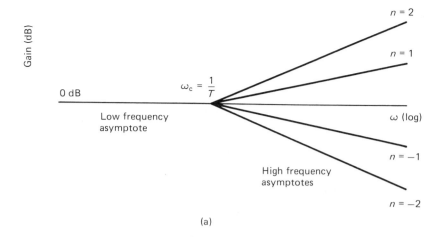

(a)

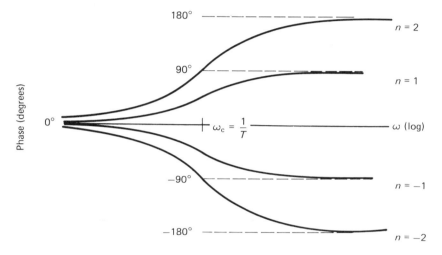

Fig 7.12

(b)

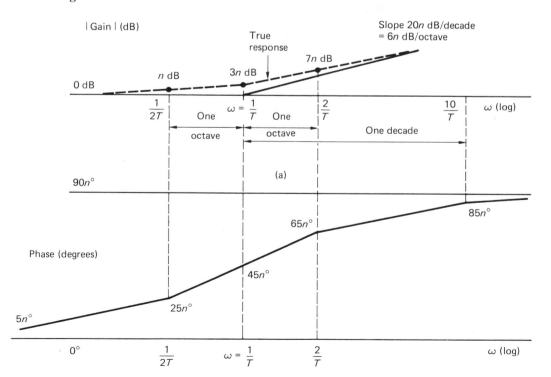

Fig 7.13

(b)

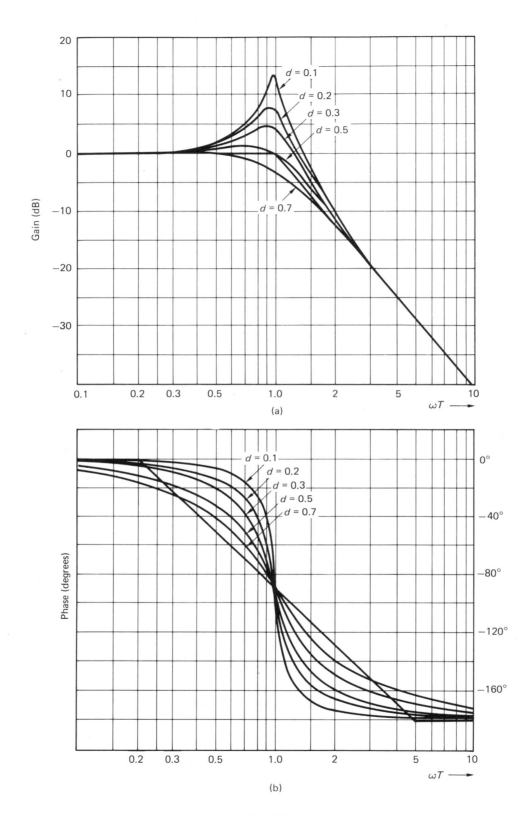

Fig 7.14

The Bode diagram is shown in Figure 7.14. The high frequency asymptote has a slope of -40 dB/decade. Note. The gain response when d = 1.0 (called critical damping) is the same as the one obtained from Equation 7.7 when $n = -2$ since

$$\frac{1}{(1 + j\omega T)^2} = \frac{1}{1 + j2\omega T - \omega^2 T^2}$$

7.2 Worked Examples

Example 7.1

Use 2-cycle log-linear graph paper to construct the linear asymptotes of the gain (dB)-frequency (rad/s) response for the voltage transfer function,

$$\frac{V_o}{V_1} = \frac{10(1 + 0.1 j\omega)}{j\omega(1 + 0.5 j\omega)}$$

Hence sketch the actual gain-frequency curve.

Solution 7.1

The gain function can be expressed as the product

$$G(j\omega) = (j\omega 0.1)^{-1} \times (1 + j\omega 0.1) \times (1 + j\omega 0.5)^{-1}$$
$$= \quad A \quad \times \quad B \quad \times \quad C$$

Hence the total gain will be the sum of the individual gains when these are expressed in dB. The individual gain components and their sum are shown in Figure 7.15(a) and (b), respectively. The graph for part A (see Figure 7.15(a)) is a straight line graph passing through the 0 dB axis at 10 rad/s with a slope -6 dB/octave; at 20 rad/s it has a value -6 dB. At one decade below this, i.e., at 2 rad/s, its value is (20–6), i.e., 14 dB since the slope is also -20 dB/decade.

The corrections to be made at the corner frequencies are $+3$ dB at 10 rad/s for part B, and -3 dB at 2 rad/s for part C.

Example 7.2

(a) Construct the gain locus for the simple lag circuit shown in Figure 7.3 and use it to estimate the gain when the phase shift changes from 0 to $-90°$ in $10°$ steps.

(b) Compare your results with those obtained by calculation using Equation 7.2.

(c) Repeat parts (a) and (b) for the lead circuit shown in Figure 7.6 and Equation 7.4.

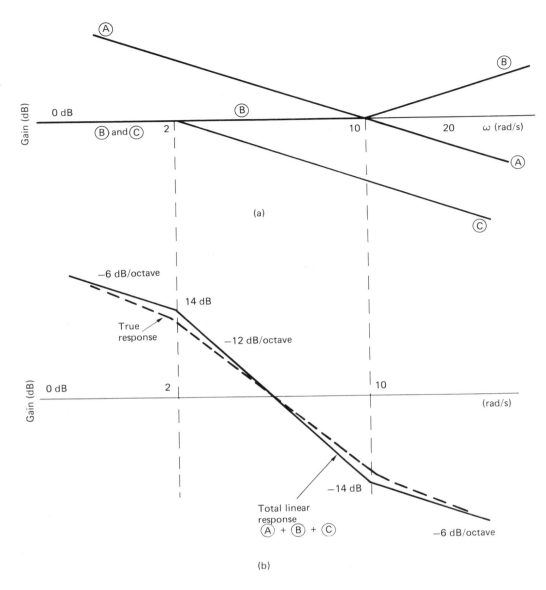

(a)

(b)

Fig 7.15

Solution 7.2

The loci are shown in Figures 7.5 and 7.8, which are independent of the circuit time constant. By calculation, using Equation 7.4:

Lag circuit Phase shift (deg)	0	−10	−20	−30	−40	−50	−60	−70	−80	−90
Lead circuit Phase shift (deg)	0	10	20	30	40	50	60	70	80	90
Gain	1.0	0.98	0.94	0.87	0.77	0.64	0.5	0.34	0.17	0

Example 7.3

(a) Determine the transfer function $G(j\omega)$ which satisfies the linearised gain-frequency response shown in full line in Figure 7.16.

(b) Estimate the frequency at unity gain and the phase shift at this frequency.

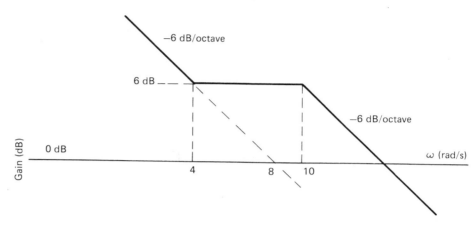

Fig 7.16

Solution 7.3

Always consider the contribution to the gain-frequency response at the lowest frequencies shown; in this case it shows slope of -6 dB/octave which must come from a $(j\omega T_1)^{-1}$ term. If it continued to fall, it would reach the 0 dB axis one octave above 4 rad/s, i.e., at 8 rad/s (refer to the graph), so $T_1 = 1/8 = 0.125$ s.

The negative slope of the $(j\omega T_1)^{-1}$ contribution is offset above 4 rad/s by a $(1 + j\omega T_2)$ section whose corner frequency is 4 rad/s, so $T_2 = 0.25$ s.

Finally, there is another corner frequency at 10 rad/s followed by a slope of -6 dB/octave, which is from a $(1 + j\omega T_3)^{-1}$ term, where $T_3 = 1/10 = 0.1$ s. Result,

$$G(j\omega) = \frac{1}{0.125j\omega} \times (1 + 0.25j\omega) \times \frac{1}{(1 + 0.1j\omega)}$$

$$= \frac{(1 + 0.25j\omega)}{0.125j\omega(1 + 0.1j\omega)} = \frac{8(1 + 0.25j\omega)}{j\omega(1 + 0.1j\omega)}$$

Example 7.4

(a) Derive the voltage transfer function $G(j\omega) = V_o/V_1$ for the circuit shown in Figure 7.17 when $R_1 = 10$ kΩ, $R_2 = 10/9$ kΩ and $C = 0.01$ microfarad.

(b) Hence draw the linearised Bode diagram of gain (dB) and phase against frequency (rad/s) for the range $10^3 < \omega < 10^6$ rad/s

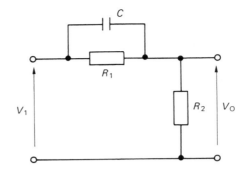

Fig 7.17

Solution 7.4

(a) Comparing Figures 7.17 and 7.2, we have

$$\frac{V_o}{V_1} = \frac{Z_2}{Z_1 + Z_2}$$

where

$$Z_1 = \frac{\dfrac{R_1}{j\omega C}}{R_1 + \dfrac{1}{j\omega C}} = \frac{R_1}{1 + j\omega C R_1}$$

and
$$Z_2 = R_2$$

Therefore

$$\frac{V_o}{V_1} = \frac{R_2(1 + j\omega C R_1)}{R_2(1 + j\omega C R_1) + R_1} = \frac{R_2(1 + j\omega C R_1)}{R_1 + R_2 + j\omega C R_1 R_2}$$

$$= \frac{R_2}{(R_1 + R_2)} \cdot \frac{(1 + j\omega T_1)}{(1 + j\omega T_2)}$$

where $T_1 = C R_1$

and
$$T_2 = \frac{C R_1 R_2}{(R_1 + R_2)}$$

Substituting values gives

$$\frac{V_o}{V_1} = \frac{0.1(1 + j\omega 10^{-4})}{(1 + j\omega 10^{-5})}$$

Note. The ratio $R_2/(R_1 + R_2)$ (0.1 in this example), is the gain of the circuit when a constant voltage (d.c.) is applied.

(b) $V_o/V_1 = 0.1(1 + j\omega 10^{-4})(1 + j\omega 10^{-5})^{-1}$

$$= A \times B \times C$$

When the gain is expressed in decibels, the Bode diagram is the sum of the 3 separate graphs:

(1) For part A, gain $= 20\log 0.1 = -20$ dB.

(2) See the generalised response (Figure 7.12) for part B of the transfer function, where $n = 1$ and $\omega_{C1} = 1/T_1 = 10^4$ rad/s.

(3) As for (2) for part C of the transfer function but $n = -1$ and $\omega_{C2} = 1/T_2 = 10^5$ rad/s.

The phase shift contributions come from parts B and C and we use the generalised phase graph of Figure 7.13(b).
For part B, start at $\omega_{C1} = 10^4$ rad/s with a phase shift of $45°$
For part C, start at $\omega_{C2} = 10^5$ rad/s with a phase shift of $-45°$.
The results are shown in Figure 7.18.

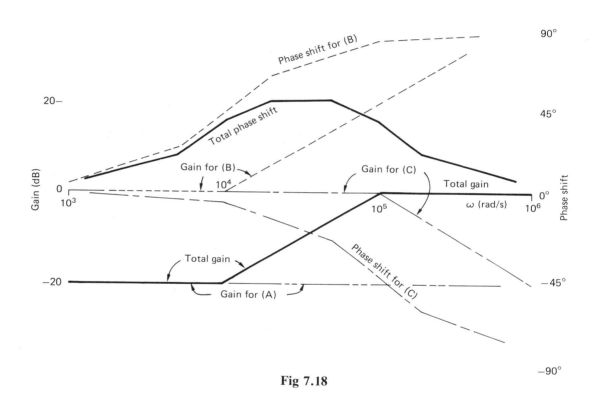

Fig 7.18

Example 7.5

(a) Sketch the Bode diagram for the transfer function

$$G(j\omega) = \frac{40 \times 10^6}{4 \times 10^6 + j\omega 1600 - \omega^2}$$

(b) Write and run a computer program or use a programmable calculator to produce a table of gain(dB) and phase values for a range of angular frequencies for comparison with part **(a)**.

155

Solution 7.5

(a) Re-write the function in standard form to compare with Equation 7.8 to give

$$G(j\omega) = 10 \times \frac{1}{1 + j\omega 0.4 \times 10^{-3} - 0.25 \times 10^{-6}\omega^2}$$

Equating coefficients gives: $T^2 = 0.25 \times 10^{-6}$, hence $T = 0.5$ ms and $2dT = 0.4 \times 10^{-3}$, so $d = 0.4$.

Use Figure 7.14 to obtain the gain- and phase-frequency responses for the frequency-dependent term. The total gain will be 20 dB higher due to the constant gain of 10, giving the gain and phase curves in Figure 7.19.

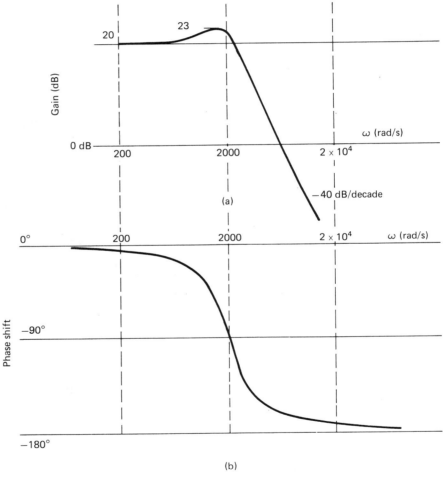

Fig 7.19

(b) By calculation

Frequency (rad/s)	200	1000	1600	1800	2000	2200	2400	3000
Gain (dB)	20	21.4	22.7	22.6	21.9	20.9	19.5	15.2

Example 7.6

(a) Show that the relationship between V_o and V_1 in Figure 7.20 is

$$\frac{V_o}{V_1} = \frac{1 + j\omega T}{1 + j\omega a T}$$

If V_1 is a sinusoidal supply,

$$a = \frac{R_1 + R_2}{R_2} \quad \text{and} \quad T = R_2 C_2$$

Plot on log-linear graph paper the linear approximations for the voltage gain in dB against angular frequency and hence sketch the actual voltage gain curve in the range $10^2 < \omega < 10^5$ rad/s given that $R_1 = 90$ kΩ, $R_2 = 10$ kΩ and $C = 0.01$ microfarad.

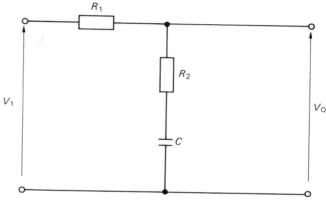

Fig 7.20

(b) Calculate the phase shift through the network when $\omega = 3.0 \times 10^3$ rad/s.

Solution 7.6

$$\frac{V_o}{V_1} = \frac{Z_2}{Z_1 + Z_2} = \frac{R_2 + \dfrac{1}{j\omega C_2}}{R_1 + R_2 + \dfrac{1}{j\omega C_2}} = \frac{1 + j\omega C_2 R_2}{1 + j\omega C_2(R_1 + R_2)} = \frac{1 + j\omega T}{1 + j\omega a T}$$

where

$$T = C_2 R_2 \quad \text{and} \quad a = \frac{(R_1 + R_2)}{R_2}$$

Using the data, $a = (90 + 10)/10 = 10$ and $T = 10 \times 10^3 \times 0.01 \times 10^{-6}$ $= 10^{-4}$ s

Corner frequencies are $\omega_{C1} = \dfrac{1}{aT} = 10^3$ rad/s for the denominator

and

$$\omega_{C2} = \frac{1}{T} = 10^4 \text{ rad/s for the numerator.}$$

The gain(dB)-frequency graph is constructed using linear asymptotes on 3-cycle log-linear paper and shown in Figure 7.21.

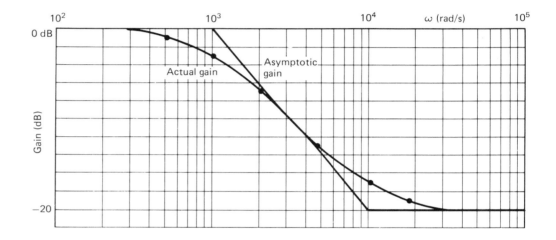

Fig 7.21

(b) When $\omega = 3 \times 10^3$ rad/s

$$\frac{V_o}{V_1} = \frac{1 + j0.3}{1 + j3} = \frac{1.044 \,\underline{/16.7^\circ}}{3.162 \,\underline{/71.6^\circ}}$$

Hence, resultant phase shift $= 16.7^\circ - 71.6^\circ = -54.9^\circ$, i.e., V_o lags V_1 by 54.9°.

Example 7.7

(a) Assuming an ideal operational amplifier in the circuit in Figure 7.22, show that the voltage gain is expressed by

$$\frac{V_o}{V_1} = \frac{1}{1 + j\omega 2T_1 - 2\omega^2 T_1^2}$$

158

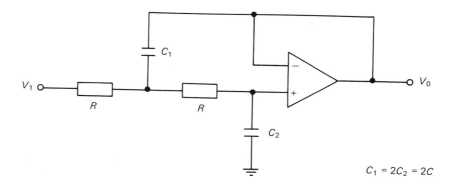

Fig 7.22

where $T_1 = RC$
(b) Sketch the gain-frequency response.
(c) What is the bandwidth of the circuit?

Solution 7.7

(a) Replace the $R, R, 2C$ star network by its equivalent delta network. This is shown in Figure 7.23.

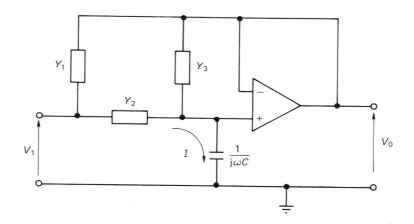

Fig 7.23

For the ideal amplifier $V_+ = V_-$, so Y_3 has no effect. From Figure 7.22, we see that $V_- = V_o$. Also, since no current enters the amplifier terminals, the current through Y_2 must flow through C_2, hence

$$I = (V_1 - V_o)Y_2 = j\omega C V_o$$

Using star-delta conversion,

$$Y_2 = \frac{\dfrac{1}{R^2}}{\dfrac{2}{R} + j2\omega C} = \frac{1}{2R(1 + j\omega CR)}$$

159

That is

$$\frac{(V_1 - V_o)}{2R(1 + j\omega CR)} = j\omega CV_o$$

or

$$V_1 = V_o(1 - 2\omega^2 C^2 R^2 + j\omega 2CR)$$

Hence

$$\frac{V_o}{V_1} = \frac{1}{1 + 2(j\omega T_1) - (\sqrt{2}\omega T_1)^2} \quad \text{where } T_1 = RC$$

(b) The equation above has the same form as Equation 7.8, and inspection shows that $dT = T_1$ and $T^2 = 2T_1^2$. That is, $T = \sqrt{2}T_1$ and $d = 1/\sqrt{2}$; the corresponding gain-frequency response is shown in Figure 7.24.

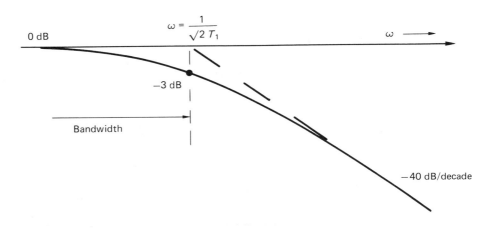

Fig 7.24

(c) The bandwidth is given by the value of the frequency at which the voltage gain has fallen by a factor of $1/\sqrt{2}$.

From part **(a)**,

$$\text{gain} = \frac{1}{\sqrt{[(1 - 2\omega^2 T_1^2)^2 + 4\omega^2 T_1^2]}}$$

Now when $\omega > 0$, the low-frequency gain > 1, and the gain falls to $1/\sqrt{2}$ when

$$(1 - 2\omega^2 T_1)^2 + 4\omega^2 T_1 = 2$$

or

$$4\omega^4 T_1 = 1$$

Giving

$$\omega = \frac{1}{\sqrt{2}T_1} = \frac{1}{T} = \text{bandwidth.}$$

160

Example 7.8

Write and then run a SPICE program (see Appendix 3 for details of SPICE) which will plot the graphs of voltage gain expressed in dB and phase shift against frequency for the circuit and data given in Worked Example 7.4. Use ten frequency values per decade in the range 100 Hz to 100 kHz. Compare the results with those obtained in Worked Example 7.4.

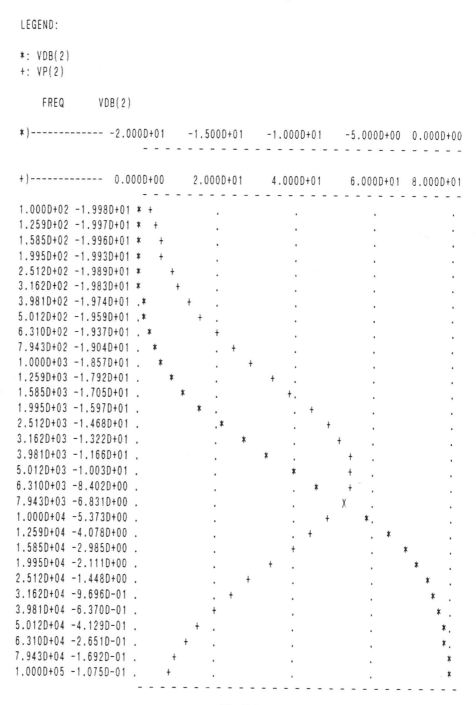

```
LEGEND:

*: VDB(2)
+: VP(2)

     FREQ      VDB(2)

*)------------- -2.000D+01    -1.500D+01    -1.000D+01    -5.000D+00  0.000D+00
                - - - - - - - - - - - - - - - - - - - - - - - - - - - - - - - -

+)------------- 0.000D+00     2.000D+01     4.000D+01     6.000D+01  8.000D+01
                - - - - - - - - - - - - - - - - - - - - - - - - - - - - - - - -
1.000D+02 -1.998D+01 * +              .              .              .
1.259D+02 -1.997D+01 *   +            .              .              .
1.585D+02 -1.996D+01 *     +          .              .              .
1.995D+02 -1.993D+01 *     +          .              .              .
2.512D+02 -1.989D+01 *        +       .              .              .
3.162D+02 -1.983D+01 *           +    .              .              .
3.981D+02 -1.974D+01 .*            +  .              .              .
5.012D+02 -1.959D+01 .*              +.              .              .
6.310D+02 -1.937D+01 . *             .+             .              .
7.943D+02 -1.904D+01 .   *           . +            .              .
1.000D+03 -1.857D+01 .     *         .    +         .              .
1.259D+03 -1.792D+01 .        *      .       +      .              .
1.585D+03 -1.705D+01 .          *    .          +.  .              .
1.995D+03 -1.597D+01 .             * .            +.              .
2.512D+03 -1.468D+01 .             .*             .  +            .
3.162D+03 -1.322D+01 .             .   *          .     +         .
3.981D+03 -1.166D+01 .             .       *      .       +       .
5.012D+03 -1.003D+01 .             .          *   .        +      .
6.310D+03 -8.402D+00 .             .              .  *     +      .
7.943D+03 -6.831D+00 .             .              .      X        .
1.000D+04 -5.373D+00 .             .              .    +    *.    .
1.259D+04 -4.078D+00 .             .              .  +        *   .
1.585D+04 -2.985D+00 .             .          +   .              * .
1.995D+04 -2.111D+00 .             .       +      .              *
2.512D+04 -1.448D+00 .             .    +         .              . *
3.162D+04 -9.696D-01 .             .  +           .              .*
3.981D+04 -6.370D-01 .             +              .              * .
5.012D+04 -4.129D-01 .         +    .              .             *.
6.310D+04 -2.651D-01 .       +      .              .             *.
7.943D+04 -1.692D-01 .     +        .              .              *
1.000D+05 -1.075D-01 .    +         .              .              *
                - - - - - - - - - - - - - - - - - - - - - - - - - - - - - - - -
```

Fig 7.25

Solution 7.8

A suitable input file is:

```
Network Figure 7.17
R1   1   2   10K
R2   2   0   1.11111K
C    1   2   0.01U
V1   1   0   AC   1
.AC DEC 10 100 100K
.PLOT AC VDB(2) VP(2)
.END
```

The resultant print-out when this program is run is shown in Figure 7.25.

7.3 Unworked Problems

Problem 7.1

Derive the voltage transfer function $\dfrac{V_o}{V_1}(j\omega)$ for each of the circuits in Figure 7.26.

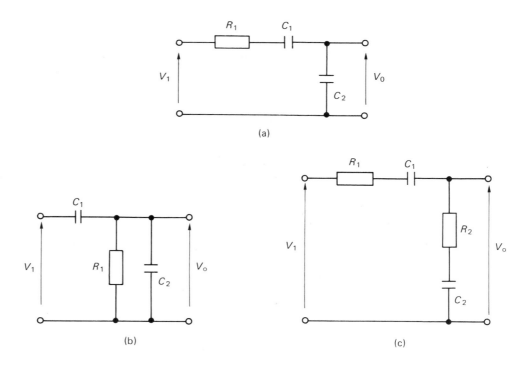

Fig 7.26

[(a) $\dfrac{a}{(1 + j\omega T)}$ where $a = \dfrac{C_1}{C_1 + C_2}$; $T = \dfrac{R_1 C_1 C_2}{(C_1 + C_2)}$

(b) $\dfrac{j\omega T_1}{1 + j\omega T_2}$ where $T_1 = R_1 C_1$; $T_2 = R_1(C_1 + C_2)$

(c) $\dfrac{a(1 + j\omega T_2)}{(1 + j\omega T_1)}$ where $a = \dfrac{C_1}{C_1 + C_2}$; $T_1 = \dfrac{C_1 C_2(R_1 + R_2)}{(C_1 + C_2)}$;

and $T_2 = R_2 C_2$]

Problem 7.2

Sketch the Bode diagrams for each of the circuits in Figure 7.26 when $R_2 = 2R_1 = 2$ ohm and $C_2 = 2C_1 = 2$ farad in each case.
[Bode diagrams are shown in Figure 7.27.]

Problem 7.3

Assume an ideal operational amplifier in the circuit shown in Figure 7.28 and derive the complex voltage gain equation. What filter characteristic does this represent?

$[\dfrac{V_o}{V_1} = \dfrac{(j\omega T)^2}{(1 + j\omega T)^2}$ where $T = RC$; Second order high pass filter]

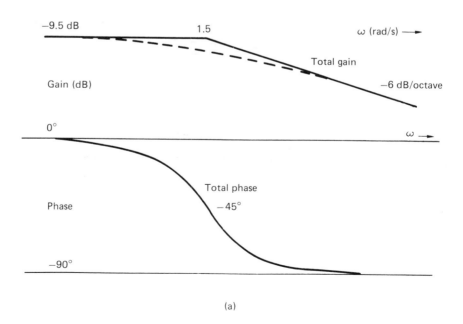

(a)

Fig 7.72 (continued on next page)

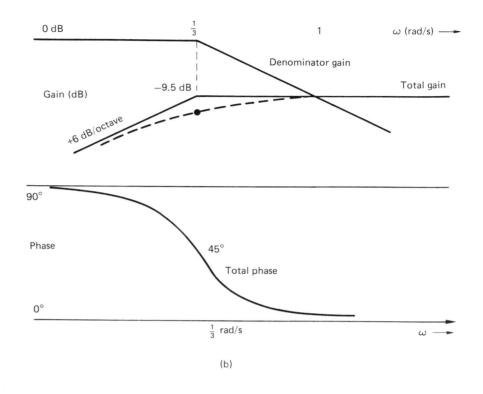

(b)

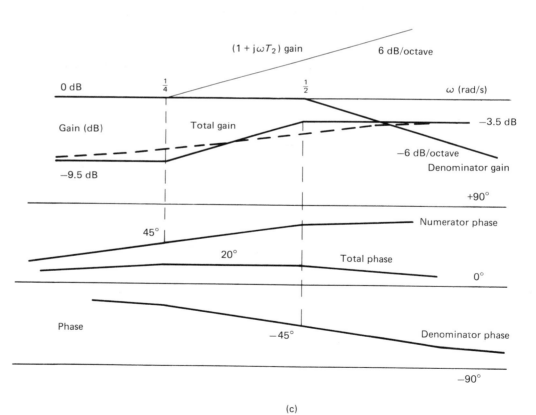

(c)

Fig 7.27

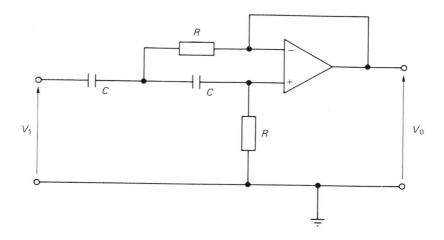

Fig 7.28

Problem 7.4

For the two circuits shown in Figures 7.3 and 7.6, $R = 100 \text{ k}\Omega$ and $C = 0.01$ microfarad. Calculate the magnitude of the voltage gain and the phase shift of the circuits at 300 Hz.

[0.469, 62° lagging; 0.883, 28° leading]

Problem 7.5

The voltage transfer function of a circuit element is expressed as

$$\frac{V_o}{V_1} = \frac{250}{j\omega(j\omega + 5)}$$

(a) Construct the linearised graphs of gain and phase vs frequency (Bode diagram).
(b) Use the graphs to estimate (i) the phase shift at unity gain, (ii) the frequency in hertz when the gain is unity.
(c) Calculate the gain and phase shift at 1.5 Hz.

[**(a)** The linearised Bode diagram is shown in Figure 7.29. **(b)** (i) 161°;
(ii) 2.5 Hz; **(c)** Voltage gain = 2.49 = 7.9 dB; phase shift = −152°]

Problem 7.6

An instrumentation system has a transfer function, relating input x to output y, given by

$$\frac{y}{x} = \frac{\omega_n^2}{\omega_n^2 - \omega^2 + j2d\omega\omega_n}$$

where d is the damping ratio and ω_n is the undamped natural frequency of the system.

If $d = 0.5$, calculate the percentage magnification (compared to the zero frequency gain) when the input signal frequency is $0.8\omega_n$.
[14%]

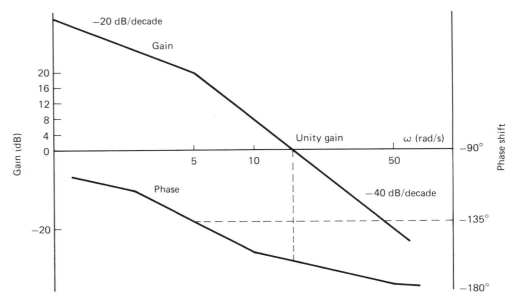

Fig 7.29

Problem 7.7

Determine the transfer functions $G(j\omega)$ which satisfy the linearised gain-frequency responses shown in Figures 7.30(a) and (b).

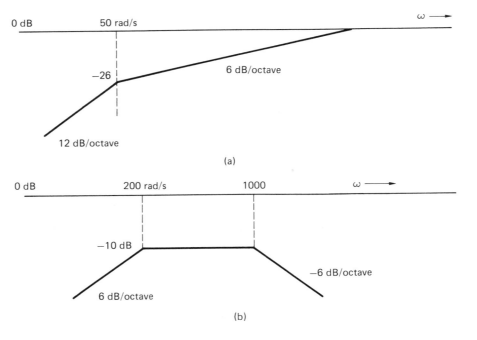

Fig 7.30

[(a) $\quad G(j\omega) = \dfrac{-2 \times 10^{-5}\omega^2}{(1 + j\omega20 \times 10^{-3})(1 + j\omega10^{-3})}$

(b) $\quad G(j\omega) = \dfrac{j\omega1.58 \times 10^{-3}}{(1 + j\omega5 \times 10^{-3})(1 + j\omega10^{-3})]}$

Problem 7.8

Derive the voltage transfer function $\dfrac{V_o}{V_1}(j\omega)$ for the network shown in Figure 7.31.

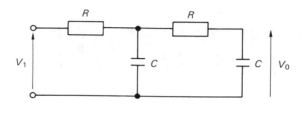

Fig 7.31

Note: The result is not the same as that obtained from two simple RC lag networks (Figure 7.3) multiplied together.

[$\quad \dfrac{V_o}{V_1} = \dfrac{1}{1 - \omega^2T^2 + j\omega3T}$ where $T = RC$.

See note at end of the Fact Sheet in this chapter.]

8 Apparent Power, Power, Reactive VA and Power Factor Improvement

8.1 Fact Sheet

(a) Average Power in an A.C. Circuit

If a voltage $v = V_M \sin \omega t$ is applied to a passive circuit, and the current in the circuit is $i = I_M \sin (\omega t - \phi)$, the instantaneous power, p, consumed is

$$p = vi = V_M I_M \sin(\omega t) \cdot \sin(\omega t - \phi) = \tfrac{1}{2} V_M I_M [\cos \phi - \cos(2\omega t - \phi)]$$

Since the term $\cos(2\omega t - \phi)$ has zero average value over one cycle, the *average power* consumed per cycle is

$$P = \tfrac{1}{2} V_M I_M \cos \phi = VI \cos \phi$$

where V and I are the r.m.s. values of the voltage and current, respectively.

Typical waveforms are shown in Figure 8.1. Since the voltage (or current) is sometimes negative when the current (or voltage) is positive, the instantaneous power waveform (which is the instantaneous product of the voltage and current waveforms) has both positive and negative values during the cycle. The reader should note that the power waveform is at twice the frequency of both the voltage and current waveforms.

In the waveforms in Figure 8.1, the voltage waveform at $\omega t = 0$ passes through zero and becomes positive and, at the same time, the current waveform is negative and is approaching zero. For this reason, we say in this case that the current waveform in the figure *lags behind* the voltage waveform (or, alternat-

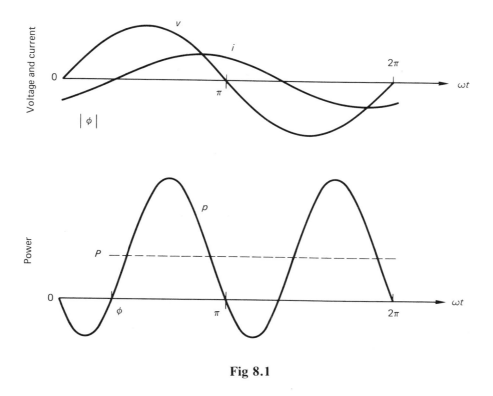

Fig 8.1

ively, we could say that the voltage waveform *leads* the current. However, it is the usual practice in electrical engineering to say what the current does with respect to the voltage).

(b) Apparent Power (*S*) and Power Factor (p.f.)

The equation for the average power in an a.c. circuit can be written

$$P = VI \cos \phi = S \cos \phi = \text{apparent power} \times \text{power factor}$$

where *S* is the *apparent power* (or the volt-ampere product) consumed by the circuit, and *power factor* = cos ϕ.

However, since cos ϕ is positive when $-90 < \phi < 90$, it is usual to qualify the power factor with information relating to the sign of the phase angle. Electrical engineers therefore speak of a *leading p.f.* when the current waveform leads the voltage waveform, and of a *lagging p.f.* when the current lags behind the voltage, as is the case in Figure 8.1. In all practical cases, the power factor lies in the range zero to unity.

(c) The Power Triangle and Quadrature Power

Since the power consumed by a circuit is expressed in the form $P = S \cos \phi$, power can be represented in the form of a power triangle as shown in Figure 8.2. The third side, *Q* of the triangle is the *quadrature power* or *reactive volt amperes*,

169

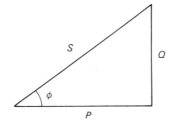

Fig 8.2

(*reactive VA*), expressed in VAr. The relationships may be summarized as follows.

$$\text{apparent power, } S = VI = I^2Z \text{ VA}$$

$$\text{power, } P = VI \cos \phi = I^2R \text{ W}$$

$$\text{quadrature power, } Q = VI \sin \phi = I^2X \text{ VAr}$$

where Z, R, and X are the respective modulus of the impedance, resistance, and reactance of the circuit.

(d) Power Calculations with Complex Values

Consider the voltage and current phasors in Figure 8.3. The power consumed by the circuit is given by

$$VI \cos \phi = VI \cos (\alpha - \beta)$$

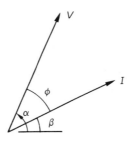

Fig 8.3

However, the product of the complex voltage and current in the diagram gives $V\angle\alpha \times I\angle\beta = VI\angle(\alpha + \beta)$. Clearly, to obtain the power consumed, the angle of the product should be $(\alpha - \beta)$. To obtain this, it is necessary to *multiply the complex voltage by the conjugate* (see Appendix 1 for details) *of the complex current*, or I^*. That is

$$S = VI^* = V\angle\alpha \times I\angle-\beta = S\angle\phi = P + jQ$$

That is,

$$P = \text{Re } VI^*$$

$$Q = \text{Im } VI^*$$

$$S = |VI^*|$$

The reader should note that it has been agreed internationally that the *reactive power of an inductive load is positive* (see Worked Example 8.1).

(e)   Power Factor Improvement

Some domestic equipment and most industrial equipment are inherently inductive, and draw current at a lagging power factor. This has a number of disadvantages (the reader should refer to textbooks on the subject for a full discussion), the principal one being that, for a given power consumed, the current required increases rapidly as the power factor gets lower (note a low leading power factor has the same effect). It is therefore advantageous from the viewpoint of the generating authority that the user should improve his power factor from a low lagging value to one which is closer to unity power factor. Clearly, it is not always practical for the user to improve his power factor to unity, but the supply authorities encourage the industrial user to do so by including a punitive low power factor clause in the electricity tariff.

There are two general methods used to improve the power factor of plant. The first is to connect a capacitor bank in parallel with any load with a low lagging power factor. The second is to replace machines, e.g., induction motors, which run at a low power factor with machines such as synchronous motors which can be arranged to run at a leading power factor.

Power factor correction by capacitors in single phase systems is described below. For information on power factor correction in three phase systems, the reader is referred to specialized texts on electrical power engineering.

The following discussion refers to single phase loads, but can be read as applying to three phase loads since certain types of load and machines (namely *balanced loads*) can be reduced to a single phase equivalent.

Note that power electronic devices such as GTO converters can force the converter current to lead, thereby providing power factor correction.

Power factor improvement by capacitor

The circuit diagram and corresponding phasor diagram for power factor correction by capacitor in a single phase system are shown in Figure 8.4, (a) and (b) respectively. The load has a low lagging power factor and draws a current of I_L at a phase angle of ϕ_L. To improve the power factor of the load, a capacitor is connected as near to the terminals of the load as possible. This has the effect not only of improving the phase angle to ϕ, but also it reduces the magnitude of the load current drawn from I_L to I. The reader should note that, since the in-phase component of the total current is unaltered, the connection of the capacitor does not change the power consumed by the load.

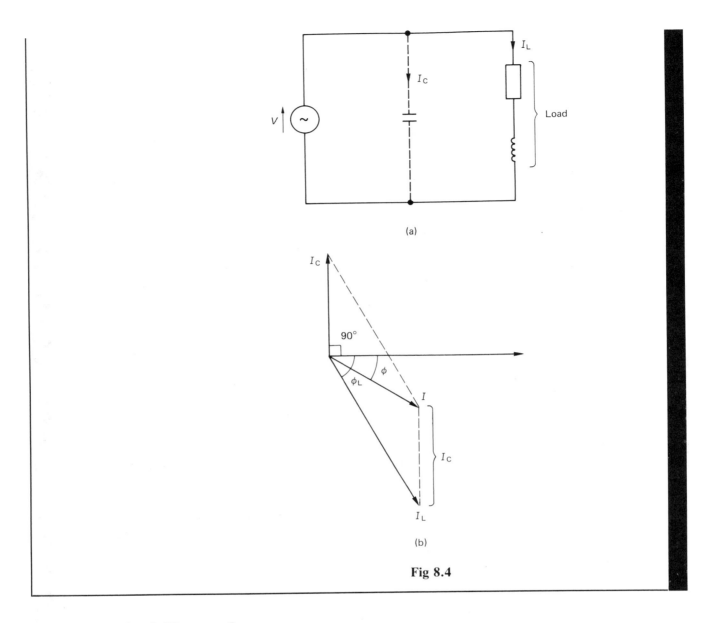

(a)

(b)

Fig 8.4

8.2   Worked Examples

Example 8.1

A voltage of $v = 212.1 \sin \omega t$ V is applied to an impedance of $3.61\angle56.31°$ ohm. Determine the resistance and reactance of the circuit, together with the power, the VA, and the VAr consumed. Calculate the current in the circuit and its power factor. Draw the power triangle for the circuit.

Solution 8.1

The impedance of the circuit is

$$\mathbf{Z} = 3.61\angle56.31° = 2 + j3 \text{ ohm}$$

that is

$$\text{circuit resistance, } R = 2 \text{ ohm}$$

and, since there is a '$+j$' term in the expression

$$\text{circuit inductive reactance, } X_L = 3 \text{ ohm}$$

The supply voltage can be expressed in the form

$$V = \frac{212.1}{\sqrt{2}} \angle 0° = 150 \angle 0° \text{ V}$$

and the current in the circuit is

$$I = \frac{V}{Z} = \frac{150 \angle 0°}{3.61 \angle 56.31°} = 41.55 \angle -56.31° \text{ A}$$

and

$$\text{power factor} = \cos(-56.31°) = 0.983 \text{ (lagging)}$$

The power, the VA, and the VAr consumed can be calculated in any one of a number of ways, including the following.

Method 1

$$\text{power, } P = |I|^2 R = 41.55^2 \times 2 = 3\,453 \text{ W}$$

$$\text{volt amperes, } S = |I|^2 |Z| = 41.55^2 \times 3.61 = 6\,232 \text{ VA}$$

$$\text{reactive VA, } Q = |I|^2 X_L = 41.55^2 \times 3 = 5\,179 \text{ VAr lagging}$$

Method 2

$$\text{power, } P = |V||I| \cos\phi = 150 \times 41.55 \cos(-56.31°) = 3\,457 \text{ W}$$

$$\text{volt amperes, } S = |V||I| = 150 \times 41.55 = 6\,232 \text{ VA}$$

$$\text{reactive VA, } Q = |V||I| \sin\phi = 150 \times 41.55 \times \sin(-56.31°)$$

$$= -5\,185 \text{ VAr or } 5\,185 \text{ VAr lagging}$$

There are two points to note here. The first is that some of the answers provided by method 2 differ by about 0.1 per cent from those produced by method 1 because of the rounding errors in the calculation. The second is the negative mathematical sign associated with the reactive VA consumed by the circuit: more is said about this below.

Method 3

$$S = VI^* = 150 \angle 0° \times 41.55 \angle 56.31° = 6232 \angle 56.31°$$

$$= 3\,457 + j\,5\,185 \text{ VA}$$

Hence,

$$\text{volt amperes, } S = 6232 \text{ VA}$$

$$\text{power, } P = 3457 \text{ W}$$

reactive VA, $Q = 5185$ VAr lagging

The reader will note that the mathematical sign associated with the VAr consumed is reversed between methods 2 and 3. This is because the convention adopted for method 3 produces a positive result with a lagging load. However, in this book, the power triangle for any problem is drawn according to the results obtained by method 2 (see Figure 8.5).

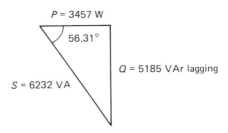

Fig 8.5

Example 8.2

A voltage $v = 200 \sin (\omega t - 20°)$ V results in a current of $i = 30 \sin (\omega t + 30°)$ mA in a circuit. Determine the value of the elements in the circuit, and draw the power triangle for the circuit.

Solution 8.2

The voltage is expressed in polar form as follows

$$V_S = \frac{200}{\sqrt{2}} \angle{-20°} = 141.42 \angle{-20°} \text{ V}$$

and the current is

$$I = \frac{30}{\sqrt{2}} \angle 30° = 21.21 \angle 30° \text{ mA}$$

Hence,

$$Z = \frac{V_S}{I} = \frac{141.42 \angle{-20°}}{21.21 \times 10^{-3} \angle 30°} = 6668 \angle{-50°} = 4286 - \text{j}5108 \text{ ohm}$$

That is, the circuit comprises a resistance of 4286 ohm in series with a capacitor of reactance 5108 ohm (or, alternatively, it comprises a 10 373 ohm resistor in parallel with a capacitor of reactance 8703 ohm). Now

$$S = VI^* = 141.42 \angle{-20°} \times 21.21 \times 10^{-3} \angle{-30°} = 3 \angle{-50°}$$

$$= 1.93 - \text{j}2.3 \text{ VA}$$

That is,

volt amperes consumed, $S = 3$ VA

power consumed, $P = 1.93$ W

reactive VA consumed, $Q = 2.3$ VAr leading

The corresponding power triangle is shown in Figure 8.6.

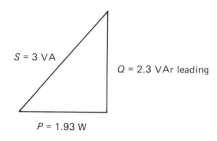

Fig 8.6

Example 8.3

Calculate the power, the VA, and the VAr consumed by the circuits in Figure 8.7. In each case, draw the power triangle for the circuit, and calculate the power factor in each case.

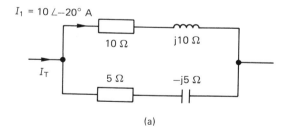

(a)

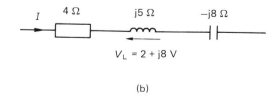

(b)

Fig 8.7

175

Solution 8.3

Circuit (a)

$$\text{circuit impedance, } \boldsymbol{Z}_{\text{E}} = \frac{(10\sqrt{2})\angle 45° \times (5\sqrt{2})\angle -45°}{(10 + j10) + (5 - j5)}$$

$$= 6.325\angle -18.43° \text{ ohm}$$

Since the same voltage appears across each branch of the parallel circuit, then $\boldsymbol{I}_{\text{T}}\boldsymbol{Z}_{\text{E}} = \boldsymbol{I}_1\boldsymbol{Z}_1$, hence

$$\boldsymbol{I}_{\text{T}} = \boldsymbol{I}_1 \frac{\boldsymbol{Z}_1}{\boldsymbol{Z}_{\text{E}}} = 10\angle -20° \times \frac{10\sqrt{2}\angle 45°}{6.325\angle -18.43°} = 22.36\angle 43.43° \text{ A}$$

and the voltage across the circuit is

$$\boldsymbol{V}_{\text{S}} = \boldsymbol{I}_1\boldsymbol{Z}_1 = 10\angle -20° \times 10\sqrt{2}\angle 45° = 141.42\angle 25° \text{ V}$$

The VA consumed by the circuit is

$$\boldsymbol{S} = \boldsymbol{V}_{\text{S}}\boldsymbol{I}_{\text{T}}^* = 141.42\angle 25° \times 22.36\angle -43.43° = 3\ 162\angle -18.43°$$

$$= 3000 - j1000 \text{ VA}$$

That is,

volt amperes consumed, $S = 3162$ VA

power consumed, $P = 3000$ W

reactive VA consumed, $Q = 1000$ VAr leading

The power factor of circuit (a) is

$$\cos(43.43° - 25°) = 0.95 \text{ leading.}$$

The power triangle for circuit (a) is shown in Figure 8.8(a).

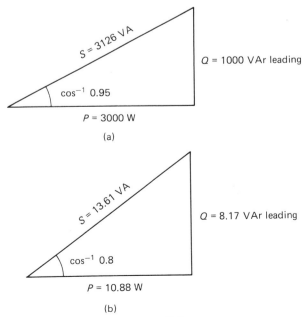

(a)

(b)

Fig 8.8

Circuit (b)

The current drawn by circuit (b) is

$$I = \frac{V_L}{Z_L} = \frac{2 + j8}{j5} = \frac{8.25\angle 76°}{5\angle 90°} = 1.65\angle -14° \text{ A}$$

The total impedance of the circuit is

$$Z_E = 4 + j(5-8) = 5\angle -36.9° \text{ ohms}$$

and the voltage across the circuit is

$$V_E = IZ_E = 1.65\angle -14° \times 5\angle -36.9° = 8.25\angle -50.9° \text{ V}$$

The VA consumed is calculated below

$$S = V_E I^* = 8.25\angle -50.9° \times 1.65\angle 14° = 13.61\angle -36.9°$$
$$= 10.88 - j8.17 \text{ VA}$$

or

volt amperes consumed, $S = 13.61$ VA

power consumed, $P = 10.88$ W

reactive VA consumed, $Q = 8.17$ VAr leading

The power factor of circuit (b) is cos $[-50.9° - (-14°)] = 0.8$ leading.

Example 8.4

Calculate the power, the VA, and the VAr consumed by the two-branch parallel circuit in Figure 8.9; draw the power triangle for the circuit. What value of capacitor C need be connected in parallel with the circuit in order to improve the overall power factor to 0.9 lagging? What is the VAr rating of the capacitor?

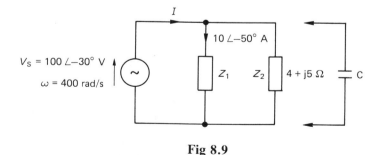

Fig 8.9

Solution 8.4

The value of impedance Z_1 is

$$Z_1 = \frac{V_S}{I_1} = \frac{100\angle -30°}{10\angle -50°} = 10\angle 20° = 9.4 + j3.42 \text{ ohm}$$

177

Also $Z_2 = 4 + j5 = 6.4\angle 51.34°$, so that the effective impedance of the parallel circuit is

$$Z_E = \frac{Z_1 Z_2}{Z_1 + Z_2} = \frac{10\angle 20° \times 6.4\angle 51.34°}{(9.4 + j3.42) + (4 + j5)} = 4.04\angle 39.2° \text{ ohm}$$

The total current drawn by the circuit is given by

$$I = \frac{V_S}{Z_E} = \frac{100\angle -30°}{4.04\angle 39.2°} = 24.75\angle -69.2° \text{ A}$$

and the VA consumed can be calculated as follows:

$$S = VI^* = 100\angle -30° \times 24.75\angle 69.2° = 2475\angle 39.2°$$

$$= 1\,918 + j1\,564 \text{ VA}$$

Hence,

$$\text{volt amperes consumed, } S = 2475 \text{ VA}$$

$$\text{power consumed, } P = 1918 \text{ W}$$

$$\text{reactive VA consumed, } Q = 1564 \text{ VAr lagging}$$

and

$$\text{power factor} = \cos[-30° - (-69.2°)] = 0.775 \text{ lagging.}$$

The corresponding power triangle is shown in Figure 8.10(a). Figure 8.10(b) shows that to improve the overall power factor of the circuit to 0.9 lagging, the capacitor rating is

$$Q_C = 1564 - 1918 \tan(\cos^{-1} 0.9) = 1565 - 929 = 635 \text{ VAr}$$

that is, the capacitor must have a rating of 635 VAr. The current drawn by the capacitor is

$$|I_C| = Q_C/|V_S| = 635/100 = 6.35 \text{ A}$$

Since $|I_C| = \dfrac{|V_C|}{X_C} = \dfrac{|V_C|}{1/\omega C} = \omega C|V_C|$, then

$$C = \frac{|I_C|}{\omega|V_C|} = \frac{6.35}{400 \times 100} = 158.8 \times 10^{-6} \text{ F or 158.8 microfarad}$$

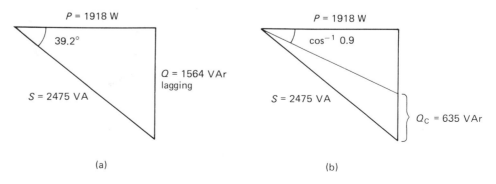

(a)

(b)

Fig 8.10

178

Example 8.5

In order to improve the overall power factor of a 400 V single phase induction motor to 0.92 lagging, a capacitor is connected to its terminals. If the total load current drawn by the combination is 9 A, and the capacitor current is 8 A, calculate the power consumed by the motor, the power factor of the motor, and the current drawn by the motor. Draw the phasor diagram for the circuit, and calculate the kVAr rating of the capacitor.

Solution 8.5

The phasor diagram is drawn in Figure 8.11, where I_L is the total current drawn by the combination. The inphase component of the total current is

$$|I_{\text{motor}}| \cos \phi_M = 0.92 I_L = 0.92 \times 9 = 8.28 \text{ A}$$

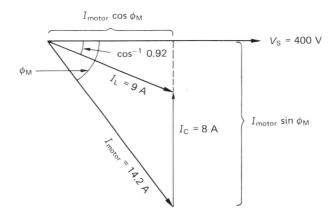

Fig 8.11

The quadrature component of the motor current is

$$|I_{\text{motor}}| \sin \phi_M = I_C + 8.28 \tan(\cos^{-1} 0.92)$$
$$= 8 + 8.28 \tan 23.1° = 11.53 \text{ A}$$

Hence,

$$|I_{\text{motor}}| = \sqrt{[(I_{\text{motor}} \cos \phi_M)^2 + (I_{\text{motor}} \sin \phi_M)^2]}$$
$$= \sqrt{(8.28^2 + 11.53^2)} = 14.2 \text{ A}$$

and the power factor of the motor is given by

$$\cos \phi_M = \frac{|I_{\text{motor}}| \cos \phi_M}{|I_{\text{motor}}|} = \frac{8.28}{14.2} = 0.583 \text{ lagging}$$

The kVAr rating of the capacitor is calculated as follows

$$|V_S||I_C|/1000 = 400 \times 8/1000 = 3.2 \text{ kVAr}$$

Example 8.6

A substation supplies the following single phase loads:

> load 1: 250 kW at a power factor of 0.95 leading
>
> load 2: 400 kVA at a power factor of 0.7 lagging
>
> load 3: 300 kVAr at a power factor of 0.8 lagging
>
> load 4: 150 kW at unity power factor.

Calculate the total load, and draw the power triangle for the load. Determine the reactive power which must be connected in order to improve the overall power factor to 0.95 lagging.

Solution 8.6

The individual VA's and the total power triangle are shown in Figure 8.12(a). The power and the VAr for each load are now calculated.

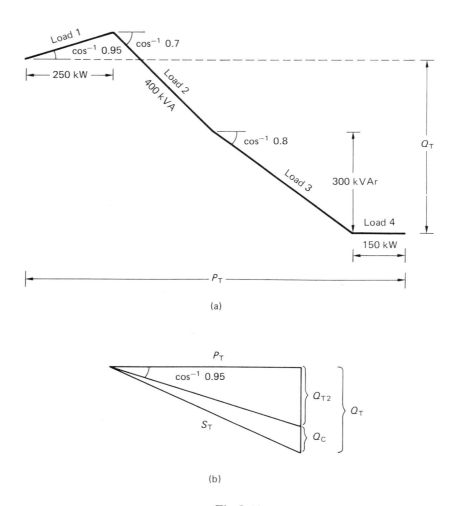

(a)

(b)

Fig 8.12

Load 1

Given $P_1 = 250$ kW, power factor $= 0.95$

$\phi_1 = \cos^{-1} 0.95 = 18.2°$;

$Q_1 = P_1 \tan \phi_1 = 250 \times \tan(\cos^{-1} 0.95) = 82.2$ kVAr leading.

Load 2

Given $S_2 = 400$ kVA, power factor $= 0.7$ lagging

$\phi_2 = \cos^{-1} 0.7 = 45.57°$ lag; $P_2 = S_2 \cos \phi_2 = 400 \times 0.7 = 280$ kW;

$Q_2 = S_2 \sin \phi_2 = 400 \sin 45.57° = 285.7$ kVAr lagging.

Load 3

Given $Q_3 = 300$ kVAr lagging, power factor $= 0.8$ lagging

$\phi_3 = \cos^{-1} 0.8 = 36.87°$ lagging;

$P_3 = Q_3/\tan \phi_3 = 300/\tan 36.87° = 400$ kW.

Load 4

Given $P_4 = 150$ kW, power factor $= 1$

$\phi_4 = 0$; $Q_4 = 0$

Hence,

$$\text{total kW load, } P_T = 250 + 280 + 400 + 150 = 1\,080 \text{ kW}$$

and (lagging kVAr taken to have a negative sign)

$$\text{total kVAr load, } Q_T = 82.2 - 285.7 - 300 + 0$$
$$= -503.5 \text{ kVAr (i.e., lagging)}$$

Therefore

$$\text{total VA load, } S_T = \surd(P_T^2 + Q_T^2) = \surd(1080^2 + (-503.5)^2)$$
$$= 1191.6 \text{ kVA}$$

and the load power factor is

$$\cos \phi_T = \frac{P_T}{S_T} = \frac{1080}{1191.6} = 0.906 \text{ lagging}$$

The diagram associated with the improvement of the power factor to 0.95 lagging is shown in Figure 8.12(b). The kVAr rating of the power factor correction plant is

$$Q_C = Q_T - Q_{T2} = 503.5 - P_T \times \tan(\cos^{-1} 0.95)$$
$$= 503.5 - (1080 \times \tan(\cos^{-1} 0.95)) = 503.5 - 355$$
$$= 148.5 \text{ kVAr leading}$$

Example 8.7

A 240 V, 50 Hz, 500 W single-phase induction motor has a full load efficiency of 80 per cent at a power factor of 0.75 lagging. Calculate the power, the VA, and the VAr consumed by the motor; determine a complex expression in rectangular form for the motor current.

The full load power factor is improved to 0.95 lagging by means of a capacitor connected to the motor terminals. Determine the reactance and the capacitance of the capacitor and its current. Also calculate the rating of the capacitor.

Solution 8.7

The full load power taken by the motor is given by

$$\text{motor input power} = \frac{\text{output power}}{\text{efficiency}} = \frac{500}{0.8} = 625 \text{ W}$$

and

$$\text{VA consumed by the motor} = \frac{\text{input power}}{\text{power factor}} = \frac{625}{0.75} = 833.3 \text{ VA}$$

$$\text{VAr consumed by the motor} = \sqrt{(\text{VA}^2 - \text{P}^2)} = \sqrt{(833.3^2 - 625^2)}$$
$$= 551.2 \text{ VAr}$$

The corresponding power triangle is shown in Figure 8.13.

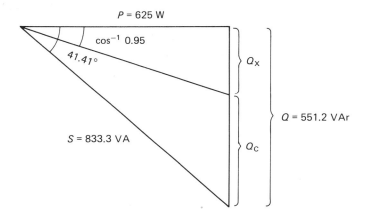

Fig 8.13

The modulus of the current drawn by the motor is

$$I = \frac{P}{V \cos \phi} = \frac{625}{240 \times 0.75} = 3.47 \text{ A}$$

Since the power factor is 0.75 lagging

$$\phi = \cos^{-1} 0.75 = 41.41° \text{ lagging}$$

Hence,

$$I = 3.47\angle -41.41° = 2.6 - j2.3 \text{ A}$$

To improve the power factor to 0.95 lagging (see Figure 8.13), the VAr rating of the capacitor is

$$Q_C = 551.2 - Q_X = 551.2 - 625\tan(\cos^{-1} 0.95)$$

$$= 551.2 - 205.4 = 345.8 \text{ VAr leading}$$

but

$$Q_C = V_S I_C = V_S \frac{V_S}{1/\omega C} = V_S^2 \omega C$$

or

$$C = \frac{Q_C}{V_S^2 \omega} = \frac{345.8}{240^2 \times 2\pi \times 50} = 19.11 \times 10^{-6} \text{ F or } 19.11 \text{ microfarad}$$

and the modulus of the capacitor current is

$$I_C = \frac{Q_C}{V_S} = \frac{345.8}{240} = 1.44 \text{ A}$$

Example 8.8

Calculate the current in each branch of Figure 8.14, and calculate the power, the VA, and the VAr consumed by the circuit.

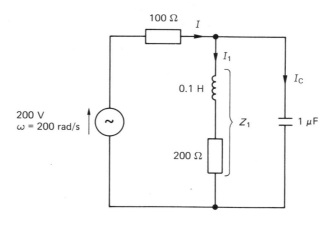

Fig 8.14

Solution 8.8

The reactance of the capacitor is

$$X_C = 1/\omega C = 1/(200 \times 1 \times 10^{-6}) = 5000 \text{ ohm}$$

183

Hence the impedance of the capacitor is

$$Z_C = 5000\angle -90° = -j5000 \text{ ohm}$$

The impedance of the inductive branch of the parallel circuit is calculated as follows

$$Z_1 = R + j\omega L = 200 + j(200 \times 0.1) = 200 + j20 = 201\angle 5.71° \text{ ohm}$$

and the effective impedance of the complete circuit is

$$Z_E = 100 + \frac{5000\angle -90° \times 201\angle 5.71°}{-j5000 + (200 + j20)} = 100 + 201.7\angle 3.41°$$

$$= 100 + (201.3 + j12) = 301.3 + j12 = 301.5\angle 2.28° \text{ ohm}$$

From Ohm's law, the current drawn by the circuit is

$$I = \frac{V_S}{Z_E} = \frac{200\angle 0°}{301.5\angle 2.28°} = 0.6633\angle -2.28° = 0.6628 - j0.026 \text{ A}$$

The current in each branch can be calculated as follows

$$Z_1 + Z_C = (200 + j20) - j5000 = 200 - j4980$$

$$= 4984\angle -87.7° \text{ ohm}$$

Hence, $$I_C = I \times \frac{Z_1}{Z_1 + Z_C} = 0.6633\angle -2.88° \times \frac{201\angle 5.71°}{4984\angle -87.7°}$$

$$= 0.027\angle 90.53° \text{ A}$$

and

$$I_1 = I \times \frac{Z_C}{Z_1 + Z_C} = 0.6636\angle -2.88° \times \frac{5000\angle -90°}{4984\angle -87.7°} = 0.6655\angle -5.18° \text{ A}$$

The VA consumed by the circuit is

$$S = VI^* = 200\angle 0° \times 0.6633\angle 2.28° = 132.66\angle 2.28°$$

$$= 132.55 + j5.28 \text{ VA}$$

That is,

$$S = 132.66 \text{ VA}$$

$$P = 132.55 \text{ W}$$

$$Q = 5.28 \text{ VAr lagging}$$

Alternatively, we may say that

$$S = |V||I| = 200 \times 0.6633 = 132.66 \text{ VA}$$

$$P = 100I^2 + 200I_1^2 = (100 \times 0.663^2) + (200 \times 0.6655^2) = 132.53 \text{ W}$$

$$Q = \sqrt{(S^2 - P^2)} = \sqrt{(132.66^2 - 132.53^2)} = 5.87 \text{ VAr}$$

Note that the small difference between the two sets of results is due to rounding errors in the two methods of calculation.

Example 8.9

A 10 kVA single-phase transformer supplies a load of 8 kVA at a power factor of 0.5 lagging. What additional power, in kW, may be connected to the transformer at a power factor of **(a)** 0.5 lagging, **(b)** unity power factor to fully load the transformer?

Solution 8.9

Since the rating of a power transformer is current-limited (due to the heating effect of current), it is also kVA limited. That is a 10 kVA transformer can only supply a maximum load of 10 kVA at any power factor.

(a) *0.5 p.f. lagging load*

The position is shown in Figure 8.15, where the maximum output from the transformer is limited by the 10 kVA arc. Since the transformer is already supplying 8 kVA at 0.5 p.f. lagging, it can only supply another 2 kVA at the same power factor. The power consumed by the original load is

$$P_1 = S_1 \cos \phi = 8 \times 0.5 = 4 \text{ kW}$$

and at full load

$$P_1 + P_A = 10 \cos \phi = 10 \times 0.5 = 5 \text{ kW}$$

where P_A is the additional power supplied at 0.5 p.f. lagging.
Hence,

$$P_A = 1 \text{ kW}$$

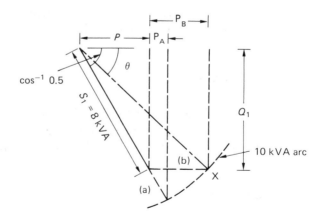

Fig 8.15

(b) *Unity power factor load*

In this case, the system operates at point X in Figure 8.15.

$$Q_1 = S_1 \sin \theta = 8 \sin (\cos^{-1} 0.5) = 6.93 \text{ kVAr}$$

and

$$\theta = \sin^{-1}(Q_1/10) = \sin^{-1}(6.93/10) = 43.87° \text{ lagging}$$

that is,

$$P_1 + P_B = 10 \cos \theta = 10 \cos 43.87° = 7.21 \text{ kW}$$

where P_B is the additional power supplied at unity power factor.
    Hence,

$$P_B = 7.21 - 4 = 3.21 \text{ kW}$$

8.3 Unworked Problems

Problem 8.1

A voltage of $v = 100 \sin(\omega t - 30°)$ V is applied to a coil of resistance 10 ohm and inductance 0.1 H. If $\omega = 500$ rad/s, deduce an expression for the current in the circuit, and calculate the VA, the power, and the VAr consumed by the circuit.
[1.96 sin $(\omega t - 108.7°)$ A; 98.3 VA; 19.26 W; 96.38 VAr (lagging)]

Problem 8.2

A circuit which consumes 1 kW at a power factor of 0.7 lagging, is connected in parallel with a circuit consuming 1.5 kW at a power factor of 0.6 leading, the modulus of the current in the second circuit being 10 A. Determine (a) the resistance and reactance of each element in the circuit, (b) the overall VA and VAr consumed.
[(a) $R_1 = 30.61$ ohm, $X_{L1} = 31.26$ ohm, $R_2 = 15$ ohm, $X_{C2} = 20$ ohm;
(b) 2.69 kVA, 0.98 kVAr lagging]

Problem 8.3

When a voltage of $3300\angle 30°$ V is applied to an impedance of $10\angle 50°$ ohm, calculate the VA, the power and the VAr consumed.
[1.089 MVA; 0.7 MW; 0.834 MVAr lagging]

Problem 8.4

Impedances of $Z_1 = (4 + j6)$ ohm and $Z_2 = (10 - j12)$ ohm are connected in series. If they carry a current of $10\angle 20°$ A, calculate for each impedance, the VA, the power, and the VAr consumed. What is the power factor of the complete circuit? Draw the power triangle for each impedance and for the series circuit.
[$S_1 = 721$ VA, $P_1 = 400$ W, $Q_1 = 600$ VAr lagging; $S_2 = 1562$ VA, $P_2 = 1000$ W, $Q_2 = 1200$ VAr leading; 0.919 leading]

Problem 8.5

What is the reactance of a pure inductor which must be connected in parallel with the circuit in Problem 8.4 in order to alter the overall power factor of the circuit to 0.95 lagging?
[21.9 ohm]

Problem 8.6

A voltage of $100\angle-50°$ V is applied to a 2-branch parallel circuit in which $Z_1 = 4\angle50°$ ohm and $Z_2 = 5\angle-60°$ ohm. Calculate the VA, the power, and the VAr for each branch and for the complete circuit, and draw the power triangle for the circuit.
[Circuit 1: 2500 VA, 1607 W, 1915 VAr lagging; Circuit 2: 2000 VA, 1000 W, 1732 VAr leading; Total: 2614 VA, 2607 W, 183 VAr lagging]

Problem 8.7

The following loads are connected in parallel with one another.

$$P_1 = 10 \text{ kW at } 0.8 \text{ power factor lagging}$$

$$S_2 = 20 \text{ kVA at } 0.9 \text{ power factor leading}$$

$$Q_3 = 15 \text{ kVAr at } 0.7 \text{ power factor lagging}$$

Evaluate the VA, the power, and the VAr for each load, and for the total load. Draw the power triangle for each load and for the total load.
[Load 1: 12.5 kVA, 10 kW, 7.5 kVAr lagging; Load 2: 20 kVA, 18 kW, 8.72 kVAr leading; Load 3: 21 kVA, 14.7 kW, 15 kVAr lagging; Total: 44.87 kVA, 42.7 kW, 13.78 kVAr lagging]

Problem 8.8

An industrial load of 200 kW has a lagging power factor of 0.6. What is the kVAr rating of a capacitor bank needed to correct the power factor to (a) 0.9 lagging, (b) 0.9 leading?
[(a) 169.81 kVAr; (b) 363.53 kVAr]

Problem 8.9

A 4 kW single-phase induction motor has a full-load efficiency of 80 per cent, and a power factor of 0.75 lagging. If the supply is 250 V, 50 Hz, calculate the current drawn by the motor. If the overall power factor is to be improved to 0.9 lagging by connecting a capacitor in parallel with the motor, determine the current drawn by the combination, the kVAr rating of the capacitor bank, and the capacitance of the capacitor.
[26.7 A; 22.2 A; 1.99 kVAr; 101.2 microfarad]

Problem 8.10

A 20 kVA single-phase transformer supplies full load kVA at a power factor of 0.7 lagging. (a) What maximum additional load and at what power factor can the transformer supply? (b) If the power factor of the original load connected to the transformer is improved to 0.85 lagging (i.e., no change in power), what additional power can be supplied at a power factor of unity?
[(a) 28.56 kVAr at 90° leading; (b) 4 kW]

Problem 8.11

Calculate the power, the reactive power, and the apparent power for a load which has a voltage of $(20 - j10)$ V across it, and carries a current of $(10 - j20)$ mA.

(Staffordshire Polytechnic)

[0.4 W; 0.3 VAr; 0.5 VA]

Problem 8.12

A supply of $10 \sin \omega t$ V energizes a series circuit comprising a 1 H inductance and a 1 ohm resistance. If the voltage across the resistor lags behind the supply voltage by 30°, calculate the angular frequency (ω) of the supply, and the power dissipated in the resistor.

(Staffordshire Polytechnic)

[0.5773 rad/s; 37.5 W]

188

9   Circuit Theorems I

9.1   Fact Sheet

(a)   Mesh Current Analysis of A.C. Circuits

The general rules applying to mesh current analysis of d.c. circuits also apply to a.c. circuits, with the exception that impedance values are used where resistances were used formerly.

The mesh current equations for the circuit in Figure 9.1 are

$$
\begin{bmatrix} E_A \\ -E_B \\ E_C \end{bmatrix} = \begin{bmatrix} Z_A + Z_B + Z_C & -Z_B & -Z_C \\ -Z_B & Z_B + Z_D + Z_E & -Z_E \\ -Z_C & -Z_E & Z_C + Z_E + Z_F \end{bmatrix} \begin{bmatrix} I_1 \\ I_2 \\ I_3 \end{bmatrix}
$$

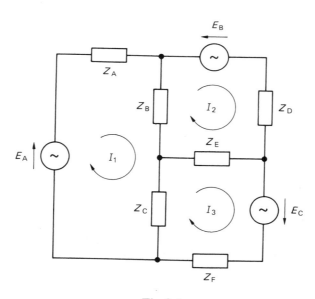

Fig 9.1

or, in generalized matrix form this becomes

$$
\begin{bmatrix} E_1 \\ E_2 \\ E_3 \end{bmatrix} = \begin{bmatrix} Z_{11} & Z_{12} & Z_{13} \\ Z_{21} & Z_{22} & Z_{23} \\ Z_{31} & Z_{32} & Z_{33} \end{bmatrix} \begin{bmatrix} I_1 \\ I_2 \\ I_3 \end{bmatrix}
$$

where E_1, E_2, and E_3 are the voltages driving currents I_1, I_2, and I_3 in a clockwise direction around the meshes. The currents are evaluated using the the techniques outlined in Chapter 2.

(b) Node Voltage Analysis of A.C. Circuits

The rules applying to d.c. node voltage analysis apply to a.c. circuits. The matrix form of the node voltage equations (node 0 being taken as reference) for the circuit in Figure 9.2 is

$$
\begin{bmatrix} I_A + I_B \\ -I_B \\ -I_A \end{bmatrix} = \begin{bmatrix} Y_A + Y_B + Y_C & -Y_B & -Y_C \\ -Y_B & Y_B + Y_D + Y_F & -Y_F \\ -Y_C & -Y_F & Y_C + Y_E + Y_F \end{bmatrix} \begin{bmatrix} V_1 \\ V_2 \\ V_3 \end{bmatrix}
$$

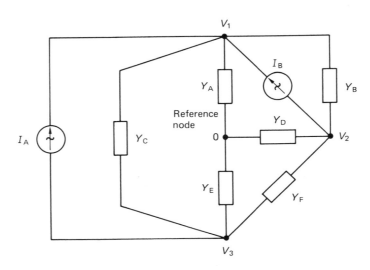

Fig 9.2

The corresponding generalized matrix form of equations are

$$
\begin{bmatrix} I_1 \\ I_2 \\ I_3 \end{bmatrix} = \begin{bmatrix} Y_{11} & Y_{12} & Y_{13} \\ Y_{21} & Y_{22} & Y_{23} \\ Y_{31} & Y_{32} & Y_{33} \end{bmatrix} \begin{bmatrix} V_1 \\ V_2 \\ V_3 \end{bmatrix}
$$

(c) Millman's Theorem or The Parallel Generator Theorem

This theorem is a version of nodal analysis, and is particularly useful in the solution of three-phase, unbalanced, star-connected systems. However, it can be used with any multi-phase, unbalanced star-connected system, and for the solution of multi voltage-source d.c. systems.

The theorem states that, in an *n*-phase, *n*-wire unbalanced star-connected system, the potential of the star point of the load (S) with respect to the neutral point (N) of the supply is

$$V_{SN} = \frac{\sum\limits_{K=1}^{K=n} E_{KN}Y_K}{\sum\limits_{K=1}^{K=n} Y_K} \quad V$$

The most popular case is that of the three-phase, three-wire unbalanced star-connected system, shown in Figure 9.3, where

$$V_{SN} = \frac{E_1Y_1 + E_2Y_2 + E_3Y_3}{Y_1 + Y_2 + Y_3} \quad V$$

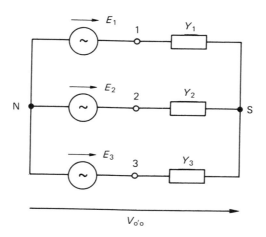

Fig 9.3

(d) Thévenin's Theorem

Any one-port active network can be replaced by a single generating source consisting of an active voltage source (sinusoidal if a.c.), in series with an impedance (resistance if d.c.), as shown in Figure 9.4. This is summarized by *Thévenin's theorem* as follows.

An active network having terminals A and B to which an electrical load is connected, behaves as though it contained a single source of e.m.f., E, having an internal impedance Z (or resistance R if d.c.). E is measured at the terminals with the load disconnected; Z is the impedance measured between the terminals A and B with the load disconnected, and each internal source within the network replaced by its internal impedance.

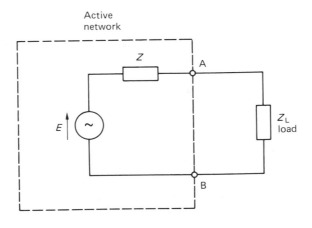

Fig 9.4

(e) Norton's Theorem

Any one-port active network can be replaced by a single generating source comprising an active current source, I (a.c. or d.c., as appropriate), in parallel with an internal admittance Y (or conductance G if a d.c. source), as shown in Figure 9.5. This is summarized below.

An active network having terminals A and B to which an electrical load may be connected, behaves as though it contained a single current source I, having internal admittance Y. I is the current which would flow between terminals A and B when they are short-circuited together; Y is the admittance measured between A and B with the load disconnected, and each source within the network is replaced by its internal admittance.

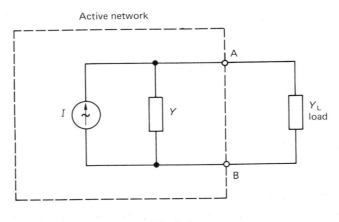

Fig 9.5

(f) Equivalence between Thévenin's and Norton's Equivalent Circuits

The two circuits in Figures 9.4 and 9.5 are equivalent when

$$Z = 1/Y$$

and

$$E = IZ = I/Y$$

(g) Duality

Two circuits are said to be the *dual* of one another if the mesh equations of one circuit have the same mathematical form as the node equations of the other.

Consider the circuits in Figure 9.6. The equations are as follows.

Mesh equation for
circuit (a)
$$v = v_1 + v_2$$
$$= Ri + L\, di/dt$$

Node equation for
circuit (b)
$$i = i_1 + i_2$$
$$= Gv + C\, dv/dt$$

The two circuits are the duals of each other because the mesh equation of Figure 9.6(a) has the same mathematical form as the node equation of the circuit in Figure 9.6(b). To convert circuit (a) to circuit (b), the voltage source is replaced by a current source, the series circuit is replaced by a parallel circuit, a resistance is replaced by a conductance, and an inductor is replaced by a capacitor. To summarize, the following are duals.

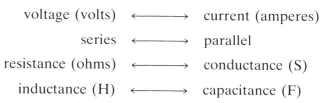

voltage (volts) $\longleftrightarrow$ current (amperes)

series $\longleftrightarrow$ parallel

resistance (ohms) $\longleftrightarrow$ conductance (S)

inductance (H) $\longleftrightarrow$ capacitance (F)

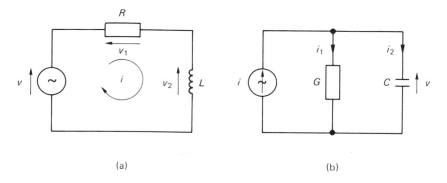

(a)   (b)

Fig 9.6

Moreover, any initial voltage on a capacitor has its dual in the same value of initial current in the inductor in the dual circuit, and vice versa.

Thus, once a circuit has been analysed, its dual has also been analysed!

Consider the circuit in Figure 9.7(a). Its dual is obtained by

1. Placing a node (node 0) outside the circuit.

2. Placing a node inside each mesh (nodes 1–3).

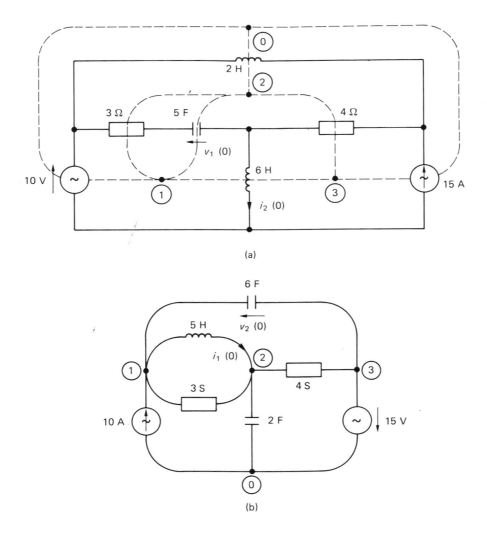

(a)

(b)

Fig 9.7

3. Drawing a dotted line through each element, each line terminating on a node in an adjacent mesh.

4. Drawing the dual of the original circuit by inserting the dual of each element in the original circuit on the dotted line.

5. Showing the voltage or current of each source on the dual using the rules outlined below (this also applies to initial voltage across each capacitor, and initial current in each inductor).

The resulting dual is shown in Figure 9.7(b). It should be noted that although the two diagrams are the duals of one another, *they are not equivalent circuits*. That is, if a voltage of 3 V causes a current of 1 A to flow in one element of a series circuit then, in the dual, a current of 3 A in a parallel circuit causes 1 V to appear across the dual element.

Consider the two paths between nodes 1 and 2 in Figure 9.7(a). One of them passes through a 3 ohm resistor, and the other through a 5 F capacitor. Since these are in series in the original circuit, the dual circuit contains a 3 S conductance in parallel with a 5 H inductor.

One method of deducing the direction of the voltage and current sources (including initial values) in the dual is as follows. Rotate the arrow (voltage or current) in the original circuit in a *clockwise direction* until it lies on a dotted line linking the nodes drawn in spaces in the original circuit. The new direction of the arrow indicates the direction of the corresponding current (or voltage) arrow on the dual.

9.2 Worked Examples

Example 9.1

Calculate I_1, I_2 and V_L in Figure 9.8 using mesh current analysis.

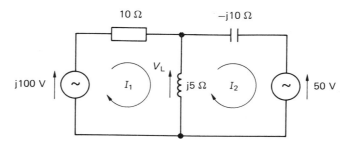

Fig 9.8

Solution 9.1

The mesh equations are

$$j100 = (10 + j5)I_1 - j5I_2$$
$$-50 = \qquad -j5I_1 - j5I_2$$

and are written in matrix form as follows

$$\begin{bmatrix} j100 \\ -50 \end{bmatrix} = \begin{bmatrix} 10 + j5 & -j5 \\ -j5 & -j5 \end{bmatrix} \begin{bmatrix} I_1 \\ I_2 \end{bmatrix}$$

I_1 is obtained using Cramer's rule as follows

$$I_1 = \frac{\begin{vmatrix} j100 & -j5 \\ -50 & -j5 \end{vmatrix}}{\begin{vmatrix} 10 + j5 & -j5 \\ -j5 & -j5 \end{vmatrix}} = \frac{559.02\angle -26.57°}{70.71\angle -45°}$$

$$= 7.91\angle 18.43° = 7.5 + j2.5 \text{ A}$$

and

$$I_2 = \frac{\begin{vmatrix} 10 + j5 & j100 \\ -j5 & -50 \end{vmatrix}}{\begin{vmatrix} 10 + j5 & -j5 \\ -j5 & -j5 \end{vmatrix}} = \frac{1030.8\angle 194.03°}{70.71\angle -45°}$$

$$= 14.58\angle 239.03° = -7.5 - j12.5 \text{ A}$$

The voltage V_L is calculated below

$V_L = (I_1 - I_2)Z_L$ where Z_L is the impedance of the inductance

$$= [(7.5 + j2.5) - (-7.5 - j12.5)]j5 = (15 + j15)j5$$

$$= 21.21\angle 45° \times 5\angle 90° = 106.05\angle 135° \text{ V}$$

Example 9.2

Using mesh analysis, solve the circuit in Figure 9.9 for I_1 and I_2, and hence calculate the total power consumed.

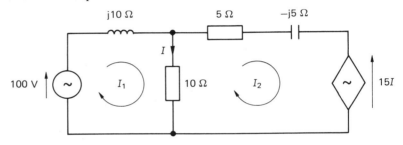

Fig 9.9

Solution 9.2

The equation for mesh 1 is

$$100 = (10 + j10)I_1 - 10I_2$$

and the equation for mesh 2 is

$$-15I = -10I_1 + (15 - j5)I_2$$

But,

$$I = I_1 - I_2$$

so that the equation for mesh 2 becomes

$$0 = 5I_1 - j5I_2$$

The equations are written in the general matrix form as follow

$$\begin{bmatrix} 100 \\ 0 \end{bmatrix} = \begin{bmatrix} 10 + j10 & -10 \\ 5 & -j5 \end{bmatrix} \begin{bmatrix} I_1 \\ I_2 \end{bmatrix}$$

196

Solving by Cramer's rule gives

$$I_1 = \frac{\begin{vmatrix} 100 & -10 \\ 0 & -j5 \end{vmatrix}}{\begin{vmatrix} 10+j10 & 10 \\ 5 & -j5 \end{vmatrix}} = \frac{500\angle{-90°}}{111.8\angle{-26.57°}} = 4.47\angle{-63.43°} = 2 - j4 \text{ A}$$

and

$$I_2 = \frac{\begin{vmatrix} 10+j10 & 100 \\ 5 & 0 \end{vmatrix}}{\begin{vmatrix} 10+j10 & -10 \\ 5 & -j5 \end{vmatrix}} = \frac{500\angle{180°}}{111.8\angle{-26.57°}} = 4.47\angle{-153.43°} = -4 - j2 \text{ A}$$

and

$$I = I_1 - I_2 = (2 - j4) - (-4 - j2) = 6 - j2$$
$$= 6.325\angle{-18.43°} \text{ A}$$

The total power consumed is

$$10I^2 + 5I_2^2 = (10 \times 6.325^2) + (5 \times 4.47^2) = 400 + 100$$
$$= 500 \text{ W}$$

Example 9.3

Write down the mesh current equations for the circuit in Figure 9.10, and determine the value of I_3.

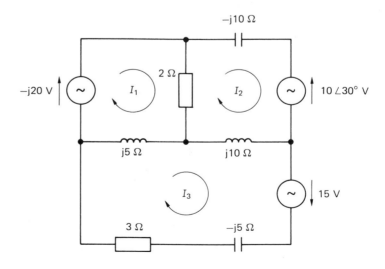

Fig 9.10

Solution 9.3

The equation for mesh 1 is

$$-j20 = (2 + j5)I_1 - 2I_2 - j5I_3$$

The e.m.f. acting in the direction of I_2 in mesh 2 is $-10\angle30°$ V, which is expressed in rectangular form as $(-8.66 - j5)$ V, giving the following equation for mesh 2

$$-8.66 - j5 = -2I_1 + 2I_2 - j10I_3$$

The equation for mesh 3 is given below

$$15 = -j5I_1 - j10I_2 + (3 + j10)I_3$$

In matrix form, the equations are

$$\begin{bmatrix} -j20 \\ -8.66 \ -j5 \\ 15 \end{bmatrix} = \begin{bmatrix} 2+j5 & -2 & -j5 \\ -2 & 2 & -j10 \\ -j5 & -j10 & 3+j10 \end{bmatrix} \begin{bmatrix} I_1 \\ I_2 \\ I_3 \end{bmatrix}$$

Solving for I_3 by Cramer's rule gives

$$I_3 = \frac{\begin{vmatrix} 2+j5 & -2 & -j20 \\ -2 & 2 & -8.66-j5 \\ -j5 & -j10 & 15 \end{vmatrix}}{\begin{vmatrix} 2+j5 & -2 & -j5 \\ -2 & 2 & -j10 \\ -j5 & -j10 & 3+j10 \end{vmatrix}} = \frac{1191.3\angle6.76°}{635.14\angle56.56°}$$

$$= 1.876\angle-49.8° = 1.21 - j1.43 \text{ A}$$

Example 9.4

Using mesh analysis, calculate I_1, I_2 and V_{WX} in Figure 9.11.

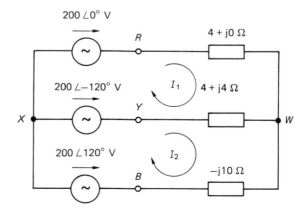

Fig 9.11

Solution 9.4

In loop 1, the e.m.f. acting in the direction of I_1 is

$$200\angle 0° - 200\angle -120° = 200 - (-100 - j173.2) = 300 + j173.2 \text{ V}$$

and the e.m.f. in loop 2 acting in the direction of I_2 is

$$200\angle -120° - 200\angle 120° = (-100 - j173.2) - (-100 + j173.2)$$

$$= -j346.4 \text{ V}$$

The mesh current equations for the two loops are

$$300 + j173.2 = (8 + j4)I_1 - (4 + j4)I_2$$

$$-j346.4 = -(4 + j4)I_4 + (4 - j6)I_2$$

which are written in matrix form as follows

$$\begin{bmatrix} 300 + j173.2 \\ -j346.4 \end{bmatrix} = \begin{bmatrix} 8 + j4 & -4 - j4 \\ -4 - j4 & 4 - j6 \end{bmatrix} \begin{bmatrix} I_1 \\ I_2 \end{bmatrix}$$

Solving by Cramer's rule gives

$$I_1 = \frac{\begin{vmatrix} 300 + j173.2 & -4 - j4 \\ -j346.4 & 4 - j6 \end{vmatrix}}{\begin{vmatrix} 8 + j4 & -4 - j4 \\ -4 - j4 & 4 - j6 \end{vmatrix}} = \frac{4399\angle -34.52°}{85.04\angle -48.81°}$$

$$= 51.73\angle 14.29° = 50.13 + j12.77 \text{ A}$$

and

$$I_2 = \frac{\begin{vmatrix} 8 + j4 & 300 + j173.2 \\ -4 - j4 & -j346.4 \end{vmatrix}}{\begin{vmatrix} 8 + j4 & -4 - j4 \\ -4 - j4 & 4 - j6 \end{vmatrix}} = \frac{2087\angle -24.9°}{85.04\angle -48.81°}$$

$$= 24.54\angle 23.91° = 22.43 + j9.95 \text{ A}$$

The voltage V_{WX} can be calculated using data from any branch linking W to X. Taking the top branch

$$V_{WX} = (200 + j0) - (4 + j0)I_1$$

$$= 200 - 4(50.13 + j12.77) = -0.52 - j51.08 = 51.08\angle -90.6° \text{ V}$$

Example 9.5

Solve Example 9.4 using Millman's theorem.

Solution 9.5

Using the notation in Figure 9.3.

$$V_{RX} = E_1 = 200\angle 0° = 200 + j0 \text{ V}$$

$$V_{YX} = E_2 = 200\angle -120° = -100 - j173.2 \text{ V}$$

$$V_{BX} = E_3 = 200\angle 120° = -100 + j173.2 \text{ V}$$

and

$V_{WX} = V_{SN}$ (see section (c) of the Fact Sheet). Using the theory in section (c) of the Fact Sheet

$$V_{SN} = \frac{E_1 Y_1 + E_2 Y_2 + E_3 Y_3}{Y_1 + Y_2 + Y_3}$$

$$= \frac{\dfrac{200\angle 0°}{4\angle 0°} + \dfrac{200\angle -120°}{4\sqrt{2}\angle 45°} + \dfrac{200\angle 120°}{10\angle -90°}}{\dfrac{1}{4\angle 0°} + \dfrac{1}{4\sqrt{2}\angle 45°} + \dfrac{1}{10\angle -90°}} = \frac{19.21\angle -94.4°}{0.376\angle -3.8°}$$

$$= 51.08\angle -90.6° = -0.52 - j51.08 \text{ V}$$

The current in the $(4 + j0)$ ohms impedance is

$$I_1 = \frac{(200 + j0) - (-0.52 - j51.08)}{4 + j0} = 51.73\angle 14.29° \text{ A}$$

Referring to Figure 9.3, the reader will observe that the current in the $-j10$ ohm impedance flows in the opposite direction to I_2 in Figure 9.11, hence

$$-I_2 = \frac{(-100 + j173.2) - (-0.53 - j51.08)}{-j10}$$

$$= 24.54\angle 203.91° \text{ A}$$

or

$$I_2 = 24.54\angle 23.91° \text{ A}$$

Example 9.6

Determine, using mesh current analysis, the VA, the power and the VAr consumed by the circuit in Figure 9.12

Solution 9.6

In this case it is only necessary to solve for I_1 and, using the relationship $S = V_S I_1^*$, the required values can be obtained.

Since $V_S = 100\angle 15° = 96.59 + j25.88 \text{ V}$

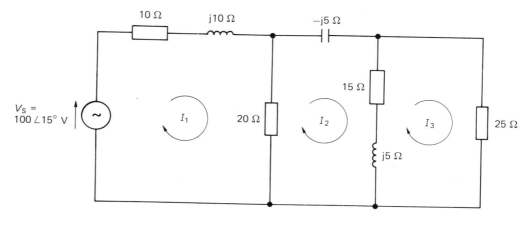

Fig 9.12

the mesh current equations for Figure 9.12 are

$$96.59 + j25.88 = (30 + j10)I_1 - 20I_2$$
$$0 = -20I_1 + 35I_2 - (15 + j5)I_3$$
$$0 = -(15 + j5)I_2 + (40 + j5)I_3$$

which, expressed in matrix form become

$$\begin{bmatrix} 96.59 + j25.88 \\ 0 \\ 0 \end{bmatrix} = \begin{bmatrix} 30 + j10 & -20 & 0 \\ -20 & 35 & -(15 + j5) \\ 0 & -(15 + j5) & (40 + j5) \end{bmatrix} \begin{bmatrix} I_1 \\ I_2 \\ I_3 \end{bmatrix}$$

Solving for I_1 by Cramer's rule gives

$$I_1 = \cfrac{\begin{vmatrix} 96.59 + j25.88 & -20 & 0 \\ 0 & 35 & -15 - j5 \\ 0 & -15 - j5 & 40 + j5 \end{vmatrix}}{\begin{vmatrix} 30 + j10 & -20 & 0 \\ -20 & 35 & -15 - j5 \\ 0 & -15 - j5 & 40 + j5 \end{vmatrix}} = \frac{120\ 022\angle 16.19°}{22\ 486\angle 28.56°}$$

$$= 5.34\angle -12.37° \text{ A}$$

That is,

volt amperes consumed, $S = 534$ VA

power consumed, $P = 474.2$ W

reactive VA consumed, $Q = 245.5$ VAr lagging

Example 9.7

Using node voltage analysis, calculate the voltage V_1 in Figure 9.13.

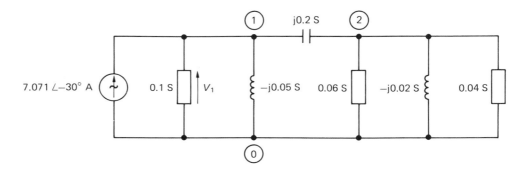

Fig 9.13

Solution 9.7

The total admittance connected to node 1 is

$$Y_{11} = 0.1 + j(-0.05 + 0.2) = 0.1 + j0.15 \text{ S}$$

and that connected to node 2 is

$$Y_{22} = (0.06 + 0.04) + j(-0.02 + 0.2) = 0.1 + j0.18 \text{ S}$$

Since the current entering node 1 is

$$7.071\angle -30° = 6.12 - j3.54 \text{ A}$$

the node voltage equations are

$$6.12 - j3.54 = (0.1 + j0.15)V_1 \qquad -j0.2V_2$$
$$0 = \qquad - j0.2V_1 \quad + (0.1 + j0.18)V_2$$

which are written in matrix form as follows

$$\begin{bmatrix} 6.12 - j3.54 \\ 0 \end{bmatrix} = \begin{bmatrix} 0.1 + j0.15 & -j0.2 \\ -j0.2 & 0.1 + j0.18 \end{bmatrix} \begin{bmatrix} V_1 \\ V_2 \end{bmatrix}$$

Solving by Cramer's rule gives

$$V_1 = \frac{\begin{vmatrix} 6.12 - j3.54 & -j0.2 \\ 0 & 0.1 + j0.18 \end{vmatrix}}{\begin{vmatrix} 0.1 + j0.15 & -j0.2 \\ -j0.2 & 0.1 + j0.18 \end{vmatrix}} = \frac{1.456\angle 30.9°}{0.0402\angle 55.13°} = 36.2\angle -24.23° \text{ V}$$

The reader is asked to note that Worked Examples 9.6 and 9.7 are electrically identical, and the voltage V_1 in Example 9.7 is equal to the voltage across the 20 ohm resistor in figure 9.12. It will prove an interesting exercise to verify this.

Example 9.8

Using node voltage analysis, determine the *transfer function* (see also Chapter 7) which relates V_B to V_A in Figure 9.14.

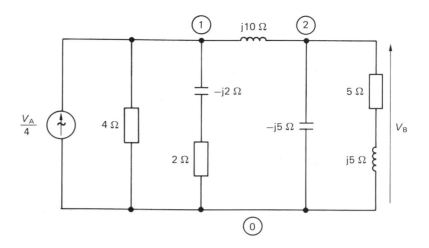

Fig 9.14

Solution 9.8

Applying KCL to node 1 yields

$$\frac{V_A}{4} = \left(\frac{1}{4} + \frac{1}{2 - j2} + \frac{1}{j10} \right) V_1 - \frac{1}{j10} \ V_2$$

and applying KCL to node 2 gives

$$0 = -\frac{1}{j10} \ V_1 + \left(\frac{1}{j10} + \frac{1}{-j5} + \frac{1}{5 + j5} \right) V_2$$

These are expressed in matrix form as follows:

$$\begin{bmatrix} \dfrac{V_4}{4} \\[2mm] 0 \end{bmatrix} = \begin{bmatrix} \dfrac{1}{4} + \dfrac{1}{2 - j2} + \dfrac{1}{j10} & \dfrac{-1}{j10} \\[4mm] \dfrac{-1}{j10} & \dfrac{1}{j10} - \dfrac{1}{j5} + \dfrac{1}{5 + j5} \end{bmatrix} \begin{bmatrix} V_1 \\[2mm] V_2 \end{bmatrix}$$

where $V_2 = V_B$. Since V_A is unknown, and we merely wish to obtain the relationship between V_B and V_A, we will assume that $V_A = 1\angle 0°$ V. Solving for V_2 (or V_B) by Cramer's rule gives

$$V_2 = V_B = \cfrac{\begin{vmatrix} \dfrac{1}{4} + \dfrac{1}{2 - j2} + \dfrac{1}{j10} & \dfrac{1}{4} \\[4mm] \dfrac{-1}{j10} & 0 \end{vmatrix}}{\begin{vmatrix} \dfrac{1}{4} + \dfrac{1}{2 - j2} + \dfrac{1}{j10} & \dfrac{-1}{j10} \\[4mm] \dfrac{-1}{j10} & \dfrac{1}{j10} - \dfrac{1}{j5} + \dfrac{1}{5 + j5} \end{vmatrix}}$$

203

$$= \frac{0.025\angle-90°}{0.0618\angle14°} = 0.405\angle-104° \text{ V}$$

That is, the transfer function relating V_B to V_A is

$$\frac{V_B}{V_A} = 0.405\angle-104°$$

Example 9.9

Determine **(a)** the Thévenin and **(b)** the Norton equivalent of the circuit connected between terminals A and B of Figure 9.15.

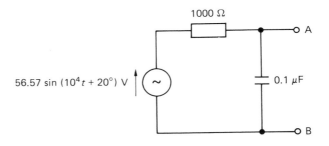

Fig 9.15

Solution 9.9

The polar complex representation of the supply voltage is

$$V_S = \frac{56.57}{\sqrt2} \angle20° = 40\angle20° \text{ V}$$

(a) *Thévenins Equivalent Circuit*

Since no load is connected to the terminals of the circuit, the Thévenin voltage, V_T, is equal to the voltage V_{AB} between the terminals of the capacitor.

$$V_T = V_{AB} = V_S \times \frac{1/j\omega C}{R + 1/j\omega C} = \frac{V_S}{1 + j\omega CR}$$

$$= \frac{40\angle20°}{1 + j(10^4 \times 0.1 \times 10^{-6} \times 1000)} = \frac{40\angle20°}{1 + j1}$$

$$= 28.28\angle-25° \text{ V}$$

The internal impedance of the source is obtained by replacing the voltage source by its internal impedance (which is zero ohms in this case), and calculating the impedance between the terminals A and B.
    Now

$$X_C = 1/\omega C = 1/(10^4 \times 0.1 \times 10^{-6}) = 1000 \text{ ohm}$$

Hence, the internal impedance, Z_T, between A and B is

$$Z_T = \frac{1000 \times (-j1000)}{1000 - j1000} = 707.1\angle-45° \text{ ohm}$$

The Thévenin equivalent circuit of Figure 9.15 is shown in Figure 9.16(a).

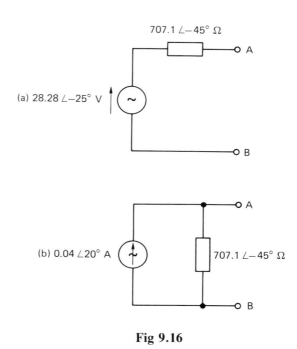

Fig 9.16

(b) *Norton's Equivalent Circuit*

The complex expression for Norton's current source, I_N, is obtained by calculating the current which flows in a short-circuit between the output terminals A and B. when the short-circuit is applied, the capacitor is effectively shorted out, and the current is

$$I_N = \frac{V_S}{1000} = \frac{40\angle20°}{1000} = 0.04\angle20° \text{ A}$$

The internal impedance of Norton's source is calculated in the same way as for the Thévenin source, i.e., it is $701.1\angle-45°$ ohm (see Figure 9.16(b)) or, alternatively, the impedance can be replaced by the admittance Y_N as follows

$$Y_N = 1/707.1\angle-45° = 0.00142\angle45° \text{ S}$$

Alternatively, we may say

$$I_N = V_T/Z_T = 28.28\angle-25°/707.1\angle-45° = 0.04\angle20° \text{ A}$$

and

$$Y_N = 1/Z_T = 0.00142\angle45° \text{ S}$$

Example 9.10

Replace the active network in Figure 9.17 with its Norton equivalent circuit. Hence calculate the current which would flow in a 0.1 S conductance connected between A and B.

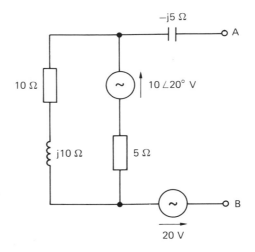

Fig 9.17

Solution 9.10

The value of the Norton current source, I_N (see Figure 9.18(a)), is equal to the current flowing in a short-circuit between terminals AB. Since $10\angle 20°$ V $= 9.4 + j3.42$ V, the mesh current equations for Figure 9.18(a) are written in matrix form as follows.

$$\begin{bmatrix} -9.4 - j3.42 \\ -10.6 + j3.42 \end{bmatrix} = \begin{bmatrix} 15 + j10 & -5 \\ -5 & 5 - j5 \end{bmatrix} \begin{bmatrix} I_1 \\ I_N \end{bmatrix}$$

Hence,

$$I_N = \frac{\begin{vmatrix} 15 + j10 & -9.4 - j3.42 \\ -5 & -10.6 + j3.42 \end{vmatrix}}{\begin{vmatrix} 15 + j10 & -5 \\ -5 & 5 - j5 \end{vmatrix}} = \frac{250.7\angle 196.64°}{103.1\angle -14.04°} = 2.43\angle 210.68° \text{ A}$$

The internal impedance between terminals A and B (see Figure 9.18(b)) is

$$Z = -j5 + \frac{5(10 + j10)}{5 + (10 + j10)} = -j5 + (3.84 + j0.77)$$

$$= 5.71\angle -47.77° \text{ ohm}$$

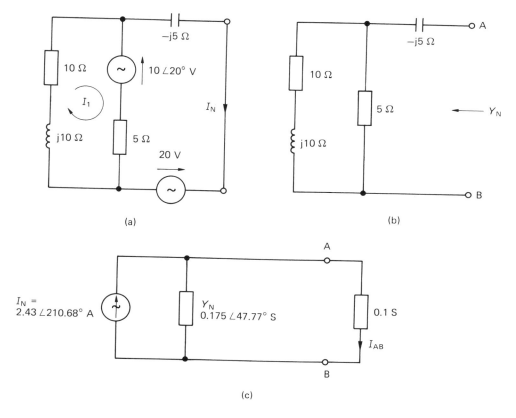

Fig 9.18

Hence, the internal admittance of the Norton source is

$$Y_N = 1/Z = 0.175\angle 47.77° = 0.118 + j0.13 \text{ S}$$

The effective admittance of the parallel circuit (including the 0.1 S load) connected to the pure current source is

$$(0.118 + j0.13) + 0.1 = 0.218 + j0.13 = 0.254\angle 30.8° \text{ S}$$

The current in the 0.1 S load (see Figure 9.18(c)) connected between A and B is

$$I_{AB} = 2.43\angle 210.68° \times \frac{0.1\angle 0°}{0.254\angle 30.8°} = 0.96\angle 179.88° \text{ A}$$

The current is assumed to flow from A to B. Alternatively, the current can be thought of as $0.96\angle -0.12°$ A flowing from B to A.

Example 9.11

Deduce (a) Thévenin's, (b) Norton's equivalent circuit between terminals A and B in Figure 9.19. Hence calculate the current which flows in an impedance of (i) $(10 + j0)$ ohm, (ii) $(0 + j10)$ ohms connected between A and B.

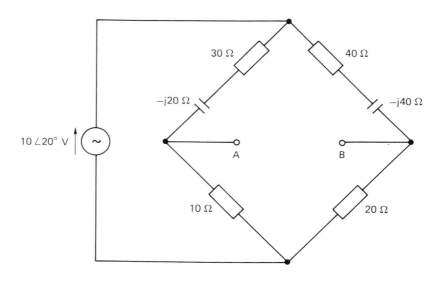

Fig 9.19

Solution 9.11

Both sources have the same internal impedance, and is calculated below (see Figure 9.20(a)). The voltage source is replaced by its internal impedance (which is zero in this case), giving

$$Z_{AB} = \frac{10(30 - j20)}{10 + (30 - j20)} + \frac{20(40 - j40)}{20 + (40 - j40)} = 23.38 - j4.08$$

$$= 23.73\angle{-9.9°} \text{ ohm}$$

and

$$Y_{AB} = 1/Z_{AB} = 0.042\angle{9.9°} = 0.041 + j0.007 \text{ S}$$

(a) Thévenin's Source

The Thévenin's voltage, V_{AB}, (see Figure 9.20(b)) is calculated below

$$V_{AB} = V_{AC} - V_{BC} = 10\angle{20°} \left\{ \frac{10}{10 + (30 - j20)} - \frac{20}{20 + (40 - j40)} \right\}$$

$$= 0.6\angle{-99.4°} \text{ V}$$

The corresponding Thévenin equivalent circuit is shown in figure 9.21(a).

(i) For $Z_L = (10 + j0)$ ohm

$$I_L = \frac{0.61\angle{-99.4°}}{(10 - j0) + (23.38 - j4.08)} = 0.018\angle{-92.43°} \text{ A}$$

(ii) For $Z_L = (0 + j10)$ ohm

$$I_L = \frac{0.61\angle{-99.4°}}{(0 + j10) + (22.38 - j4.08)} = 0.025\angle{-113.6°} \text{ A}$$

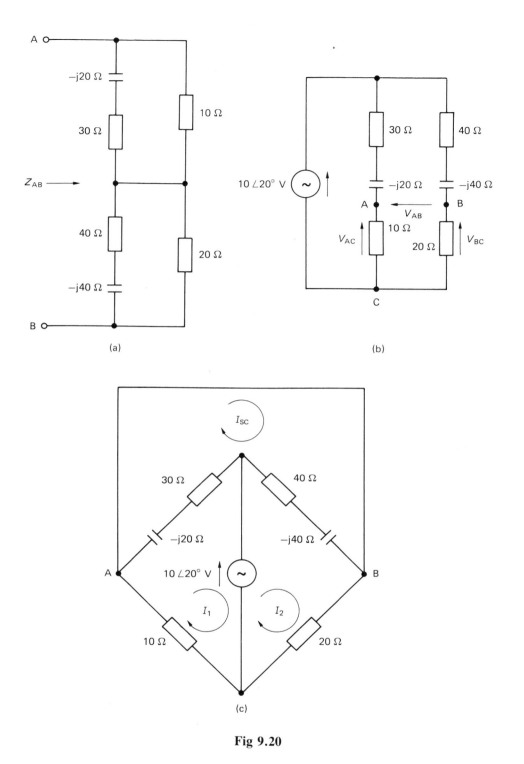

(a)

(b)

(c)

Fig 9.20

(b) *Norton Source*

The Norton source current, I_{SC}, (see Figure 9.20(c)) is calculated below. Since $10\angle 20° \text{ V} = (9.4 + j3.42) \text{ V}$, the matrix form of mesh current equations for Figure 9.20(c) are

$$\begin{bmatrix} -9.4 - j3.42 \\ 9.4 + j3.42 \\ 0 \end{bmatrix} = \begin{bmatrix} 40 - j20 & 0 & -30 + j20 \\ 0 & 60 - j40 & -40 + j40 \\ -30 + j20 & -40 - j40 & 70 - j60 \end{bmatrix} \begin{bmatrix} I_1 \\ I_2 \\ I_{SC} \end{bmatrix}$$

where I_{SC} is the current produced by the ideal Norton source.

Solving for I_{SC} by Cramer's rule gives

$$I_{SC} = \frac{\begin{vmatrix} 40 - j20 & 0 & -9.4 - j3.42 \\ 0 & 60 - j40 & 9.4 + j3.42 \\ -30 + j20 & -40 + j40 & 0 \end{vmatrix}}{\begin{vmatrix} 40 - j20 & 0 & -30 + j20 \\ 0 & 60 - j40 & -40 + j40 \\ -30 + j20 & -40 + j40 & 70 - j60 \end{vmatrix}} = \frac{2000\angle 200°}{76\,550\angle -70.14°}$$

$$= 0.026\angle -89.86° \text{ A}$$

(i) $Y_L = 1/(10 + j0) = 0.1 + j0 \text{ S}$

The admittance connected to the ideal current source (see Figure 9.21(b)) is

$$(0.041 + j0.007) + 0.1 = 0.141 + j0.007 = 0.141\angle 284° \text{ S}$$

Hence,

$$I_L = 0.026\angle -89.86° \times \frac{0.1\angle 0°}{0.141\angle 2.84°} = 0.018\angle -92.7° \text{ A}$$

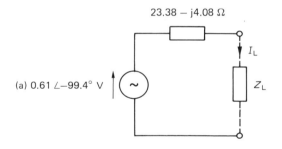

(a) 0.61 ∠−99.4° V

23.38 − j4.08 Ω

I_L

Z_L

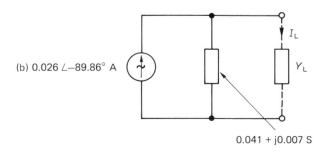

(b) 0.026 ∠−89.86° A

I_L

Y_L

0.041 + j0.007 S

Fig 9.21

(ii) $Y_L = 1/(0 + j10) = 0 - j0.1$ S

The admittance connected to the ideal current source, in this case, is

$$(0.041 + j0.007) - j0.1 = 0.041 - j0.093 = 0.102\angle -66.2° \text{ S}$$

and

$$I_L = 0.026\angle -89.86° \times \frac{0.1\angle -90°}{0.102\angle -66.2°} = 0.025\angle -113.66° \text{ A}$$

Marginal differences between the Thévenin and Norton solutions are due to rounding errors in the calculation.

Note: The Norton source current can, alternatively, be calculated from the relationship

$$I_{\text{NORTON}} = \frac{V_{\text{THÉVENIN}}}{Z_{\text{INTERNAL}}} = \frac{0.61\angle -99.4°}{23.73\angle -9.9°} = 0.026\angle -89.5° \text{ A}$$

Example 9.12

Construct the dual of the circuit in Figure 9.22.

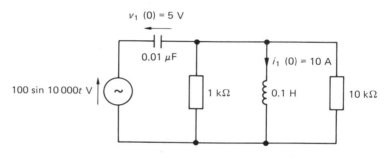

Fig 9.22

Solution 9.12

The circuit is redrawn in Figure 9.23(a) together with the outline of the dual circuit (shown dotted). The dual circuit is drawn in full line in Figure 9.23(b), together with the component values and the initial values for the dual circuit. The corresponding values for the two circuits are listed below.

Initial circuit value	*Corresponding dual circuit value*
100 sin 10 000t V	100 sin 10 000t A
0.01 microfarad	0.01 microhenry
1 kΩ	10^{-3} s
0.1 H	0.1 F
10 kΩ	10^{-4} S
$v_1(0) = 5$ V	$i_2(0) = 5$ A
$i_1(0) = 10$ A	$v_2(0) = 10$ V

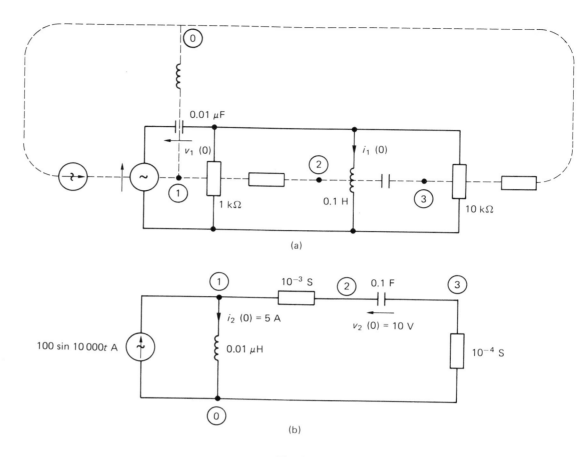

Fig 9.23

The direction of the voltages and currents in the dual circuit have been deduced in accordance with the method outlined in the Fact Sheet for this chapter.

Unworked Problems

Problem 9.1

Calculate I_1 and I_2 in Figure 9.24 if $\omega = 500$ rad/s.
$[I_1 = 0.447\angle71.57° \text{ A}; I_2 = 0.57\angle60.26° \text{ A}]$

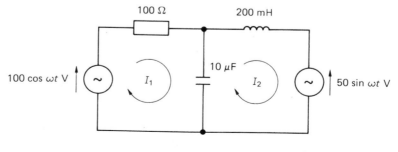

Fig 9.24

Problem 9.2

Write the mesh current equations for the circuit in Figure 9.25, and solve them for I_3.

$$[5\angle 60° = j2.5I_1 \qquad\qquad + j0.5I_2 \qquad\qquad - j4I_3$$
$$0 = j0.5I_1 \quad + (1 - j0.75)I_2 \qquad\qquad + j0.25I_3$$
$$0 = -j4I_1 \qquad\qquad + j0.25I_2 \quad + (2 + j3.75)I_3$$

$$I_3 = 2.22\angle 103.24° \text{ A}]$$

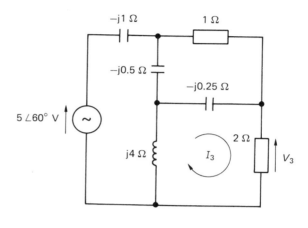

Fig 9.25

Problem 9.3

Use node voltage analysis to evaluate V_3 in Problem 9.2.
$[4.44\angle 103.24° \text{ V}]$

Problem 9.4

Use node voltage analysis to determine V_1 and I in Figure 9.26.
$[5.37\angle 20.17° \text{ V}; 0.76\angle -24.85° \text{ A}]$

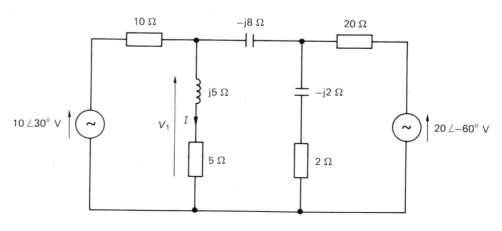

Fig 9.26

Problem 9.5

A 3-phase, 3-wire system has a balanced supply and unbalanced load (see Chapter 12 for details of balanced and unbalanced systems) as follows:

$$V_{1N} = 1000\angle 0° \text{ V}, \ V_{2N} = 1000\angle -120° \text{ V}, \ V_{3N} = 1000\angle 120° \text{ V}$$

and

$$Z_{1S} = 10\angle 0° \text{ ohm}, \ Z_{2S} = 15\angle -15° \text{ ohm}, \ Z_{3S} = 20\angle 20° \text{ ohm}$$

Determine the value of V_{SN}, I_1, I_2, I_3, and the voltage across each load.
[$V_{SN} = 357.6\angle -11.6°$ V; $I_1 = 65.36\angle 6.32°$ A; $I_2 = 77.56\angle -122°$ A;
$I_3 = 63.3\angle 112.19°$ A; $V_{1S} = 653.65\angle 6.32°$ V; $V_{2S} = 1163.4\angle -137°$ V;
$V_{2S} = 1163.4\angle -137°$ V; $V_{3S} = 1266\angle 132.2°$ V]

Problem 9.6

The generator in Problem 9.5 develops a fault, unbalancing the phase voltages, which become

$$V_{1N} = 800\angle 20° \text{ V}, \ V_{2N} = 1200\angle -140° \text{ V}, \ V_{3N} = 1300\angle 120° \text{ V}$$

Evaluate the new value of V_{SN}, the line currents, and the voltage across each phase of the load.
[$V_{SN} = 149\angle 55.1°$ V; $I_1 = 68.35\angle 12.8°$ A; $I_2 = 89.63\angle -123.3°$ A;
$I_3 = 62.21\angle 106.2°$ A; $V_{1S} = 683.5\angle 12.8°$ V; $V_{2S} = 1344.4\angle -138.3°$ V;
$V_{3S} = 1244\angle 126.2°$ V]

Problem 9.7

In a 3-phase, star-star connected system

$$V_{1N} = 250\angle -20° \text{ V}, \ V_{2N} = 200\angle -90° \text{ V}, \ V_{3N} = 300\angle 150° \text{ V}$$

$$Z_{1S} = 10\angle -30° \text{ ohm}, \ Z_{2S} = 5\angle 0° \text{ ohm}$$

What value of Z_{3S} makes V_{SN} zero?
[$6.92\angle 25.38°$ ohm]

Problem 9.8

Deduce the Thévenin equivalent circuit between the terminals Y and Z in Figure 9.27 if X is (a) a 20 V ideal voltage source (its top terminal being positive with respect to the bottom terminal), (b) a 10 A current source (the current flowing downwards).
[(a) $V_{TH} = 15$ V (Y positive), $R_{TH} = 3.75$ ohm; (b) $V_{TH} = 50$ V (Y negative), $R_{TH} = 7.5$ ohm]

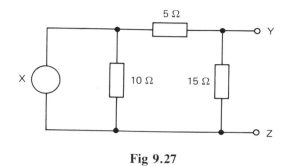

Fig 9.27

Problem 9.9

Deduce the Thévenin equivalent circuit with respect to terminals A and B of Figure 9.28. Calculate the current which flows in an impedance of (3 + j4) ohm connected between A and B.

[$V_{TH} = 13.42\angle146.57°$ V, $Z_{TH} = 84.85\angle-45°$ ohm; $0.16\angle188.2°$ A]

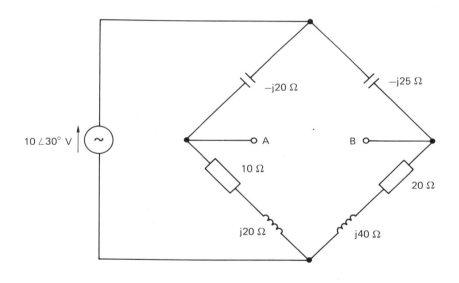

Fig 9.28

Problem 9.10

Deduce the Norton equivalent circuit for Figure 9.29 with respect to terminals A and B. If an impedance of $10\angle-20°$ ohm is connected between A and B, calculate the current flowing in the load. Convert the Norton equivalent circuit to its coresponding Thévenin equivalent circuit.

[$I_N = 5.76\angle58.23°$ A, $Y_N = 0.0398\angle-84.29°$ S; $5.87\angle81.39°$ A; $V_{TH} = 144.6\angle142.52°$ V, $Z_{TH} = 25.12\angle84.29°$ ohm]

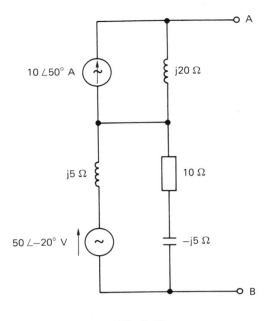

Fig 9.29

Problem 9.11

Deduce the Norton equivalent circuit with respect to terminals A and B of Figure 9.30. Hence calculate the current flowing in a 10-ohm resistance connected between A and B.

$[I_N = 2.676$ A; $G_N = 0.539$ S; $I_{AB} = 0.419$ A$]$

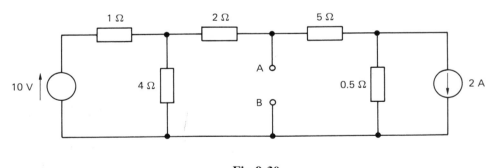

Fig 9.30

Problem 9.12

Draw the dual of the circuit in Figure 9.31(a).

[See Figure 9.31(b) for solution]

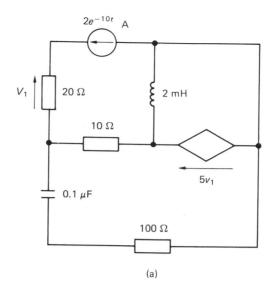

(a)

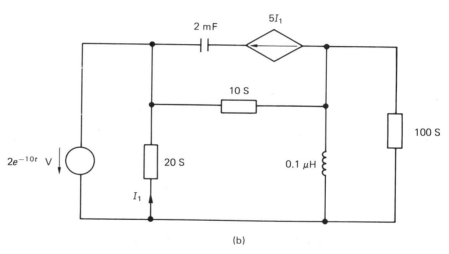

(b)

Fig 9.31

Problem 9.13

Using mesh analysis, determine the current I_2, in polar form, for the circuit shown in Figure 9.32.

[$0.63\angle 131.8°$ A]

(Liverpool Polytechnic)

Problem 9.14

Derive the Thévenin equivalent circuit of Figure 9.33 relative to terminals AB and hence (i) write the value, in Cartesian terms, of the load impedance Z_L that should be connected across terminals AB such that maximum power is deve-

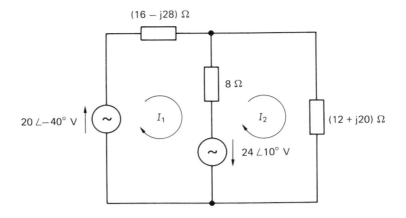

Fig 9.32

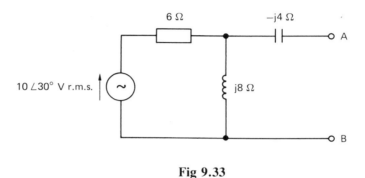

Fig 9.33

loped in Z_L and (ii) determine the maximum load power (see Chapter 10 for details of the maximum power transfer theorem).

(Liverpool Polytechnic)

[$V_{TH} = 8\angle 66.87°$ V, $Z_{TH} = 4\angle -16.26°$ ohm; assuming that the load resistance and reactance are independently variable
(i) 3.84 + j1.12 ohm; (ii) 4.15 W]

Problem 9.15

(a) For the circuit in Figure 9.34, determine the Thévenin equivalent circuit between terminals A and B. (b) Use the equivalent circuit obtained in part (a) to calculate the current through a load resistance of 15 ohm connected between A and B.

(Staffordshire Polytechnic)

[(a) $V_{TH} = 25$ V; $R_{TH} = 10$ ohm; (b) 1.0 A]

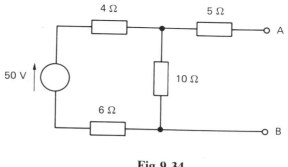

Fig 9.34

Problem 9.16

(a) Determine the Thévenin equivalent circuit with respect to terminals A and B in Figure 9.35. (b) Calculate the current in a 7-ohm resistor connected between terminals A and B.

(Staffordshire Polytechnic)

[(a) V_{TH} = 6 V (terminal A positive), R_{TH} = 5 ohm; (b) 0.5 A (flowing from A to B)]

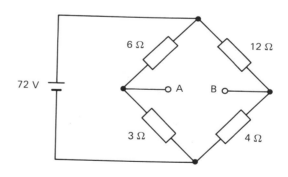

Fig 9.35

Problem 9.17

Use Thévenins theorem to calculate the current in the 1 ohm resistor in Figure 9.36.

(Staffordshire Polytechnic)

V_{TH} = 12 V; R_{TH} = 4 ohm; 2.4 A]

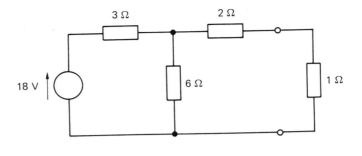

Fig 9.36

Problem 9.18

Given that, in Figure 9.37

$V_{AN} = 10 \sin \omega t$ V; $V_{BN} = 10 \sin (\omega t - 2\pi/3)$ V; $V_{CN} = 10 \sin (\omega t + 2\pi/3)$ V

and $\omega = 1$ rad/s, calculate V_{SN}.

(Staffordshire Polytechnic)

[7.32 $\sin (\omega t - \pi)$ V]

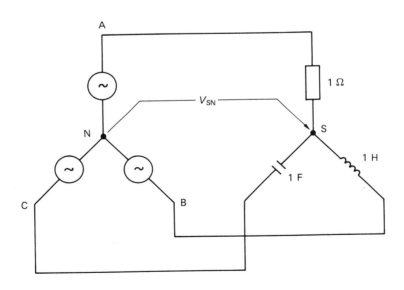

Fig 9.37

10 Circuit Theorems II

10.1 Fact Sheet

(a) The General Star-mesh Transformation (Rosen's Theorem)

The general star network of N components in Figure 10.1(a), can be converted into the general mesh network in Figure 10.1(b). The equivalent admittance connected between the pair of terminals U and V in the network is

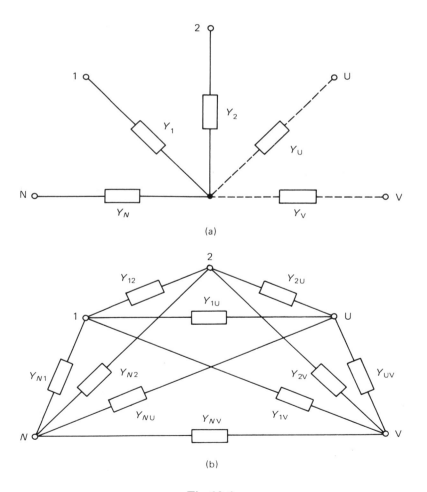

Fig 10.1

$$Y_{UV} = \frac{Y_U Y_V}{\displaystyle\sum_{K=1}^{K=N} Y_K}$$

Although a particular mesh-star transformation exists (see section (b) below), a general mesh-star transformation does not.

(b) Star-delta and Delta-star Transformation

A network comprising three elements connected in *star* or *tee* (see Figure 10.2(a)) can be converted into three elements connected in *delta* or *mesh* (see Figure 10.2(b)), and vice versa.

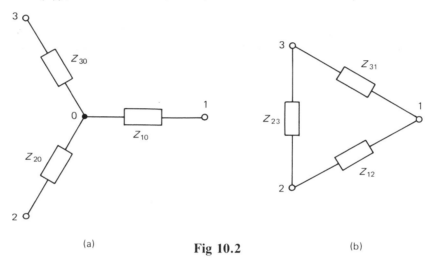

(a)   **Fig 10.2**   (b)

The following is a simplification of the general star-mesh transformation to give the *star-delta* or *tee-pi transformation*.

$$Z_{12} = Z_{10} + Z_{20} + \frac{Z_{10}Z_{20}}{Z_{30}} \qquad Y_{12} = \frac{Y_{10}Y_{20}}{Y_{10} + Y_{20} + Y_{30}}$$

$$Z_{23} = Z_{20} + Z_{30} + \frac{Z_{20}Z_{30}}{Z_{10}} \qquad Y_{23} = \frac{Y_{20}Y_{30}}{Y_{10} + Y_{20} + Y_{30}}$$

$$Z_{31} = Z_{30} + Z_{10} + \frac{Z_{30}Z_{10}}{Z_{20}} \qquad Y_{31} = \frac{Y_{30}Y_{10}}{Y_{10} + Y_{20} + Y_{30}}$$

The *delta-star* or *pi-tee* transformation is as follows.

$$Z_{10} = \frac{Z_{12}Z_{13}}{Z_{12} + Z_{23} + Z_{31}} \qquad Y_{10} = Y_{31} + Y_{21} + \frac{Y_{31}Y_{21}}{Y_{32}}$$

$$Z_{20} = \frac{Z_{23}Z_{12}}{Z_{12} + Z_{23} + Z_{31}} \qquad Y_{20} = Y_{21} + Y_{23} + \frac{Y_{21}Y_{23}}{Y_{31}}$$

$$Z_{30} = \frac{Z_{13}Z_{23}}{Z_{12} + Z_{23} + Z_{31}} \qquad Y_{30} = Y_{31} + Y_{32} + \frac{Y_{31}Y_{32}}{Y_{12}}$$

(c) Superposition Theorem

This theorem can be stated as follows.

> In any linear bilateral network containing several *independent* sources, the voltage across (or the current in) any element or source is the sum of the individual voltages (or currents) produced by each independent source acting alone (every other source in the network meanwhile being replaced by its internal impedance).

When the circuit contains *dependent* sources, the superposition theorem can only be used when the control variable is external to the network containing the sources.

Since power is proportional to the square (which is nonlinear) of voltage (or current), superposition cannot be applied directly to the computation of power.

(d) Reciprocity Theorem

This theorem, which refers to linear, bilateral, *single-source* networks, can be stated in two ways as follows:

1. If an e.m.f., E, is applied to a linear, bilateral network at one point, and it produces a current I at a second point then, when the e.m.f., E, is applied at the second point, it produces current I at the first point.
2. If a current I flowing between terminals A and B in a network produces voltage V between terminals C and D in the network then, when I flows between terminals C and D it produces voltage V between A and B.

However, in case 1, the currents at other points in the network change when the position of the voltage source changes. Likewise in case 2, the voltage between other points in the network change when the position of the current source changes.

(e) Compensation Theorem or Substitution theorem

This states that an impedance Z which carries current I, may be replaced by a *compensation e.m.f.* whose magnitude and polarity are equal to the p.d. IZ. Also, if the voltage across an element or branch of impedance Z is V, then the element or branch may be replaced by a current source $I = V/Z$.

It follows that if the impedance of any branch is changed by δZ, the *incremental change* of current δI in that branch would be the same as that produced by a voltage source $\delta V = I\,\delta Z$ if introduced in the *same branch* (Note: if δZ was an increase in impedance, δV would oppose the current in the branch to achieve the same result).

(f) Maximum Power Transfer Theorem

The power which is transferred from an active network to a load depends on a number of factors, the most important of which are as follows.

1. If the load is a pure resistance, maximum power is transferred to the load when the resistance of the load is equal to the magnitude of the internal impedance of the active network.
2. If the load comprises a fixed reactance in series with a variable resistance, maximum power is transferred when the resistance of the load is equal to the sum of the magnitude of the internal impedance of the active network and the reactance of the load.
3. If the load has a variable impedance but a constant power factor, maximum power is transferred to the load when the magnitude of the load impedance is equal to the magnitude of the internal impedance of the source.
4. If the load resistance and the load reactance are independently variable, maximum power is transferred to the load when the load impedance is equal to the complex conjugate of the internal impedance of the source.

10.2 Worked Examples

Example 10.1

Convert the 4-branch star network in figure 10.3(a) into its equivalent mesh network in Figure 10.3(b).

Solution 10.1

The star network values are converted initially to their polar admittance form as follows.

$$Y_{AN} = \frac{1}{5} = 0.2 + j0 = 0.2\angle 0° \text{ S}$$

$$Y_{BN} = \frac{1}{3 + j4} = 0.12 - j0.16 = 0.2\angle -53.13° \text{ S}$$

$$Y_{CN} = \frac{1}{4 + j3} = 0.16 - j0.12 = 0.2\angle -36.87° \text{ S}$$

$$Y_{DN} = \frac{1}{1.414 + j1.414} = 0.354 - j\,0.354 = 0.5\angle -45° \text{ S}$$

and

$$\sum_{N=1}^{N=4} Y_N = 0.834 - j0.634 = 1.05\angle -37.24° \text{ S}$$

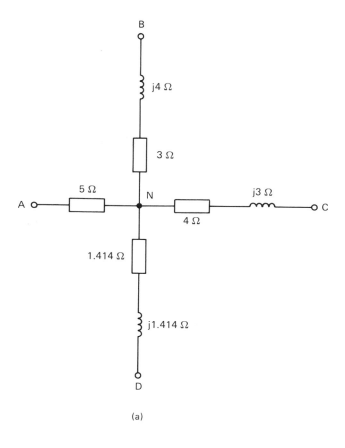

(a)

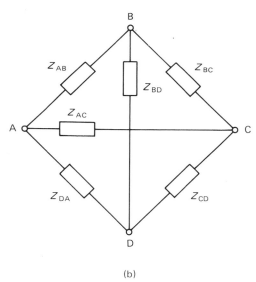

(b)

Fig 10.3

The elements in Figure 10.3(b) are calculated below. Rosen's theorem states that

$$Y_{AB} = \frac{Y_{AN}Y_{BN}}{\Sigma Y} = \frac{0.2\angle 0° \times 0.2\angle -53.13°}{1.05\angle -37.24°} = 0.038\angle -15.89° \text{ S}$$

or

$$\boldsymbol{Z}_{AB} = 26.32\angle 15.89° \text{ ohm}$$

Similarly

$$\boldsymbol{Y}_{BC} = 0.038\angle -52.76° \text{ S or } \boldsymbol{Z}_{BC} = 26.32\angle 52.76° \text{ ohm}$$

$$\boldsymbol{Y}_{CD} = 0.095\angle -44.63° \text{ S or } \boldsymbol{Z}_{CD} = 10.53\angle 44.63° \text{ ohm}$$

$$\boldsymbol{Y}_{DA} = 0.095\angle -7.76° \text{ S or } \boldsymbol{Z}_{DA} = 10.53\angle 7.76° \text{ ohm}$$

$$\boldsymbol{Y}_{BD} = 0.095\angle -60.89° \text{ S or } \boldsymbol{Z}_{BD} = 10.53\angle 60.89° \text{ ohm}$$

$$\boldsymbol{Y}_{AC} = 0.038\angle 0.37° \text{ S or } \boldsymbol{Z}_{AC} = 26.32\angle -0.37° \text{ ohm}$$

Example 10.2

Convert the delta-connected set of capacitors in Figure 10.4 into their star equivalent, and calculate the value of the current I.

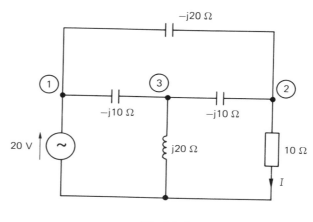

Fig 10.4

Solution 10.2

The three capacitive impedances in Figure 10.4 are converted into their equivalent mesh-connected impedances in Figure 10.5 as follows.

$$\Sigma\boldsymbol{Z} = \boldsymbol{Z}_{12} + \boldsymbol{Z}_{23} + \boldsymbol{Z}_{31} = -\text{j}20 - \text{j}10 - \text{j}10 = -\text{j}40 \text{ ohm}$$

Now

$$\boldsymbol{Z}_{10} = \boldsymbol{Z}_{12}\boldsymbol{Z}_{31}/\Sigma\boldsymbol{Z} = (-\text{j}20)(-\text{j}10)/(-\text{j}40) = -\text{j}5 \text{ ohm}$$

$$\boldsymbol{Z}_{20} = \boldsymbol{Z}_{23}\boldsymbol{Z}_{12}/\Sigma\boldsymbol{Z} = (-\text{j}20)(-\text{j}10)/(-\text{j}40) = -\text{j}5 \text{ ohm}$$

$$\boldsymbol{Z}_{30} = \boldsymbol{Z}_{31}\boldsymbol{Z}_{23}/\Sigma\boldsymbol{Z} = (-\text{j}10)(-\text{j}10)/(-\text{j}40) = -\text{j}2.5 \text{ ohm}$$

The mesh current equations for Figure 10.5 are

$$20 = \text{j}12.5I_1 - \text{j}17.5I$$

$$0 = -\text{j}17.5I_1 + (10 + \text{j}12.5)I$$

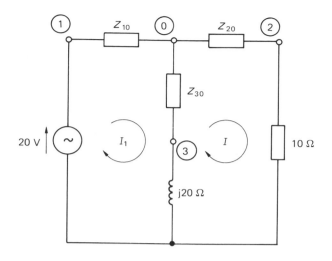

Fig 10.5

Solving for I gives

$$I = \frac{\begin{vmatrix} j12.5 & 20 \\ -j17.5 & 0 \end{vmatrix}}{\begin{vmatrix} j12.5 & -j17.5 \\ -j17.5 & 10 + j12.5 \end{vmatrix}} = \frac{350\angle 90°}{195.26\angle 39.8°} = 1.79\angle 50.2° \text{ A}$$

Example 10.3

In Figure 10.6(a), $Z_1 = 20\angle 45°$ ohm and $Z_2 = 10\angle -30°$ ohm. Determine the delta-connected equivalent circuit.

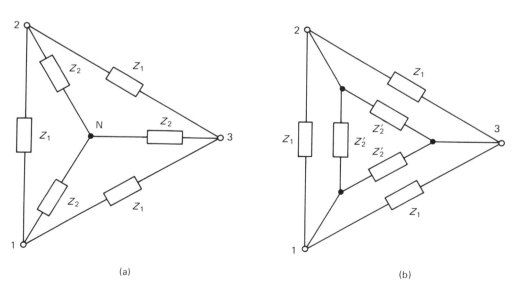

(a)   (b)

Fig 10.6

Solution 10.3

The inner star comprising the three Z_2 elements is converted into the delta-connected impedances Z_2' (see Figure 10.6(b)) as follows

$$Z_2' = Z_2 + Z_2 + \frac{Z_2 Z_2}{Z_2} = 3Z_2 = 3 \times 10\angle -30° = 30\angle -30° \text{ ohm}$$

Each Z_2' impedance is connected in parallel with a Z_1 impedance to give a net parallel impedance of

$$\frac{Z_1 Z_2'}{Z_1 + Z_2'} = \frac{20\angle 45° \times 30\angle -30°}{20\angle 45° + 30\angle -30°} = 14.95\angle 16.23° \text{ ohm}$$

That is, the network in Figure 10.6(a) can be replaced by three delta-connected impedances each of $14.95\angle 16.23° = 14.35 + j4.18$ ohm

Example 10.4

Using the superposition theorem, determine the current in each branch of the network in Figure 10.7(a).

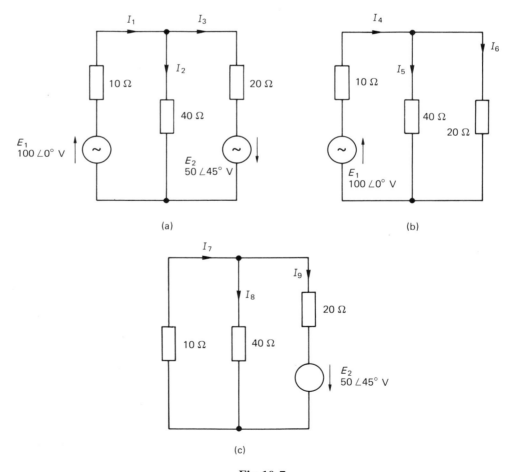

(a)

(b)

(c)

Fig 10.7

Solution 10.4

The circuit diagram for E_1 acting alone is shown in Figure 10.7(b). The current I_4 is

$$I_4 = \frac{100\angle 0°}{10 + \dfrac{40 \times 20}{40 + 20}} = \frac{100\angle 0°}{10 + 13.333} = 4.29\angle 0° \text{ A}$$

Using the current-division theory for parallel circuits

$$I_5 = 4.29\angle 0° \times \frac{20}{20 + 40} = 1.4\angle 0° \text{ A}$$

Hence,

$$I_6 = I_4 - I_5 = 4.29\angle 0° - 1.43\angle 0° = 2.86\angle 0° \text{ A}$$

The circuit diagram for E_2 acting alone is shown in Figure 10.7(c). Using a similar method of calculation, we get

$$I_9 = \frac{50\angle 45°}{20 + \dfrac{10 \times 40}{10 + 40}} = \frac{50\angle 45°}{20 + 8} = 1.79\angle 45° \text{ A}$$

Also

$$I_7 = 1.432\angle 45° \text{ A, and } I_8 = 0.348\angle 45° \text{ A}$$

Combining the values from Figure 10.7(b) and (c), we get the required values in Figure 10.7(a) as follows.

$$I_1 = I_4 + I_7 = 4.29\angle 0° + 1.432\angle 45° = 5.4\angle 10.79° \text{ A}$$

$$I_2 = I_5 + I_8 = 1.43\angle 0° + 0.358\angle 45° = 1.7\angle 8.55° \text{ A}$$

$$I_3 = I_6 + I_9 = 2.86\angle 0° + 1.79\angle 45° = 4.32\angle 17.09° \text{ A}$$

Example 10.5

If, in Figure 10.8(a) and at a frequency of 10^3 rad/s, $X_L = 20$ ohm and $X_C = 10$ ohm, determine an expression for i_L.

Solution 10.5

Since the current source and the voltage source operate at different frequencies, the principle of superposition is a convenient method of determining the expression for i_L. Moreover, since we only need to evaluate i_L, the current in the remainder of the circuit need not be calculated.

Dealing with the current source alone, and bearing in mind that the internal impedance of the voltage source is zero, and circuit diagram is that shown in Figure 10.8(b), and

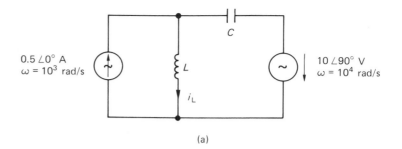

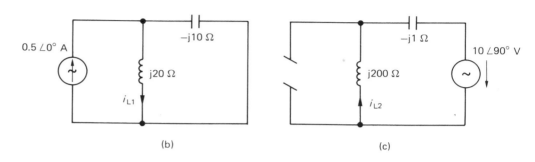

Fig 10.8

$$I_{L1} = 0.5\angle 0° \times \frac{-j10}{j20 - j10} = 0.5\angle 180° \text{ A}$$

and the corresponding maximum value of current in the inductor is $\sqrt{2} \times 0.5 = 0.707$ A, hence

$$i_{L1} = 0.707 \sin (10^3 t + 180°) \text{ A}$$

Dealing with the voltage source, whose frequency is 10^4 rad/s, the reactance values are

$$X_L = 20 \times 10^4 / 10^3 = 200 \text{ ohm}$$

$$X_C = 10 \times 10^3 / 10^4 = 1 \text{ ohm}$$

The internal impedance of the current source is infinity, resulting in the circuit diagram for the voltage source alone being as shown in Figure 10.8(c). Hence

$$I_{L2} = \frac{10\angle 90°}{j(200 - 1)} = 0.0502\angle 0° \text{ A}$$

and the maximum value of current in the inductor is 0.071 A,
    Hence,

$$i_{L2} = 0.071 \sin 10^4 t \text{ A}$$

Consequently, in Figure 10.8(a)

$$i_L = i_{L1} - i_{L2} = 0.707 \sin (10^3 t + 180°) - 0.071 \sin 10^4 t \text{ A}$$

Example 10.6

In this example, the reciprocity theorem is demonstrated as follows. Firstly the value of I_2 in Figure 10.9(a) is calculated, and then the voltage source is inserted in the branch containing the 10 ohm resistor and the current in the branch which formerly contained the voltage source is calculated. If the two values of current are equal, then reciprocity is demonstrated.

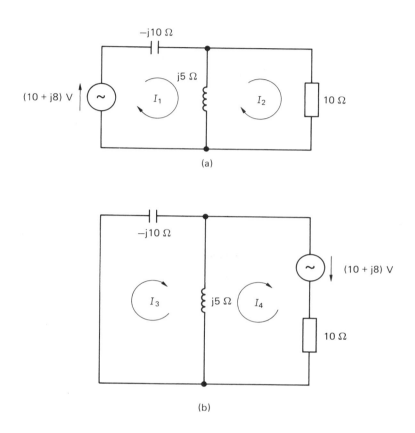

Fig 10.9

Solution 10.6

The mesh current equations for the circuit in Figure 10.9(a) are

$$10 + j8 = -j5I_1 - j5I_2$$
$$0 = -j5I_1 + (10 + j5)I_2$$

hence,

$$I_2 = \frac{\begin{vmatrix} -j5 & 10+j8 \\ -j5 & 0 \end{vmatrix}}{\begin{vmatrix} -j5 & -j5 \\ -j5 & 10+j5 \end{vmatrix}} = \frac{64.03\angle128.66°}{70.71\angle-45°} = 0.906\angle173.66° \text{ A}$$

Next, the voltage source is removed from its initial position and is inserted in the branch containing the 10 ohm resistor (the voltage source acting in the direction of the original current). The corresponding circuit is shown in Figure 10.9(b), having the mesh current equations

$$0 = -j5I_3 - j5I_4$$

$$10 + j8 = -j5I_3 + (10 + j5)I_4$$

giving

$$I_3 = \frac{\begin{vmatrix} 0 & -j5 \\ 10 + j8 & 10 + j5 \end{vmatrix}}{\begin{vmatrix} -j5 & -j5 \\ -j5 & 10 + j5 \end{vmatrix}} = \frac{64.03\angle 128.66°}{70.71\angle -45°} = 0.906\angle 173.66° \text{ A}$$

Since $I_2 = I_3$, reciprocity is demonstrated.

Example 10.7

In Figure 10.10(a) $I_1 = 0.734 + j0.459$ A and $I_2 = 0.1 + j0.189$ A. Use the compensation theorem to calculate the current distribution when the resistance of the 25 ohm resistor is changed to 20 ohm.

Solution 10.7

When the 25 ohm resistance is reduced to 20 ohms, the circuit used for the compensation theorem calculation is shown in Figure 10.10(b). Since $I_2 = 0.1 + j0.189 = 0.215\angle 61.78°$ A, the value of the compensation e.m.f. is

$$-I_2\delta Z = -0.215\angle 61.78° \times (-5) = 1.075\angle 61.78°$$

$$= 0.508 + j0.95 \text{ V}$$

The mesh current equations for Figure 10.10(b) are

$$0 = 15\delta I_1 - 10\delta I_2$$

$$0.508 + j0.95 = -10\delta I_1 + (30 - j20)\delta I_2$$

Solving by Cramer's rule gives

$$\delta I_2 = \frac{\begin{vmatrix} 0 & -10 \\ 0.508 + j0.95 & 30 - j20 \end{vmatrix}}{\begin{vmatrix} 15 & -10 \\ -10 & 30 - j20 \end{vmatrix}} = \frac{10.77\angle 61.86°}{461\angle -40.6°} = 0.023\angle 102.46°$$

$$= -0.005 + j0.022 \text{ A}$$

and

$$\delta I_2 = 0.036\angle 102.9° = -0.008 + j0.035 \text{ A}$$

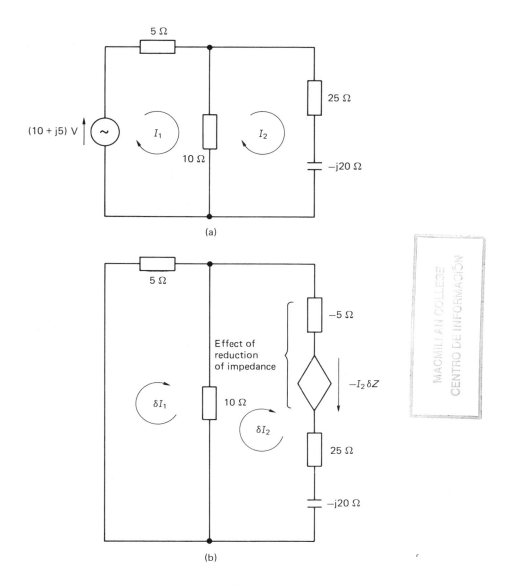

Fig 10.10

Hence the new current, I'_1, in the 5 ohm resistance in Figure 10.10(a) is

$$I'_1 = I_1 + \delta I_1 = (0.734 + j0.459) + (-0.005 + j0.022)$$
$$= 0.729 + j0.481 = 0.873\angle 33.42° \text{ A}$$

and the new current, I'_2, in the $(-j20)$ ohm capacitive reactance is

$$I'_2 = I_2 + \delta I_2 = (0.1 + j\ 0.189) + (-0.008 + j0.035)$$
$$= 0.092 + j0.224 = 0.242\angle 67.67° \text{ A}$$

Example 10.8

Replace the circuit between terminals A and B in Figure 10.11(a) by its (i) Norton's and (ii) Thévenins equivalent circuit. Determine also the value of a

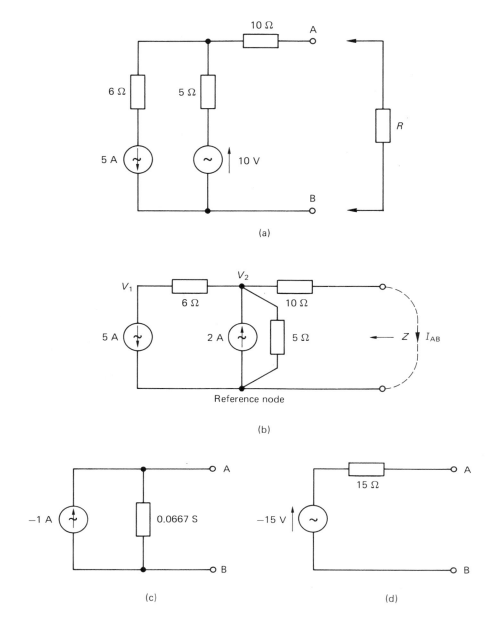

(a)

(b)

(c)

(d)

Fig 10.11

resistor R which, when connected between A and B, will receive maximum power from the circuit. Calculate the value of this power.

Solution 10.8

The voltage source in Figure 10.11(a) is converted into its equivalent current source and is reinserted into the circuit, giving Figure 10.11(b). Since the 5 A current source has infinite internal impedance, the internal impedance, $\mathbf{Z}$, of the network (see Figure 10.11(b)) is

$$\mathbf{Z} = 15 + \text{j}0 \text{ ohm}$$

and its corresponding admittance is

$$Y = 0.0667 + j0 \text{ S}$$

(i) Norton's Current Source

When terminals A and B in Figure 10.11(b) are shorted together, the node voltage equations for Figure 10.11(b) are

$$-5 = \frac{V_1}{6} - \frac{V_2}{6}$$

$$2 = \frac{-V_1}{6} + \left(\frac{1}{6} + \frac{1}{5} + \frac{1}{10}\right)V_2$$

Solving for V_2 gives

$$V_2 = \frac{\begin{vmatrix} \dfrac{1}{6} & -5 \\[2mm] -\dfrac{1}{6} & 2 \end{vmatrix}}{\begin{vmatrix} \dfrac{1}{6} & -\dfrac{1}{6} \\[2mm] -\dfrac{1}{6} & \dfrac{1}{6} + \dfrac{1}{5} + \dfrac{1}{10} \end{vmatrix}} = \frac{-0.5\angle 0°}{0.05\angle 0°} = -10\angle 0° \text{ V}$$

and the current I_{AB} flowing in the short-circuit between A and B is

$$I_{AB} = -10/10 = -1 \text{ A}$$

The corresponding Norton's equivalent circuit diagram is shown in Figure 10.11(c).

(ii) Thévenin's Voltage Source

From section (f) of the Fact Sheet for Chapter 9, the Thévenin voltage, V_{AB}, between the open-circuited terminals A and B in diagram (c) is

$$V_{AB} = I_{AB}Z = -1 \times 15 = -15 \text{ V}$$

The corresponding Thévenin's equivalent circuit is shown in Figure 10.11(d).

Maximum power will be dissipated in a resistor of resistance 15 ohm (which has a voltage of 15/2 V across it) connected to terminals AB in Figure 10.11(d); the power dissipated in it is

$$P = (-15/2)^2/15 = 3.75 \text{ W}$$

10.3 Unworked Problems

Problem 10.1

Convert the star-connected network C, C, R_1 in Figure 10.12 into a delta network, and hence show that $V_2 = 0$ when

$$R_2 = \frac{1}{R_1\omega^2 C^2} \quad \text{and} \quad \omega L = \frac{2}{\omega C}$$

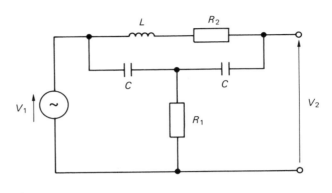

Fig 10.12

Problem 10.2

Convert the circuit in Figure 10.13 into its equivalent π network.
[$\mathbf{Z}_{AB} = 26.53\angle{-74.98°}$ ohm; $\mathbf{Z}_{AC} = 30.02\angle{23.15°}$ ohm;
$\mathbf{Z}_{BC} = 33.15\angle{53.68°}$ ohm]

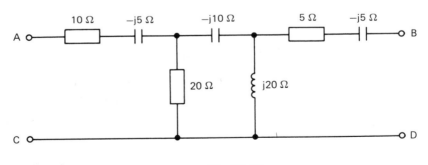

Fig 10.13

Problem 10.3

If the network in Figure 10.14 is equivalent to a balanced star-connected system of $2.77\angle{11.3°}$ ohm per phase, calculate the value of Z.
[$\mathbf{Z} = 5\angle{-45°}$ ohm]

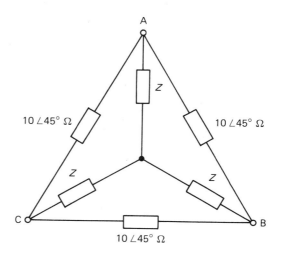

Fig 10.14

Problem 10.4

Using the superposition theorem, calculate the value of I in Figure 10.15.
[-0.6 A]

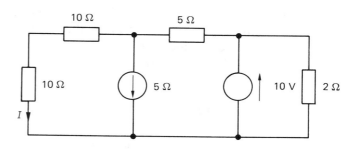

Fig 10.15

Problem 10.5

Using the superposition theorem, calculate the current in the j10 ohm inductive reactance in Worked Example 9.3 (see also Figure 9.10) due to each source separately (assume that current flows into the left-hand end of the inductor), hence determine the total current flowing in the inductor.
[$-0.983 - j1.026$ A due to E_1; $0.472 - j0.149$ A due to E_2; $0.257 - j1.246$ A due to E_3; total current $= -0.254 - j2.421$ A]

Problem 10.6

Demonstrate the validity of the reciprocity theorem by calculating I_1 in Figure 10.16 and, after inserting the voltage source in the branch where I_1 flows,

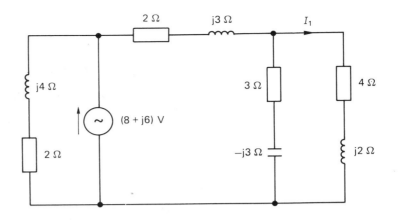

Fig 10.16

calculate the current in the branch which originally contained the voltage source. If the theorem is valid, the two values of current should be the same.
$[I_1 = (1 - j0.542) \text{ A}]$

Problem 10.7

In Problem 10.6, if the j2 ohm inductive reactance is increased in value to j3 ohm, use the compensation theorem to calculate the compensation voltage and the new value of I_1.
$[1.137\angle 61.54° \text{ V}; 1.078\angle -35.35° \text{ A}]$

Problem 10.8

If the $-j3$ ohm reactance of the capacitor in Figure 10.17 is increased to $-j4$ ohm, use the compensation theorem to calculate the change in current in the $(2 + j3)$ ohm branch of the circuit.
[A reduction of $0.08\angle -57.3°$ A]

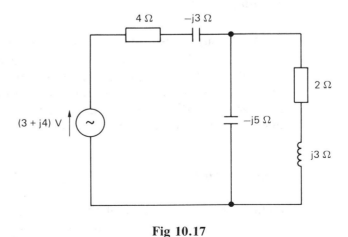

Fig 10.17

Problem 10.9

Determine the value of R in the circuit in Figure 10.18 which receives maximum power, and calculate the value of this power.
[69.13 ohm; 0.0437 W]

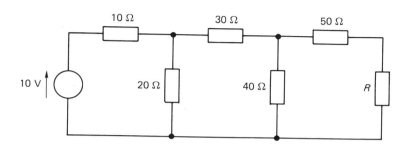

Fig 10.18

Problem 10.10

The $(4 + j2)$ ohm branch of the circuit in Problem 10.6 (Figure 10.16) is replaced by an impedance Z, whose resistance and reactance are independently variable. What value of Z will receive maximum power from the circuit, and what is the value of this power?
[$3 - j0.6$ ohm; 6W]

Problem 10.11

Using the superposition theorem, calculate the value of the current in the 6 ohm resistor in the circuit of Figure 10.19.

(Liverpool Polytechnic)

[6.56 A]

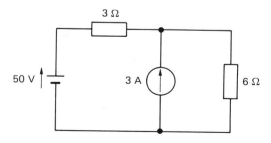

Fig 10.19

Problem 10.12

Use the principle of Superposition to determine the current in the 3 ohm resistor in Figure 10.20.

(Staffordshire Polytechnic)

[4 A]

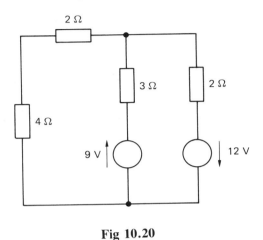

Fig 10.20

Problem 10.13

Using the Y–Δ or Δ–Y conversions, calculate the magnitude of the current drawn from the supply in the circuits in Figures 10.21(a) and (b).

(Staffordshire Polytechnic)

[(**a**) 0.002 A; (**b**) 1.414∠45° A]

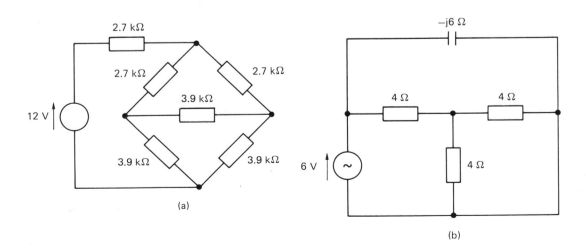

(a)

(b)

Fig 10.21

Problem 10.14

(a) Derive the values for Thévenin's equivalent circuit with respect to terminals A and B for the circuit in Figure 10.22. (b) Express, in polar form, the value of load impedance which, when connected between A and B, will cause the maximum power to be dissipated in the load. (c) Calculate the maximum power in part (b). (d) What is the value of maximum power which can be dissipated in a purely resistive load connected between A and B?

(Staffordshire Polytechnic)

[(a) $V_{TH} = 8.94\angle{-26.56°}$ V, $Z_{TH} = 108\angle{-21.8°}$ ohm;
(b) $108\angle{21.8°}$ ohm (assuming that the resistance and reactance of the load are independent); (c) 0.2 W; (d) 0.19 W]

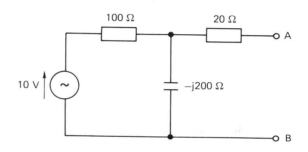

Fig 10.22

Problem 10.15

Use the Superposition theorem to calculate I in Figure 10.23.

(Staffordshire Polytechnic)

[1.6 A]

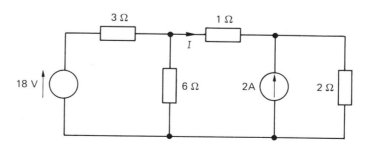

Fig 10.23

Problem 10.16

Use the Superposition theorem to calculate V_{AB} in Figure 10.24. Calculate the power supplied by each source.

(Staffordshire Polytechnic)
[8.8 V; current source supplies 35.2 W, voltage source supplies 4 W]

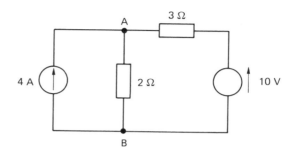

Fig 10.24

Problem 10.17

Calculate the value of R in Figure 10.25 which results in maximum power being consumed in R. Calculate the value of this power.

(Staffordshire Polytechnic)
[1 ohm; 30.25 W]

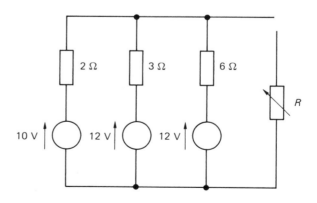

Fig 10.25

11   Coupled Circuits and the Transformer

11.1   Fact Sheet

(a)   Mutual Coupling

Two circuits are said to be *mutually coupled* when the magnetic field produced by the current in one circuit induces an e.m.f. in the other circuit. The induced e.m.f., e_2, in the second circuit is

$$e_2 = M \frac{di_1}{dt} \text{ V}$$

where M is the *mutual inductance* (in henry, H) between the two circuits, and di_1/dt is the rate of change of the current in the first circuit.

(b)   Mutually Coupled Circuits

Two circuits, which have a mutual inductance of M henrys linking them are shown in Figure 11.1.

Using the equation quoted in section (a) of this Fact Sheet, together with the notion of the dependent voltage-controlled source developed in Chapter 1, the two circuits can be shown as electrically isolated circuits in Figure 11.1(b) (note: since the current in each circuit induces a voltage in the other circuit, there is a dependent voltage source shown in each of them). The reader will note that the polarity of the voltage in the controlled voltage sources has not been shown in the diagram; the reason is that, since we do not know how the coils are wound relative to one another we cannot, at this stage, assign a polarity to the induced e.m.f.s in the two windings.

The time-domain equations for the two circuits are

$$v_1 = R_1 i_1 + L_1 \frac{di_1}{dt} \pm M \frac{di_2}{dt}$$

$$v_2 = R_2 i_2 + L_2 \frac{di_2}{dt} \pm M \frac{di_1}{dt}$$

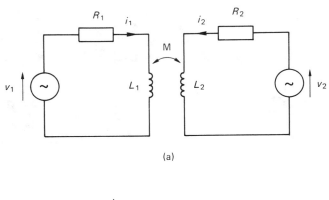

(a)

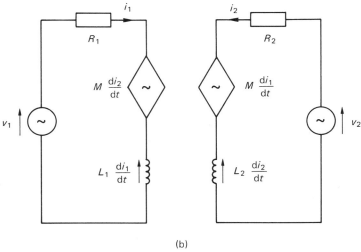

(b)

Fig 11.1

and the corresponding frequency-domain equations are

$$V_1 = (R_1 + j\omega L_1)I_1 \pm j\omega M I_2$$

$$V_2 = (R_2 + j\omega L_2)I_2 \pm j\omega M I_1$$

We can assign the correct polarity to the controlled voltage sources when the directions of the induced e.m.f.s are known, and this can be deduced from a knowledge of the *dot notation*, which is described in section (c) below.

(c) The Dot Notation

Consider the simple single-source circuit in Figure 11.2(a), comprising two magnetically coupled circuits.

Arbitrarily, a dot is placed at one end of one coil; in this case, we place a dot at the top of coil 1. When I_1 enters the dotted end of coil 1, flux Φ_1 (shown in full line) leaves the top of the coil. This enters coil 2, and induces an e.m.f. in it which, in turn, causes I_2 to flow in the second circuit. *Lenz's law* implies that the latter current produces a flux Φ_2 (shown dotted) which opposes Φ_1. To produce

244

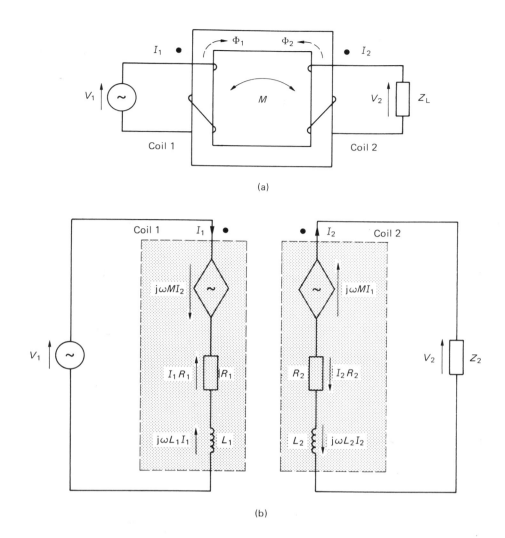

(a)

(b)

Fig 11.2

Φ_2 in the direction shown, the current I_2 must flow out of the top terminal of coil 2. In this circuit, the top terminal of the second coil is also marked with a dot for the following reason.

In the dot notation, we adopt the practice that *the ends of all mutually coupled coils, which have the same instantaneous polarity, are marked with dots.*

Since, in Figure 11.2(a), the top terminals of both coils have the same instantaneous polarity (one being forced by V_1, and the other being induced), both are marked with dots; alternatively, the bottom terminal of *each coil* could be marked with dots. Figure 11.2(b) shows how the two circuits are electrically isolated from one another by including a dependent voltage source in each coil, each having its correct polarity shown. The dependent voltage source is included *inside each coil, and nearest to the dotted end of the coil.* The dots are shown *outside* the coils.

To recapitulate, since I_1 enters the dotted end of coil 1, it produces a dependent e.m.f. in coil 2 which makes the dotted end of coil 2 positive. Since there is no external e.m.f. in the secondary circuit in Figure 11.2, current must flow out of the dotted terminal of coil 2. However, since this is the case, the polarity of the dependent voltage source in coil 1 is such that it tries to make the dotted end of coil 1 negative. Thus, a negative sign is shown at the terminal of the dependent voltage source nearest the dotted terminal of coil 1. Accordingly, we may write the following mesh equations for Figure 11.2(a)

$$V_1 = (R_1 + j\omega L_1)I_1 - j\omega M I_2$$
$$0 = -j\omega M I_1 + (R_2 + j\omega L_2)I_2 + V_2$$

where $V_2 = I_2 Z_2$

(d) T- and π-equivalent of an Inductively Coupled Circuit

Using the dot notation, it is possible to convert the magnetically coupled circuit in Figure 11.3(a) into an equivalent conductively coupled circuit (this technique is used in many computer simulations of magnetically coupled circuits). Applying the techniques outlined in section (c) above, the equivalent circuit incorporating the induced dependent voltage sources is as shown in Figure 11.3(b)

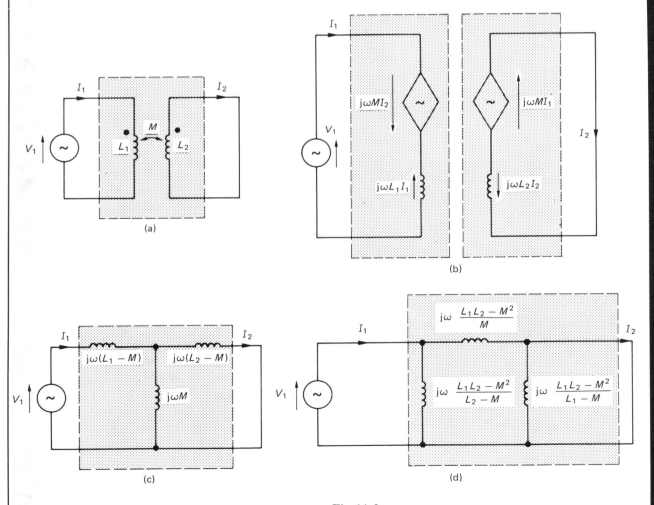

Fig 11.3

246

(Note: in this case R_1, R_2 and $\mathbf{Z}_2$ are all zero). The mesh equations for the two circuits in Figure 11.3(b) are:

$$V_1 = j\omega L_1 I_1 - j\omega M I_2 = j\omega([L_1 - M] + M)I_1 - j\omega M I_2$$

$$0 = -j\omega M I_1 + j\omega L_2 I_2 = -j\omega M I_1 + j\omega([L_2 - M] + M)I_2$$

The T-equivalent conductively coupled circuit corresponding to the second expression in each equation is shown in Figure 11.3(c), and the corresponding π-equivalent circuit is in Figure 11.3(d). Note: If the connections to one of the windings is reversed, i.e., the dot is placed on the opposite end of one of the windings (e.g., on the bottom of one of the windings in diagram (a)), the terms $(-j\omega M I_1)$ and $(-j\omega M I_2)$ in the above expressions become $(j\omega M I_1)$ and $(j\omega M I_2)$, respectively. This has the effect in Figure 11.3(c) of making the inductance in the top left-hand branch $(L_1 + M)$, the inductance in the top right-hand branch $(L_2 + M)$, and that in the common vertical branch is $-M$.

(e) Coupling Coefficient

In a practical coupled circuit, not all the magnetic flux produced by one circuit links with the other circuit. For example, in Figure 11.4, the flux linking L_1 with L_2 is Φ_{12}, and the total flux produced by L_1 is $(\Phi_{11} + \Phi_{12})$, where Φ_{11} is known as the *leakage flux*. The magnetic coupling coefficient, k, between the two coils is

$$k = \frac{\text{linking flux}}{\text{total flux}} = \frac{\Phi_{12}}{\Phi_{11} + \Phi_{12}}$$

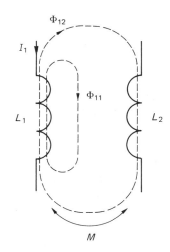

Fig 11.4

where k lies in the range $0 \leq k \leq 1$. The mutual inductance, M, between the coils is

$$M = k\sqrt{(L_1 L_2)} \quad \text{H}$$

Coils are said to be *closely coupled* if the majority of the flux leaving one coil links with other mutually coupled coils (as is the case in a power transformer).

Coils are said to be *loosely coupled* if only a small proportion of the flux leaving one coil reaches other mutually coupled coils (as is often the case in coupled circuits in communications equipment).

(f) The Ideal Two-winding Transformer

An *ideal transformer* is a lossless transformer with a coupling coefficient of unity (by its nature, this is a hypothetical transformer). This transformer (see Figure 11.5) has ampere-turn balance between the windings, and supports the same number of volts per turn on its windings, that is

$$I_1 N_1 = I_2 N_2 \quad \text{and} \quad \frac{V_1}{N_1} = \frac{V_2}{N_2}$$

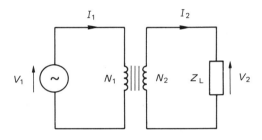

Fig 11.5

These equations are often combined in the form

$$\frac{V_1}{V_2} = \frac{N_1}{N_2} = \frac{I_2}{I_1}$$

Since the ideal transformer is lossless, then the power supplied to the primary winding is equal to the power transferred to the secondary winding, that is

$$V_1 I_1 \cos \phi = V_2 I_2 \cos \phi$$

where $\cos \phi$ is the power factor of the load.

If an impedance Z_2 is connected to a winding of N_2 turns on an ideal transformer, the impedance Z_2' seen when 'looking into' a winding of N_1 turns on the transformer is

$$Z_2' = Z_2 \left(\frac{N_1}{N_2}\right)^2 \text{ ohm}$$

(g) The Autotransformer or Single-winding Transformer

The general form of construction of this type is shown in Figure 11.6(a), and the circuit representation is in Figure 11.6(b). Assuming that it is an ideal transformer, the voltage transformation ratio is

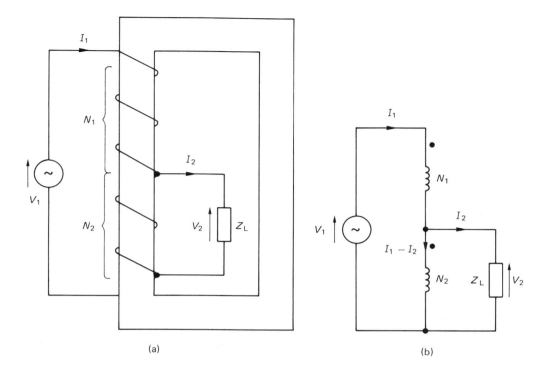

Fig 11.6

$$\frac{V_1}{V_2} = \frac{N_1 + N_2}{N_2} = \frac{N_1}{N_2} + 1 = a + 1$$

Since the transformer is assumed to be ideal, then

$$\frac{V_1}{V_2} = \frac{I_2}{I_1} = a + 1$$

and

$$V_1 I_1 \cos \phi = V_2 I_2 \cos \phi$$

where $\cos \phi$ is the power factor of the load.

11.2 Worked Examples

Example 11.1

Two identical 800-turn coils lie in parallel planes, and 50 per cent of the magnetic flux produced by one coil links with the other coil. A current of 10 A in either coil produces a magnetic flux of 0.0625 mWb; calculate the inductance of each coil and the mutual inductance between them. If the current in one coil changes from -5 A to $+5$ A in 0.01 s, what is the magnitude of the e.m.f. induced in the second coil?

Solution 11.1

The self-inductance of each coil is

$$L = \frac{N\phi}{I} = \frac{800 \times 0.0625 \times 10^{-3}}{10} = 5 \times 10^{-3} \text{ H or 5 mH}$$

The mutual inductance between the coils is given by

$$M = k\sqrt{(L_1 L_2)} \text{ H}$$

but, since $L_1 = L_2$

$$M = kL = 0.5 \times 5 = 2.5 \text{ mH}$$

and the magnitude of the e.m.f., e_2, induced in the second coil is

$$e_2 = M\frac{di_1}{dt} = 2.5 \times 10^{-3} \times \frac{5 - (-5)}{0.01} = 2.5 \text{ V}$$

Example 11.2

Deduce the dot notation for each of the coupled circuit combinations in Figure 11.7.

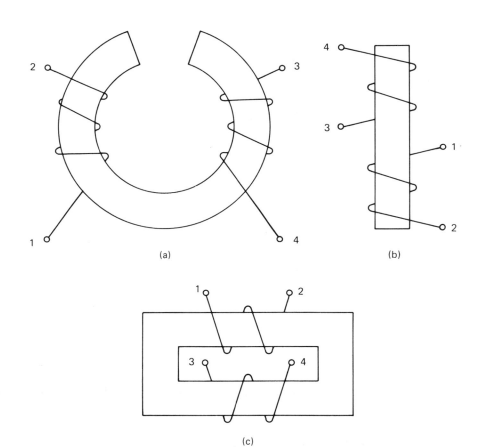

Fig 11.7

Solution 11.2

Coupled circuit (a)

We consider this in detail; the dot notation for the other circuits can be produced by a similar reasoning. A voltage V_1 with the polarity shown in Figure 11.8 is applied between terminals 1 and 2, with terminal 2 being instantaneously positive with respect to terminal 1. This causes current to enter terminal 2 and, with the winding direction shown, flux ϕ_1 leaves the top of the left-hand winding.

Lenz's law implies that the current induced in the secondary winding produces flux ϕ_2 which opposes ϕ_1. With the direction of the secondary winding shown, the current in the secondary winding must enter terminal 3 and leave terminal 4.

That is, terminals 2 and 4 have the same instantaneous polarity, and we may mark terminals 2 and 4 with dots. Similarly, terminals 1 and 3 also have the same instantaneous polarity so that we may, alternatively, mark terminals 1 and 3 with dots.

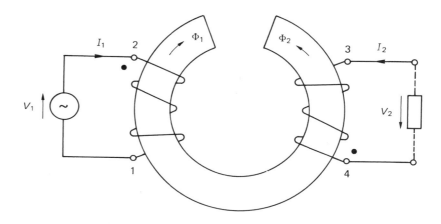

Fig 11.8

Coupled circuits (b) and (c)

Following a discussion similar to the one above, either terminals 2 and 3 can be marked with a dot *or* terminals 2 and 4 may be marked with a dot.

Example 11.3

Deduce an expression for V_1 and for V_2 in terms of I_1 and I_2 and the other parameters in Figure 11.9. Write down an expression for the voltage V_{BA}.

Solution 11.3

It is useful, initially, to convert the two magnetically-coupled circuits into two isolated electrical circuits. We do this in Figure 11.10 by introducing the mutually

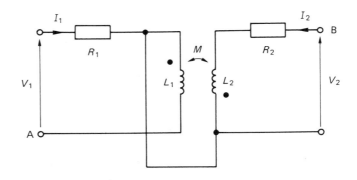

Fig 11.9

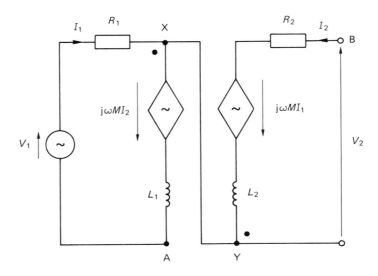

Fig 11.10

induced e.m.f.s due to I_1 and I_2 in the primary and secondary windings, respectively, using the rules described in section (c) of the Fact Sheet for this chapter. The mesh current equations for Figure 11.10 are

$$V_1 + j\omega MI_2 = (R_1 + j\omega L_1)I_1$$
$$V_2 + j\omega MI_1 = (R_2 + j\omega L_2)I_2$$

or

$$V_1 = (R_1 + j\omega L_1)I_1 - j\omega MI_2$$
$$V_2 = -j\omega MI_1 + (R_2 + j\omega L_2)I_2$$

Since no current flows in the link between X and Y in Figure 11.10, it has no effect on the above equations. However, since it connects the two windings together, we can say that

$$V_{BA} = j\omega L_1 I_1 - j\omega MI_2 + (R_2 + j\omega L_2)I_2 - j\omega MI_1$$
$$= j\omega(L_1 - M)I_1 + (R_2 + j\omega(L_2 - M))I_2$$

or, following an alternative path we also get

$$V_{BA} = V_1 - I_1R_1 + V_2$$

Also, following other paths, there are two other combinations which represent V_{BA}. The reader will find it an interesting exercise to write them down.

Example 11.4

Calculate the value of V_2 in Figure 11.11(a). What would be the value of V_2 if the voltage source was replaced by a $10\angle0°$ A current source which drives current into the upper terminal of the 0.6 H winding?

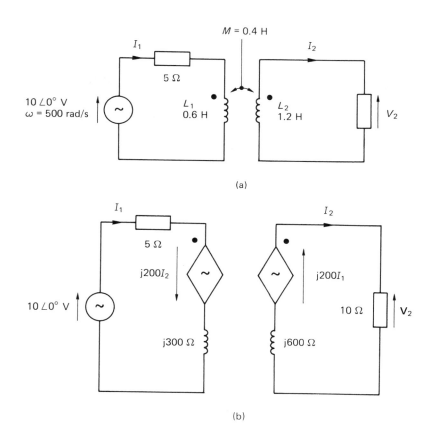

(a)

(b)

Fig 11.11

Solution 11.4

Since $\omega = 500$ rad/s

$\omega L_1 = 300$ ohm

$\omega L_2 = 600$ ohm

$\omega M = 200$ ohm

Inserting these values together with the directions of the mutually induced e.m.f.s in the equivalent circuit in Figure 11.11(b), we get the following mesh current equations for the circuit.

$$10 + j0 = (5 + j300)I_1 - j200I_2$$

$$0 = -j200I_1 + (10 + j600)I_2$$

Solving for I_2 by Cramer's rule gives

$$I_2 = \frac{\begin{vmatrix} 5 + j300 & 10 + j0 \\ -j200 & 0 \end{vmatrix}}{\begin{vmatrix} 5 + j300 & -j200 \\ -j200 & 10 + j600 \end{vmatrix}} = \frac{2000\angle 90°}{140\ 079\angle 177.5°} = 0.014\angle -87.5°$$

and

$$V_2 = 10I_2 = 0.14\angle -87.5° \text{ V}$$

The mesh equation for the secondary circuit is

$$V_2 = j200I_1 - j600I_2$$

but $V_2 = 10I_2$, or $I_2 = V_2/10$; when the voltage source is replaced by a 10 A current source, $I_1 = 10$ A. Hence,

$$V_2 = j200(10) - j600\left(\frac{V_2}{10}\right)$$

or

$$V_2(1 + j60) = j2000$$

Therefore when the transformer is driven by a current source

$$V_2 = \frac{j2000}{1 + j60} = 33.33\angle 0.95° \text{ V}$$

Example 11.5

Deduce the mesh current equations for the circuit in Figure 11.12(a).

Solution 11.5

In this case, coil L_1 carries currents I_1 and I_2 in opposite directions (see Figure 11.12(a)), so that the mutually induced e.m.f. in coil L_3 is related to $(I_1 - I_2)$ (see Figure 11.12(b)). Since only I_3 flows in L_3, there is only one mutually induced e.m.f. in coil L_1. The direction of the mutually induced e.m.f.s are deduced as follows.

Referring to Figure 11.12(b), current I_1 *enters* the dotted end of coil L_1 and I_2 *leaves* the dotted end, consequently it induces e.m.f. $j\omega M(I_1 - I_2)$ in coil L_3, which tends to make the dotted end of that coil positive. Using a similar logical argument, the reader will observe that the induced e.m.f. $j\omega MI_3$ in L_1 acts to

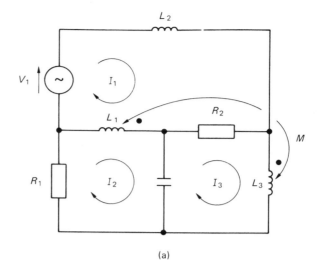

(a)

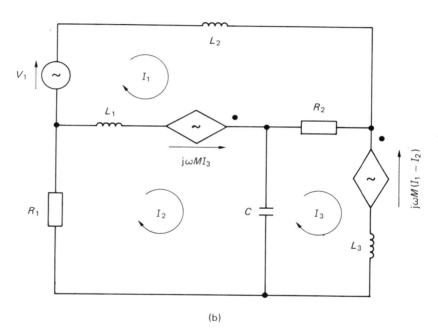

(b)

Fig 11.12

make the dotted end of coil L_1 positive. The resulting mesh current equations for the circuit in Figure 11.12(b) are

Loop 1

$$V_1 - j\omega MI_3 = [R_2 + j\omega(L_1 + L_2)]I_1 - j\omega L_1 I_2 - R_2 I_3$$

Loop 2

$$j\omega MI_3 = -j\omega L_1 I_1 + \left[R_1 + j\left(\omega L_1 - \frac{1}{\omega C}\right)\right]I_2 + \frac{1}{j\omega C}I_3$$

Loop 3

$$-j\omega M(I_1 - I_2) = -R_2 I_1 + \frac{(-1)}{j\omega C} I_2 + \left[R_2 + j\left(\omega L_3 - \frac{1}{\omega C}\right) \right] I_3$$

that is

$$V_1 = [R_2 + j\omega(L_1 + L_2)]I_1 - j\omega L_1 I_2 - (R_2 - j\omega M)I_3$$

$$0 = -j\omega L_1 I_1 + \left[R_1 + j\left(\omega L_1 - \frac{1}{\omega C}\right) \right] I_2 - j\left(\omega M - \frac{1}{\omega C}\right) I_3$$

$$0 = -(R_2 - j\omega M)I_1 - j\left(\omega M - \frac{1}{\omega C}\right) I_2 + \left[R_2 + j\left(\omega L_3 - \frac{1}{\omega C}\right) \right] I_3$$

Example 11.6

Replace the inductively-coupled section of the circuit in Figure 11.13 with a conductively-coupled section, hence calculate the value of current I.

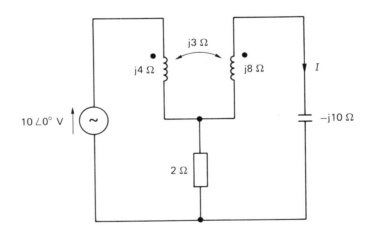

Fig 11.13

Solution 11.6

We can adopt either of two methods of dealing with this problem. The first is to isolate the two windings by introducing the mutually-induced e.m.f.s as shown in Figure 11.14(a).

Alternatively, the T-equivalent of the coupled circuit can be used to replace the magnetically-coupled section, as shown in Figure 11.14(b). Using the latter to solve the circuit, the associated mesh equations are

$$10 = (2 + j4)I_1 - (2 + j3)I$$

$$0 = -(2 + j3)I_1 + (2 - j2)I$$

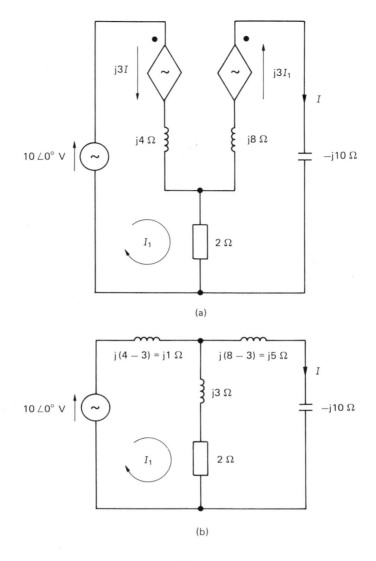

(a)

(b)

Fig 11.14

Solving for **I** gives

$$I = \frac{\begin{vmatrix} 2 + j4 & 10 \\ -2 - j3 & 0 \end{vmatrix}}{\begin{vmatrix} 2 + j4 & -2 - j3 \\ -2 - j3 & 2 - j2 \end{vmatrix}} = \frac{36.06\angle 56.31°}{18.79\angle -25.2°} = 1.92\angle 81.51° \text{ A}$$

Example 11.7

Determine the voltage transformation ratio V_2/V_1 for the ideal transformer in Figure 11.15. Calculate the value of I_1, I_2, V_1 and V_2. What value of resistance must be used to replace the 25 ohm load if maximum power is to be transferred to it, and what is the value of this maximum power?

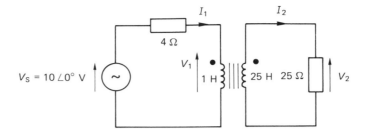

Fig 11.15

Solution 11.7

For an inductor of inductance L which is wound on a magnetic circuit of constant reluctance, $L \propto N^2$, hence

$$\frac{N_2}{N_1} = \sqrt{\frac{L_2}{L_1}} = \sqrt{\frac{25}{1}} = 5$$

That is, the transformer has a voltage step-up ratio of five. Since the transformer is 'ideal', the impedance 'seen' by the primary winding is $25/5^2 = 1.0$ ohm, so that the current in the primary winding is

$$I_1 = 10/(4 + 1) = 2 \text{ A}$$

and, since the effective impedance reflected into the primary winding is 1.0 ohm

$$V_1 = 2 \times 1 = 2 \text{ V}$$

Hence,

$$V_2 = 5 \times 2 = 10 \text{ V}$$

and

$$I_2 = 10/25 = 0.4 \text{ A}$$

In order to transfer maximum power to the load, the impedance of the secondary load referred to the primary side must be equal to the resistance of 4 ohms connected in the primary winding. That is, the load connected to the secondary terminals must be

$$4 \times 5^2 = 100 \text{ ohm}$$

When this value of resistance is connected, the current in the primary winding is

$$I_1 = 10/(4 + 4) = 1.25 \text{ A}$$

and the power consumed by the referred value of the load to the primary winding is

$$4I_1^2 = 6.25 \text{ W}$$

Note: when delivering maximum power to the load, $V_1 = 5$ V and $V_2 = 25$ V.

Example 11.8

A two-winding 40 000/4000 V transformer has a rating of 100 kVA. If the transformer is reconnected as an autotransformer, determine the voltage ratio of the transformer and its rating.

Solution 11.8

When operating as a 2-winding transformer, the full-load current carried by the 40 000 V winding is

$$\frac{100\ 000}{40\ 000} = 2.5 \text{ A}$$

and that carried by the 4000 V winding is

$$\frac{100\ 000}{4000} = 25 \text{ A}$$

The two windings are connected in series to form an autotransformer as shown in Figure 11.16. No matter which winding is taken to be winding 'A' and which winding 'B', the rated supply voltage is

$$V_1 = V_A + V_B = 40\ 000 + 4000 = 44\ 000 \text{ V}$$

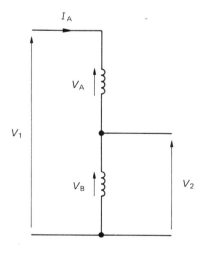

Fig 11.16

If winding 'B' is the 4000 V winding, then $V_2 = 4000$ V and $I_A = 2.5$ A. That is, the maximum input kVA is

$$\frac{44\ 000 \times 2.5}{1000} = 110 \text{ kVA}$$

If winding 'B' is the 40 000 V winding, then $V_2 = 40\,000$ V, and $I_A = 25$ A. In this case, the maximum input kVA is

$$\frac{44\,000 \times 25}{1000} = 1100 \text{ kVA}$$

That is, the autotransformer can either be rated at

44 000 to 4000 V, 110 kVA

or

44 000 to 40 000 V, 1100 kVA

11.3   Unworked Problems

Problem 11.1

Coils having 1500 and 500 turns, respectively, are wound on a magnetic circuit of reluctance 150 000 At/Wb. If the coupling coefficient between the coils is unity, calculate the mutual inductance between the coils.
[5 H]

Problem 11.2

Determine the total inductance of the series-connected coils in Figure 11.17.
[6 H]

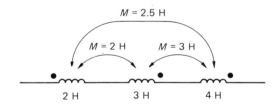

Fig 11.17

Problem 11.3

A coil of 1000 turns of wire and a search coil of 400 turns are wound on a non-magnetic former of length 80 cm and cross-sectional area 25 cm^2. If the magnetic coupling coefficient between the coils is unity, calculate (a) the mutual inductance between the coils, and (b) the e.m.f. induced in the search coil when the current in the main coil changes at the rate of 200 A/s.
[1.57 mH; 0.314 V]

Problem 11.4

Deduce the dot notation combinations for the magnetically coupled circuits in Figure 11.18.
[(a) Dots at ends 1 and 4, or 2 and 3; (b) Dots at ends 1, 4 and 5, or ends 2, 3 and 6]

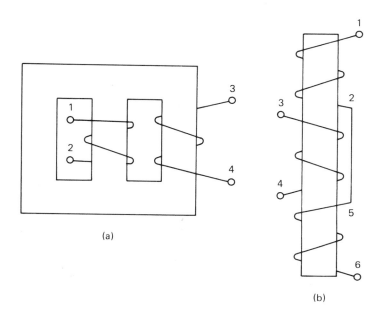

Fig 11.18

Problem 11.5

Derive mesh equations for V_1 and V_2 for the circuit in Figure 11.19.
$[V_1 = (R_1 + j\omega L_1)I_1 - j\omega MI_2; V_2 = -j\omega MI_1 + (R_2 + j\omega L_2)I_2]$

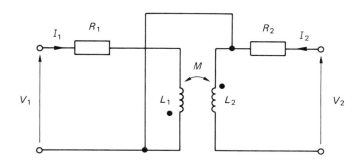

Fig 11.19

Problem 11.6

If the circuit in Figure 11.20 is energized by a voltage source of $10\angle 0°$ V, calculate the value of V_2. What is the new value of V_2 when the secondary winding is open-circuited? If the voltage source in the original circuit is replaced by a 10 A current source, calculate V_2.
$[1.48\angle 114.8°$ V; $6.98\angle -170.5°$ V; $34.87\angle -170.5°$ V$]$

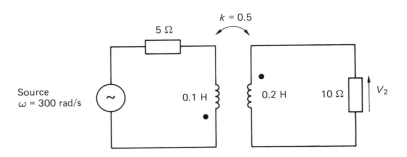

Fig 11.20

Problem 11.7

Calculate I_1 in the circuit in Figure 11.21.
$[1.29\angle -3.15°$ A$]$

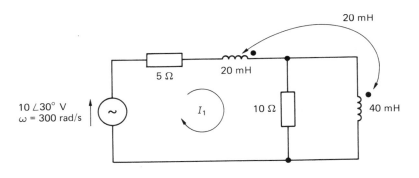

Fig 11.21

Problem 11.8

Write down the mesh current equations for the circuit in Figure 11.22.
$[-10 = (5 + j3)I_1 + j7.45I_2; 10 = j7.45I_1 + j3I_2]$

Problem 11.9

Solve the mesh equations for the circuit in Problem 11.8.
$[I_1 = 2.14\angle -107.9°$ A; $I_2 = 2.37\angle 46.6°$ A$]$

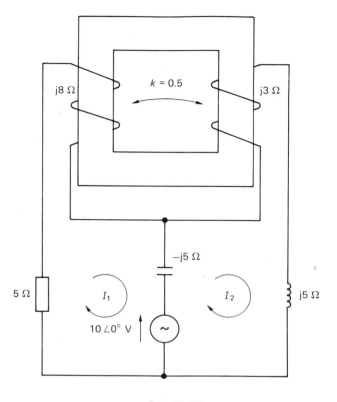

Fig 11.22

Problem 11.10

Write down the mesh current equations for the circuit in Figure 11.23.

[$10 = \quad j50I_1 \quad - j100I_2 \quad + \quad j150I_3$

$0 = -j100I_1 + (100 + j100)I_2 - 100I_3$

$0 = \quad j150I_1 - 100I_2 + (100 + j100)I_3$]

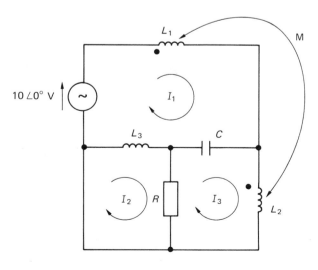

Fig 11.23

Problem 11.11

Solve the circuit equations in Problem 11.10 for I_1 if $L_1 = 0.05$ H, $L_2 = 0.2$ H, $L_3 = 0.1$ H, $M = 0.05$ H, $R = 100$ ohm, $C = 10$ microfarad, and a supply frequency of 1000 rad/s.
[$I_1 = 78.4\angle 11.3°$ mA; $I_2 = 39.2\angle 101.3°$ mA; $I_3 = 55.5\angle -123.7°$ mA]

Problem 11.12

Deduce, for the coupled circuit in Figure 11.24, (a) the T-equivalent circuit, and (b) the π-equivalent circuit. Solve the circuit for I.
[$0.485\angle 194°$ A]

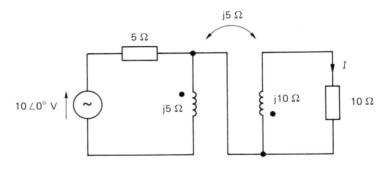

Fig 11.24

Problem 11.13

The transformer in Figure 11.25 is an ideal two-winding transformer with a voltage step-up ratio of 1:4. Calculate the value of V_2 and I_2, and the power delivered to the 10 ohm resistor. What are these values if a 100 ohm resistor is connected between X and Y?
[22.22 V; 0.111 A; 2.74 W; 16.47 V; 0.082 A; 1.36 W]

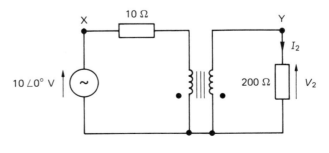

Fig 11.25

Problem 11.14

A balanced 3-phase load of 400 kW at a power factor of 0.7 lagging is energized by a 3-phase auto-transformer at a line voltage of 500 V. If the supply voltage is 440 V, calculate the line current in the supply and in the load, and determine the current in part of the transformer windings. Neglect the magnetizing current and ignore voltage drops in the transformer.
[750 A; 660 A; 660 A; 90 A]

Problem 11.15

Determine the input impedance of the circuit shown in Figure 11.26 at an angular frequency of ω rad/s.

(Liverpool Polytechnic)

$[R_1 + j\omega L_1 + \omega^2 M^2/(R_2 + j[\omega L_2 - 1/\omega C])]$

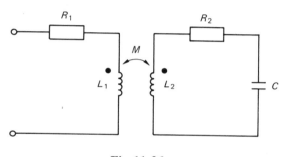

Fig 11.26

Problem 11.16

Calculate the total inductance of the series circuit in Figure 11.27.

(Staffordshire Polytechnic)

[9 H]

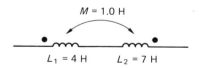

$M = 1.0$ H

$L_1 = 4$ H $L_2 = 7$ H

Fig 11.27

12 Polyphase Systems

12.1 Fact Sheet

(a) Introduction

A polyphase system is one having many phases or voltages, each being phase displaced from the next. In its simplest form, a polyphase supply can be thought of as several alternators mounted on the same shaft and whose outputs are electrically connected, but whose voltages are phase displaced from one another. Examples of phasor diagrams of a two-phase, a three-phase, and a six-phase supply are shown in diagrams (a), (b) and (c), respectively, of Figure 12.1. Since the three-phase supply is the one most widely used, we will pay special attention to it.

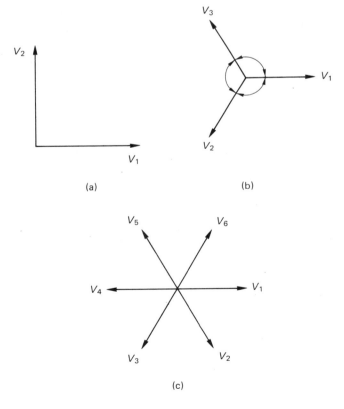

Fig 12.1

If the phase voltages have the same magnitude, and are separated from one another by the same phase angle, then the supply is said to be *balanced*. If *either* of the conditions are not met, the supply is said to be *unbalanced*.

(b)   The Three-phase Supply

The waveform diagram for a balanced three-phase supply is shown in Figure 12.2(a), and the corresponding phasor diagram for $\omega t = 0$ is shown in Figure 12.2(b). The three voltages are generated by the *red phase* (R), the *yellow phase* (Y), and the *blue phase* (B) of the alternator, each voltage being phase displaced from the next by 120°. The direction of 'rotation' of the phasors being, of course, anticlockwise.

The *phase sequence* of the supply is the sequence in which they pass, one after another in an anticlockwise direction, the same relative point in the cycle. In the case of the waveforms in Figure 12.2(a), the phase sequence is RYB. This is known as the *positive phase sequence* (PPS), and is the phase sequence adopted by the U.K. supply authorities. An alternative phase sequence, known as *negative phase sequence*, corresponds to rotating in the sequence RBY (see also section (n) in this Fact Sheet).

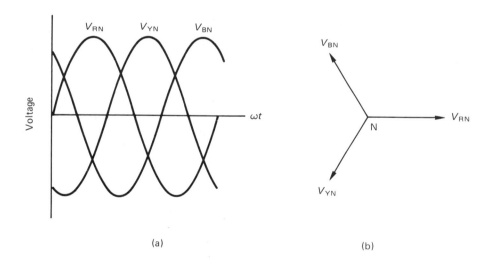

Fig 12.2

(c)   Star (Wye) Connected Systems

When three single-phase sources are connected as shown in Figure 12.3, they form a three-phase star- or wye-connected supply. In practice, the three single-phase sources would either be produced by windings on a single 3-phase alternator, or they could be from three electronic sources. Whilst three-phase voltage sources are frequently found in practice, three-phase current sources are not.

Similarly, three load impedances which have a common connection (S in Figure 12.3), are known as a star-connected load. When the terminals RYB of

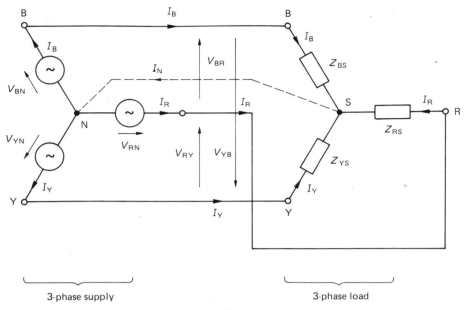

Fig 12.3

the generator are connected to corresponding terminals of the load, the complete system is known as a *star-star*, *three-phase*, *three-wire system*.

Should the common point N of the generator be directly connected to the common point S of the load, the system is described as a *star-star*, *three-phase*, *four-wire system*. The line connecting the N and S points together is known as the *neutral wire* or *neutral line*.

The common point N of the generator is known as the *neutral point* because it is usually connected to earth (neutral) potential. Point S of the load is known as the *star point* of the load. If the neutral wire has zero resistance, then points N and S are electrically equivalent, in which case we can refer to point S as though it were point N.

The star connected load is said to be *balanced* if

$$Z_{RS} = Z_{YS} = Z_{BS}$$

otherwise it is *unbalanced*.

The current which flows in a *phase* of the source (or of the load) is known as the *phase current*, and the current which flows in a *line* is a *line current*. In a star-connected system, each phase of the source and load is connected to a line, so that

$$\text{phase current} = \text{line current}$$

The phase and line currents are shown as I_R, I_Y, and I_B in Figure 12.3.

The current in the neutral wire of a star-connected, four-wire system is, by KCL

$$I_N = I_R + I_Y + I_B$$

(d) Complex Operators *h*, *a*, and λ

The reader is familiar with the complex operator j (for details see Appendix 1), which can be thought of as an operator which 'turns' a phasor through 90° in an anticlockwise direction. Here, you are introduced to the operator h (sometimes known as operator *a* or operator λ), which 'turns' a phasor through 120° in an anticlockwise direction. That is

$$h = 1\angle 120°$$

$$h^2 = 1\angle 240° = 1\angle -120°$$

$$h^3 = 1\angle 360° = 1\angle 0°$$

(e)   Phase and Line Voltages in a Star-connected System

We shall use a double-subscript notation to describe the line and phase voltages in a three-phase system. For example, in Figure 12.4

   V_{RN} = the voltage of the R line with respect to N

   V_{YB} = the voltage of the Y line with respect to line B, etc.

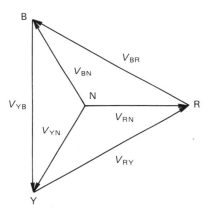

Fig 12.4

Balanced Voltages

If the supply is balanced, all the phase voltages have the same magnitude (say V_P), and these are separated from one another by 120°. Thus, the three voltages in a balanced star-connected system may be represented by

$$V_{RN} = V_P\angle 0° \text{ V}$$

$$V_{YN} = V_P\angle -120° = h^2 V_P \text{ V}$$

$$V_{BN} = V_P\angle 120° = h V_P \text{ V}$$

The *line-to-line voltages* or *line voltages* are defined as follows

   V_{BR} = the voltage of line B with respect to line R

   $= V_{BN} - V_{RN} = V_P(h - 1) = \sqrt{3}\ V_P\angle 150° \text{ V}$

$$V_{YB} = V_{YN} - V_{BN} = V_P(h^2 - h) = \sqrt{3}\, V_P\angle -90° = -j\sqrt{3}V_P \text{ V}$$

$$V_{RY} = V_{RN} - V_{YN} = V_P(1 - h^2) = \sqrt{3}\, V_P\angle 30° \text{ V}$$

That is, in a balanced three-phase star-connected supply

$$\text{line voltage} = \sqrt{3} \times \text{phase voltage}$$

or

$$V_L = \sqrt{3}\, V_P$$

Unbalanced Voltages

In this case, the line voltages *must* be calculated from the basic equations given above for V_{BR}, V_{YB} and V_{RY}.

(f) Neutral Current in a Balanced 4-wire System

If the supply voltage and the load impedances are balanced, the line currents are also balanced (see Worked Example 12.2). Since the neutral wire current is the phasor sum of the line currents, it follows that this is zero (also see Worked Example 12.2), that is

$$I_N = 0 + j0$$

In this situation, the neutral wire can be removed from the system without any effect (Note: this is not the case either when the supply is unbalanced, or when the load is unbalanced).

(g) Single-line Equivalent of a Balanced Star-connected System

When a balanced star-connected load is supplied by a balanced 3-phase set of voltages, the current in the neutral wire is zero, and the magnitude of the line (and phase) current is

$$|I_L| = |I_P| = |V_P|/|Z_P|$$

where $|Z_P|$ is the magnitude of the impedance connected in each phase.

If the load has a lagging phase angle of ϕ, each phase current will lag behind its own phase voltage by ϕ, and will be phase displaced from the other currents by 120° (see Worked Example 12.2).

(h) Unbalanced 4-wire, Star-connected Load

In this case, the line currents are unbalanced (see Worked Example 12.4) and, with few exceptions, the neutral wire current is finite.

(i) Balanced Delta-connected or Mesh-connected Systems

In a delta-connected system, the *phase current* flows in the generator winding (or the load) which is connected between a pair of lines (see Figure 12.5). Since each phase of the load is connected directly via a pair of lines to one phase of the generator, we may regard each phase of the load as being supplied by its own single-phase supply. That is Z_{RY} is supplied directly by V_{RY}, Z_{YB} is supplied directly by V_{YB}, etc. Each supply line shares the current of two loads, e.g., the R-line carries the outgoing current from V_{RY} and the return current to V_{BR}.

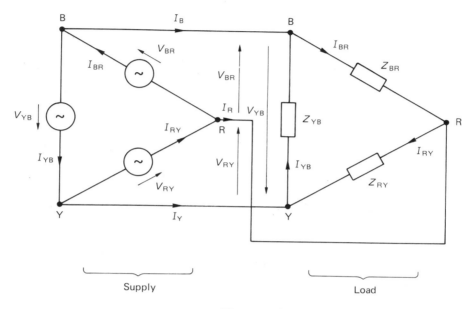

Fig 12.5

Since each phase voltage in a delta-connected system is connected to one phase of the load, then *if the supply is balanced*

$$\text{line voltage, } V_L = \text{phase voltage, } V_P$$

If the load impedances are balanced, then

$$\text{line current, } I_L = \sqrt{3}\, I_P$$

where I_L is the magnitude of the line current, and I_P is the magnitude of the phase current (see Worked Example 12.3).

(j) Summary of Relationships in Balanced Loads

The relationships between line and phase values in balanced loads is summarized below.

	Line current	Phase current	Line voltage	Phase voltage
Star	$I_L = I_P$	$I_P = I_L$	$V_L = \sqrt{3}\, V_P$	$V_P = V_L/\sqrt{3}$
Delta	$I_L = \sqrt{3}\, I_P$	$I_P = I_L/\sqrt{3}$	$V_L = V_P$	$V_P = V_L$

(k) Unbalanced Delta-connected Loads

Applying KCL to each node of the generator (or load) in Figure 12.5 yields

$$I_R = I_{RY} - I_{BR}$$
$$I_Y = I_{YB} - I_{RY}$$
$$I_B = I_{BR} - I_{YB}$$

Once the phase currents have been calculated, the line currents can be computed using these relationships (see Worked Example 12.6).

(l) Power in a 3-phase System

The power consumed in a 3-phase system, either balanced or unbalanced, is the sum of the power consumed in each phase of the load.

If the load is *balanced* (either star or delta), the power can be calculated from the equation

$$P = \sqrt{3}\, V_L I_L \cos \phi \ \text{W}$$

where V_L and I_L are the modulus of the line voltage and line current, respectively, and $\cos \phi$ is the power factor of the load.

In a balanced system, the VAr consumed is

$$Q = \sqrt{3}\, V_L I_L \sin \phi \ \text{VAr}$$

and the apparent power is

$$S = \sqrt{3}\, V_L I_L \ \text{VA}$$
$$= \sqrt{(P^2 + Q^2)}$$

(m) Power Measurement: the Two Wattmeter Method

The power indicated by a wattmeter in an a.c. circuit is equal to the product

$$\left(\begin{array}{c} \text{voltage across} \\ \text{the voltage} \\ \text{coil} \end{array}\right) \times \left(\begin{array}{c} \text{current through} \\ \text{the current} \\ \text{coil} \end{array}\right) \times \left(\begin{array}{c} \text{cosine of the angle} \\ \text{between the voltage and} \\ \text{current in the two coils} \end{array}\right)$$

The two wattmaters connected as shown in Figure 12.6 measure the total power consumed by a 3-phase, 3-wire load (whether connected in star or delta, and whether balanced or unbalanced).

The total power consumed, P_T, is given by

$$P_T = P_1 + P_2 \ \text{W}$$

where P_1 and P_2 are the readings of the wattmeters. Also

$$P_1 = \text{Re}(V_{RB} I_R^*) \ \text{W} \quad \text{and} \quad P_2 = \text{Re}(V_{YB} I_Y^*) \ \text{W}$$

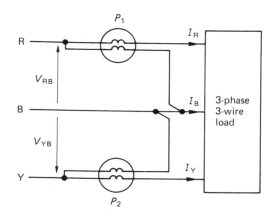

Fig 12.6

If the phase angle between the voltage across the potential coil and the current in the current coil in one of the instruments exceeds 90° (see also *balanced loads* below), that instrument gives a negative reading. The situation is corrected by reversing the connections of *either* the current coil *or* the voltage coil of the instrument (but *not* both of them), and treating the resulting reading as though it were a negative value.

Balanced loads

The phase angle, ϕ, of a balanced load can be calculated from the following

$$\tan \phi = \sqrt{3}\left(\frac{P_2 - P_1}{P_1 + P_2}\right)$$

When the phase angle is either 60° lagging or 60° leading, one of the wattmeters indicates zero, and the other indicates the total power consumed. When the phase angle exceeds 60°, one of the wattmeters gives a negative indication and the other wattmeter indicates a value in excess of the total power consumed.

The *reactive VA* consumed by a balanced load is

$$Q = \sqrt{3}(P_2 - P_1) \text{ VAr}$$

(n) Symmetrical Components

Any unbalanced set of 3-phase voltages or currents can be represented by the superposition of three sets of balanced voltages or currents, namely

1. a *positive phase sequence* (PPS) system, having the same phase sequence as the original unbalanced system (say RYB — see Figure 12.7(a)),

2. a *negative phase sequence* (NPS) system, having a phase sequence opposite to that of the original unbalanced system (say RBY — see Figure 12.7(b)), and

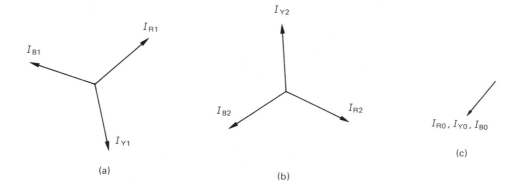

(a)

(b)

(c)

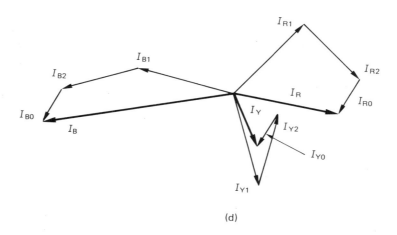

(d)

Fig 12.7

3. a *zero phase sequence* (ZPS) system, whose elements are equal in magnitude and phase to one another (see Figure 12.7(c)).

If either the 3-phase power supply or the load is unbalanced, either two sets or all three sets of symmetrical components of current flow in the circuit. The use of the symmetrical component notation simplifies calculations in such cases.

Whenever there is an asymmetrical fault on a system, e.g., one-line-to-earth, or a short-circuit between lines, etc, symmetrical components of current flow in the circuit. Many specialized fault protection circuits rely on the detection of the symmetrical components of current or voltage in order to protect equipment.

Analysis of Unbalanced Conditions

If I_R, I_Y and I_B are a 3-phase set of unbalanced currents, then

$$I_R = I_{R1} + I_{R2} + I_{R0}$$

$$I_Y = I_{Y1} + I_{Y2} + I_{Y0}$$

$$I_B = I_{B1} + I_{B2} + I_{B0}$$

where I_{R1}, I_{Y1} and I_{B1} are the PPS components, I_{R2}, I_{Y2}, and I_{B2} are the NPS components, and I_{R0}, I_{Y0} and I_{B0} are the ZPS components. For a 3-phase set of unbalanced voltages, there is a similar set of equations, i.e.,

$$V_R = V_{R1} + V_{R2} + V_{R0}, \text{ etc}$$

The phase sequence components can be calculated from the original unbalanced components using the following equations.

$$I_{R1} = (I_R + hI_Y + h^2I_B)/3$$

$$I_{R2} = (I_R + h^2I_Y + hI_B)/3$$

$$I_{R0} = (I_R + I_Y + I_B)/3$$

where $h = 1\angle120°$ (see also section (d) in this Fact Sheet), and there is a similar set of equations for the sequence components of voltages, e.g.,

$$V_{R1} = (V_R + hV_Y + h^2V_B)/3, \text{ etc.}$$

A typical set of PPS, NPS and ZPS components of current are shown in diagrams (a) to (c), respectively, of Figure 12.7. Figure 12.7(d) shows how the phasors are added in accordance to the above equations to determine the unbalanced line currents I_R, I_Y, and I_B.

The general relationship between the symmetrical components of current are as follows.

$$I_{Y1} = h^2I_{R1} \qquad I_{Y2} = hI_{R2}$$

$$I_{B1} = hI_{R1} \qquad I_{B2} = h^2I_{R2}$$

$$I_{R0} = I_{Y0} = I_{B0}$$

There are similar relationships between the symmetrical components of voltage, e.g.,

$$V_{Y1} = h^2V_{R1}, \text{ etc}$$

The Power Consumed by Symmetrical Components

The total average power consumed is the sum of the individual power due to the positive phase sequence, the negative phase sequence, and the zero phase sequence components (see Worked Example 12.10).

No average power is produced by the interaction between the voltage from one phase sequence and the current from another phase sequence.

12.2 Worked Examples

Example 12.1

Write down complex expressions for the balanced set of **(a)** positive phase sequence and **(b)** negative phase sequence system of voltages in diagrams (a) and (b), respectively, of Figure 12.8. The magnitude of the phase voltage is 400 V.

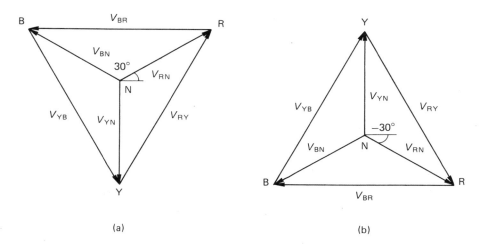

(a)   (b)

Fig 12.8

Solution 12.1

For the positive phase sequence set of balanced voltages in Figure 12.8(a), the phase voltages are

$$V_{RN} = V_P \angle 30° = 400 \angle 30° = 346.4 + j200 \text{ V}$$

$$V_{YN} = V_P \angle -90° = 400 \angle -90° = 0 - j400 \text{ V}$$

$$V_{BN} = V_P \angle 150° = 400 \angle 150° = -346.4 + j200 \text{ V}$$

and, since the line voltage is $\sqrt{3}V_P = \sqrt{3} \times 400 = 692.8$ V, the p.p.s. line voltages are

$$V_{RY} = V_L \angle 60° = 692.8 \angle 60° = 346.4 + j600 \text{ V}$$

$$V_{BR} = V_L \angle 180° = 692.8 \angle 180° = -692.8 + j0 \text{ V}$$

$$V_{YB} = V_L \angle -60° = 692.8 \angle -60° = 346.4 - j600 \text{ V}$$

For the negative phase sequence system in Figure 12.8(b), the phase voltages are

$$V_{RN} = 400 \angle -30° = 346.4 - j200 \text{ V}$$

$$V_{YN} = 400 \angle 90° = 0 + j400 \text{ V}$$

$$V_{BN} = 400 \angle -150° = -346.4 - j200 \text{ V}$$

and the n.p.s. line voltages are

$$V_{RY} = 692.8\angle{-60°} = 346.6 - j600 \text{ V}$$

$$V_{BR} = 692.8\angle{-180°} = -692.8 + j0 \text{ V}$$

$$V_{YB} = 692.8\angle{60°} = 346.4 + j600 \text{ V}$$

Example 12.2

A 3-phase, 4-wire, balanced supply with phase sequence RYB, has a line voltage of 440 V, and supplies three $10\angle30°$ ohm impedances connected in star (see Figure 12.9(a)). Calculate the line voltages, the line currents and the neutral current; draw the phasor diagram for the load.

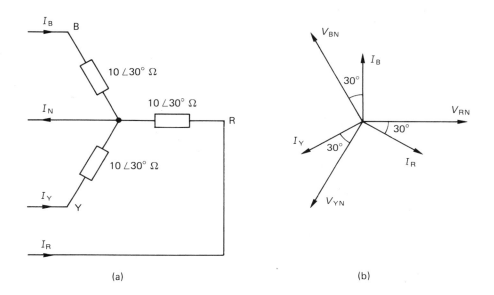

(a)

(b)

Fig 12.9

Solution 12.2

The magnitude of the phase voltage is $440/\sqrt{3} = 254$ V, hence

$$V_{RN} = 254\angle0° \text{ V}, \; V_{YN} = 254\angle{-120°} \text{ V}, \; V_{BN} = 254\angle120° \text{ V}$$

and

$$V_{RY} = V_{RN} - V_{YN} = 254\angle0° - 254\angle{-120°} = 440\angle30° \text{ V}$$

$$V_{BR} = V_{BN} - V_{RN} = 254\angle120° - 254\angle0° = 440\angle150° \text{ V}$$

$$V_{YB} = V_{YN} - V_{BN} = 254\angle{-120°} - 254\angle120° = 440\angle{-90°} \text{ V}$$

The line (and phase) currents are

$$I_R = \frac{V_{RN}}{Z_{RN}} = \frac{254\angle0°}{10\angle30°} = 25.4\angle{-30°} = 22 - j12.7 \text{ A}$$

$$I_Y = \frac{V_{YN}}{Z_{YN}} = \frac{254\angle{-120°}}{10\angle{30°}} = 25.4\angle{-150°} = -22 - j12.7 \text{ A}$$

$$I_B = \frac{V_{BN}}{Z_{BN}} = \frac{254\angle{120°}}{10\angle{30°}} = 25.4\angle{90°} = 0 + j\,25.4 \text{ A}$$

$$I_N = I_R + I_Y + I_B = 0 + j0 \text{ A}$$

Since the load is balanced, each phase current lags behind its associated phase voltage by 30° (see Figure 12.9(b)), and the current in the neutral wire is zero.

Example 12.3

If the three impedances in Worked Example 12.2 are reconnected in delta, calculate the phase and line currents in the system, and draw the phasor diagram for the load.

Solution 12.3

The circuit diagram is shown in Figure 12.10, and the line voltages are (see also Worked Example 12.2)

$$V_{RY} = 440\angle{30°} \text{ V}, \; V_{BR} = 440\angle{150°} \text{ V}, \; V_{YB} = 440\angle{-90°} \text{ V}$$

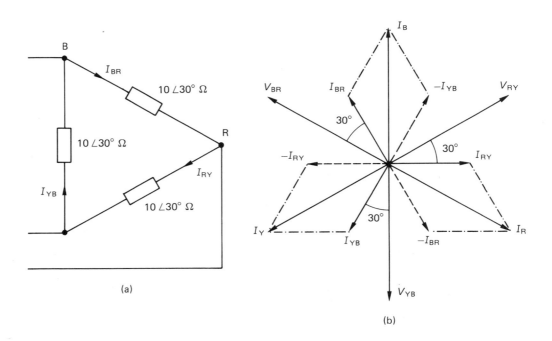

Fig 12.10

and the phase currents are

$$I_{RY} = \frac{V_{RY}}{Z_{RY}} = \frac{440\angle 30°}{10\angle 30°} = 44\angle 0° = 44 + j0 \text{ A}$$

$$I_{BR} = \frac{V_{BR}}{Z_{BR}} = \frac{440\angle 150°}{10\angle 30°} = 44\angle 120° = -22 + J38.11 \text{ A}$$

$$I_{YB} = \frac{V_{YB}}{Z_{YB}} = \frac{440\angle -90°}{10\angle 30°} = 44\angle -120° = -22 - j38.11 \text{ A}$$

and the corresponding line currents are

$$I_R = I_{RY} - I_{BR} = (44 + j0) - (-22 + j38.11) = 66 - j38.11$$
$$= 76.21\angle -30° \text{ A}$$

$$I_Y = I_{YB} - I_{RY} = (-22 - j38.11) - (44 + j0) = -66 - j38.11$$
$$= 76.21\angle -150° \text{ A}$$

$$I_B = I_{BR} - I_{YB} = (-22 + j38.11) - (-22 - j38.11) = 0 + j76.2$$
$$= 76.21\angle 90° \text{ A}$$

Note: $I_L = \sqrt{3}I_P = \sqrt{3} \times 44 = 76.21 \text{ A}$.

The corresponding phasor diagram is also shown in Figure 12.10.

Example 12.4

A balanced set of 3-phase voltages of phase sequence RYB, and line voltage 440 V, supply a 4-wire set of unbalanced star-connected impedances shown in Figure 12.11. Calculate the line currents and the current in the neutral wire. Draw the phasor diagram for the load.

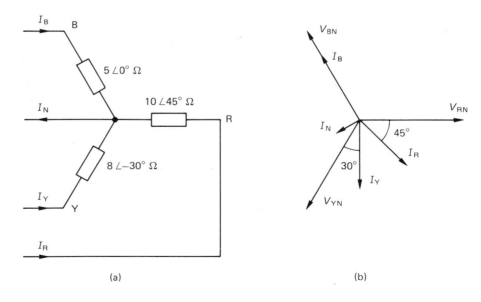

(a)   (b)

Fig 12.11

Solution 12.4

The phase voltage is $440/\sqrt{3} = 254$ V, and the current in the three phases of the load is calculated as follows.

$$I_R = \frac{V_{RN}}{Z_{RN}} = \frac{254\angle 0°}{10\angle 45°} = 25.4\angle -45° = 17.96 - j17.96 \text{ A}$$

$$I_Y = \frac{V_{YN}}{Z_{YN}} = \frac{254\angle -120°}{8\angle -30°} = 31.75\angle -90° = -j31.75 \text{ A}$$

$$I_B = \frac{V_{BN}}{Z_{BN}} = \frac{254\angle 120°}{5\angle 0°} = 50.8\angle 120° = -25.4 + j44 \text{ A}$$

The current in the neutral wire is

$$I_N = I_R + I_Y + I_B$$
$$= (17.96 - j17.96) - j31.75 + (-25.4 + j44)$$
$$= -7.44 - j5.71 = 9.38\angle -142.5° \text{ A}$$

The resulting phasor diagram is shown in Figure 12.11.

Example 12.5

If the neutral wire in Worked Example 12.4 is disconnected, calculate the value of the current in each line, the voltage between the star and neutral points, and the voltage across each phase of the load; draw the phasor diagram for the circuit.

Solution 12.5

This problem can be solved using Millman's theorem as follows. The voltage V_{SN} in Millman's theorem is equal to that of the star point of the load with respect to the neutral point of the supply. That is

$$V_{SN} = \frac{\dfrac{V_{RN}}{Z_{RS}} + \dfrac{V_{YN}}{Z_{YS}} + \dfrac{V_{BN}}{Z_{BS}}}{\dfrac{1}{Z_{RS}} + \dfrac{1}{Z_{YS}} + \dfrac{1}{Z_{BS}}}$$

$$= \frac{\dfrac{254\angle 0°}{10\angle 45°} + \dfrac{254\angle -120°}{8\angle -30°} + \dfrac{254\angle 120°}{5\angle 0°}}{\dfrac{1}{10\angle 45°} + \dfrac{1}{8\angle -30°} + \dfrac{1}{5\angle 0°}}$$

$$= \frac{25.4\angle -45° + 31.75\angle -90° + 50.8\angle 120°}{0.1\angle -45° + 0.125\angle 30° + 0.2\angle 0°}$$

$$= 24.75\angle -141.26° = -19.3 - j15.5 \text{ V}$$

The voltage across each phase of the load is calculated as follows

$$V_{RS} = V_{RN} - V_{SN} = (254 + j0) - (-19.3 - j15.5)$$
$$= 273.3 + j15.5 = 273.73\angle 3.25° \text{ V}$$

$$V_{YS} = V_{YN} - V_{SN} = (-127 - j220) - (-19.3 - j15.5)$$
$$= -107.7 - j204.5 = 231.1\angle -117.7° \text{ V}$$

$$V_{BS} = V_{BN} - V_{SN} = (-127 + j220) - (-19.3 - j15.5)$$
$$= -107.7 + j235.5 = 259\angle 114.6° \text{ V}$$

and the line currents are

$$I_R = \frac{V_{RS}}{Z_{RS}} = \frac{273.73\angle 3.25°}{10\angle 45°} = 27.373\angle -41.75° \text{ A}$$

$$I_Y = \frac{V_{YS}}{Z_{YS}} = \frac{231.1\angle -117.8°}{8\angle -30°} = 28.89\angle -87.8° \text{ A}$$

$$I_B = \frac{V_{BS}}{Z_{BS}} = \frac{259\angle 114.6°}{5\angle 0°} = 51.8\angle 114.6° \text{ A}$$

The phasor diagram for the circuit is in Figure 12.12.

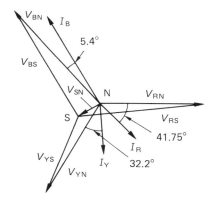

Fig 12.12

Example 12.6

An unbalanced star-connected 3-phase, 3-wire source supplies an unbalanced 3-phase delta-connected load. Calculate the current in each line, and the current in each phase of the load. The phase voltages of the supply are

$$V_{RN} = 100\angle 10° \text{ V}, \; V_{YN} = 120\angle -120° \text{ V}, \; V_{BN} = 150\angle 150° \text{ V}$$

and the phase impedances of the load are

$$Z_{RY} = 10\angle 10° \text{ ohm}, \; Z_{BR} = 15\angle -50° \text{ ohm}, \; Z_{YB} = 5\angle 0° \text{ ohm}$$

Solution 12.6

The line voltages of the system are

$$V_{RY} = V_{RN} - V_{YN} = 100\angle 10° - 120\angle -120° = 200\angle 37.42° \text{ V}$$

$$V_{BR} = V_{BN} - V_{RN} = 150\angle 150° - 100\angle 10° = 235.54\angle 165.84° \text{ V}$$

$$V_{YB} = V_{YN} - V_{BN} = 120\angle -120° - 150\angle 150° = 192\angle -68.66° \text{ V}$$

The phasor diagram showing the phase and line voltages is in Figure 12.13(a). The phase currents in the delta-connected load are calculated as follows.

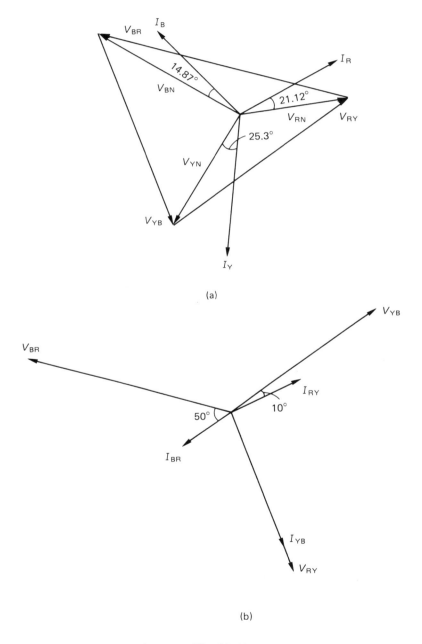

(a)

(b)

Fig 12.13

$$I_{RY} = \frac{V_{RY}}{Z_{RY}} = \frac{200\angle 37.42°}{10\angle 10°} = 20\angle 27.42° = 17.66 + j9.16 \text{ A}$$

$$I_{BR} = \frac{V_{BR}}{Z_{BR}} = \frac{235.54\angle 165.84°}{15\angle -50°} = 15.7\angle 215.84° = -12.73 - j9.19 \text{ A}$$

$$I_{YB} = \frac{V_{YB}}{Z_{YB}} = \frac{192\angle -68.66°}{5\angle 0°} = 38.4\angle -68.66° = 13.97 - j35.77 \text{ A}$$

and the associated line currents are

$$I_R = I_{RY} - I_{BR} = (17.66 + j9.16) - (-12.73 - j9.19)$$

$$= 30.39 + j18.35 = 35.5\angle 31.12°$$

$$I_Y = I_{YB} - I_{RY} = (13.97 - j35.77) - (17.66 + j9.16)$$

$$= -3.69 - j44.93 = 45.08\angle -94.7° \text{ A}$$

$$I_B = I_{BR} - I_{YB} = (-12.73 - j9.19) - (13.97 - j35.77)$$

$$= -26.7 + j26.58 = 37.67\angle 135.13° \text{ A}$$

The phasor diagram for the delta-connected load is shown in Figure 12.13(b).

Example 12.7

Calculate the VA, the power, and the VAr consumed by the circuit in Worked Example 12.2. What would be the reading on each of two wattmeters connected to the circuit in the manner shown in Figure 12.6?

Solution 12.7

Since both the supply and the load are balanced, the VA consumed can be calculated from the equation

$$S = \sqrt{3}V_L I_L = \sqrt{3} \times 440 \times 25.4 = 19\ 357 \text{ VA}$$

The power is

$$P = \sqrt{3}V_L I_L \cos \phi$$

$$= \sqrt{3} \times 440 \times 25.4 \times \cos 30° = 16\ 764 \text{ W}$$

and the VAr consumed is

$$Q = \sqrt{3}V_L I_L \sin \phi$$

$$= \sqrt{3} \times 440 \times 25.4 \times \sin 30° = 9679 \text{ VAr}$$

In Worked Example 12.2 the reading of wattmeter P_1 connected as shown in Figure 12.6 is

$$P_1 = \text{Re}(V_{RB}I_R^*)$$

where $V_{RB} = 440\angle -30°$ V, hence

$$P_1 = \text{Re}(440\angle -30° \times 25.4\angle 30°) = \text{Re}(11\ 176\angle 0°)$$

$$= \text{Re}(11\ 176 + j0) = 11\ 176 \text{ W}$$

and the indication given by P_2 is

$$P_2 = \text{Re}(V_{YB}I_Y^*) = \text{Re}(440\angle -90° \times 25.4\angle 150°) = \text{Re}(11\ 176\angle 60°)$$

$$= \text{Re}(5\ 588 + j9\ 679) = 5588 \text{ W}$$

and the total power consumed by the circuit in Worked Example 12.2 above is

$$P = P_1 + P_2 = 11\ 176 + 5588 = 16\ 764 \text{ W}$$

Example 12.8

The power consumed in a 3-phase circuit is measured by two wattmeters connected as shown in Figure 12.6. If

$$V_{RN} = 242.5\angle 0° \text{ V}, I_R = 10\angle -30° \text{ A}, I_B = 23.2\angle 132.45° \text{ A}$$

Calculate the value of I_Y, and determine the indication on each of the two wattmeters. The supply is balanced, and the phase sequence is RYB.

Solution 12.8

Since $I_R + I_Y + I_B = 0$, then

$$I_Y = -(I_R + I_B) = -(10\angle -30° + 23.2\angle 132.45°) = 14\angle -60° \text{ A}$$

With wattmeters connected as shown in Figure 12.6

$$P_1 = \text{Re}(V_{RB}I_R^*) \text{ and } P_2 = \text{Re}(V_{YB}I_Y^*)$$

Since $V_{RN} = 242.5\angle 0°$ V, then $V_{RB} = 420\angle -30°$ V, and
$V_{YB} = 420\angle -90°$ V. Hence,

$$P_1 = \text{Re}(420\angle -30° \times 10\angle 30°) = \text{Re}(4\ 200\angle 0°) = 4200 \text{ W}$$

and

$$P_2 = \text{Re}(420\angle -90° \times 14\angle 60°) = \text{Re}(5\ 880\angle -30°)$$

$$= \text{Re}(5\ 092.2 - j2\ 940) = 5092.2 \text{ W}$$

and the total power consumed is

$$P = P_1 + P_2 = 9292.2 \text{ W}$$

Example 12.9

A 3-phase, 3-wire balanced supply system of phase sequence RYB with a line voltage of 440 V has the following line currents.

$$I_R = 30\angle -90° \text{ A}, I_Y = 10\angle -100° \text{ A}, I_B = 39.89\angle 87.5° \text{ A}$$

Determine the reading on each of two wattmeters connected to read the total power, their current coils being in lines (a) R and Y, (b) Y and B, (c) R and B. V_{RN} lies in the reference direction.

Solution 12.9

(a) *Wattmeters with current coils in lines R and Y*

The wattmeter readings are

$$P_1 = \text{Re}(V_{RB}I_R^*) \quad \text{and} \quad P_2 = \text{Re}(V_{YB}I_Y^*)$$

where $V_{RB} = 440\angle{-30°}$ V and $V_{YB} = 440\angle{-90°}$ V
Hence,

$$P_1 = \text{Re}(440\angle{-30°} \times 30\angle90°) = \text{Re}(13\,200\angle60°)$$

$$= \text{Re}(6600 + j11\,432) = 6600 \text{ W}$$

$$P_2 = \text{Re}(440\angle{-90°} \times 10\angle100°) = \text{Re}(4\,400\angle10°)$$

$$= \text{Re}(4\,333 + j764) = 4333 \text{ W}$$

and the total power consumed is

$$P = P_1 + P_2 = 10\,933 \text{ W}$$

(b) *Wattmeters with current coils in lines Y and B*

The indication on the wattmeters are

$$P_1 = \text{Re}(V_{YR}I_Y^*) \quad \text{and} \quad P_2 = \text{Re}(V_{BR}I_B^*)$$

where $V_{YR} = 440\angle{-150°}$ V and $V_{BR} = 440\angle150°$ V. That is

$$P_1 = \text{Re}(440\angle{-150°} \times 10\angle100°) = \text{Re}(4400\angle{-50°})$$

$$= \text{Re}(2828 - j3370) = 2828 \text{ W}$$

$$P_2 = \text{Re}(440\angle150° \times 39.89\angle{-87.5°}) = \text{Re}(17\,552\angle62.5°)$$

$$= \text{Re}(8105 + j15\,569) = 8\,105 \text{ W}$$

Total power consumed

$$P = P_1 + P_2 = 10\,933 \text{ W}$$

(c) *Wattmeters with current coils in lines R and B*

The wattmeter indications are

$$P_1 = \text{Re}(V_{BY}I_B^*) \quad \text{and} \quad P_2 = \text{Re}(V_{RY}I_R^*)$$

where $V_{BY} = 440\angle90°$ V and $V_{RY} = 440\angle30°$ V. Hence,

$$P_1 = \text{Re}(440\angle90° \times 39.89\angle{-87.5°}) = \text{Re}(17\,552\angle2.5°)$$

$$= \text{Re}(17\,535 + j766) = 17\,535 \text{ W}$$

$$P_2 = \text{Re}(440\angle 30° \times 30\angle 90°) = \text{Re}(13\ 200\angle 120°)$$
$$= \text{Re}(-6600 + \text{j}11\ 432) = -6600 \text{ W}$$

and the total power consumed is

$$P = P_1 + P_2 = 10\ 935 \text{ W}$$

Alternative power calculation

The phase voltage is $440/\sqrt{3} = 254$ V. The power supplied by phase R is

$$P_R = V_{RN}I_R \cos \phi_R$$
$$= 254 \times 30 \times \cos(-90°) = 0 \text{ W}$$

The power supplied by phase Y is

$$P_Y = V_{YN}I_Y \cos \phi_Y$$
$$= 254 \times 10 \times \cos(-120° - (-100°)) = 2387 \text{ W}$$

and the power supplied by phase B is

$$P_B = V_{BN}I_B \cos \phi_B$$
$$= 254 \times 39.89 \cos(120° - 87.5°) = 8545 \text{ W}$$

and the total power supplied is

$$P = P_R + P_Y + P_B = 10\ 932 \text{ W}$$

Example 12.10

An unbalanced set of 3-phase voltages supplies line currents

$$I_R = 20 + \text{j}0 \text{ A}, I_Y = -16 - \text{j}12 \text{ A}, I_B = -12 + \text{j}16 \text{ A}$$

If the phase voltages of the supply are

$$V_{RN} = 100 \text{ V}, V_{YN} = -\text{j}100 \text{ V}, V_{BN} = \text{j}100 \text{ V}$$

calculate the symmetrical components of the voltage and current, and determine also the power supplied by each set of symmetrical components. What is the total power supplied?

Solution 12.10

The symmetrical components of the current are

$$I_{R1} = (I_R + hI_Y + h^2I_B)/3$$
$$= [20 + (-0.5 + \text{j}0.866)(-16-\text{j}12) + (-0.5-\text{j}0.866)(-12+\text{j}16)]/3$$
$$= 19.42 - \text{j}1.821 = 19.5\angle -5.36° \text{ A}$$

$$I_{R2} = (I_R + h^2I_Y + hI_B)/3$$
$$= [20 + (-0.5-j0.866)(-16-j12) + (-0.5+j0.866)(-12+j16)]/3$$
$$= 3.25 + j0.488 = 3.29\angle 8.54° \text{ A}$$
$$I_{R0} = (I_R + I_Y + I_B)/3$$
$$= [20 + (-16 - j12) + (-12 + j16)]/3 = -2.667 + j1.333$$
$$= 2.98\angle 153.44° \text{ A}$$

and the symmetrical components of the voltage are

$$V_{R1} = (V_R + hV_Y + h^2V_B)/3$$
$$= [100 + (-0.5 + j0.866)(-j100) + (-0.5 - j0.866)(j100)]/3$$
$$= 91.07 + j0 = 91.07\angle 0° \text{ V}$$
$$V_{R2} = (V_R + h^2V_Y + hV_B)/3$$
$$= [100 + (-0.5 - j0.866)(-j100) + (-0.5 + j0.866)(j100)]/3$$
$$= -24.4 + j0 = 24.4\angle 180° \text{ V}$$
$$V_{R0} = (V_R + V_Y + V_B)/3 = (100 - j100 + j100)/3 = 33.33 + j0$$
$$= 33.33\angle 0° \text{ V}$$

The corresponding phasor diagrams are shown in Figure 12.14. The power supplied by each of the phase sequence components is

$$P_{PPS} = 3 \times \text{power supplied by one phase of the p.p.s. supply}$$
$$= 3V_{R1}I_{R1} \times \cos (\text{angle between } I_{R1} \text{ and } V_{R1})$$
$$= 3 \times 91.07 \times 19.5 \cos (-5.36° - 0°) = 5304.3 \text{ W}$$

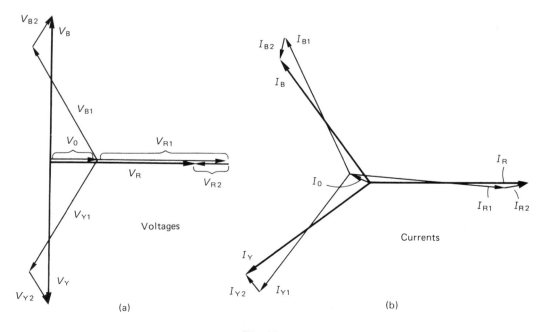

(a) Voltages   (b) Currents

Fig 12.14

$$P_{\text{NPS}} = 3 \times 24.4 \times 3.29 \cos (8.54° - 180°) = -238.2 \text{ W}$$

$$P_{\text{ZPS}} = 3 \times 33.33 \times 2.98 \cos (153.44° - 0°) = -266.5 \text{ W}$$

and

$$\text{total power} = P_{\text{PPS}} + P_{\text{NPS}} + P_{\text{ZPS}} = 4\ 799.6 \text{ W}$$

Alternatively, the power may be calculated as follows.

power supplied by phase R is $V_{\text{RN}} I_{\text{R}} \cos \phi_{\text{R}}$

$$= 100 \times 20 \times \cos 0° = 2\ 000 \text{ W}$$

power supplied by phase Y is $V_{\text{YN}} I_{\text{Y}} \cos \phi_{\text{Y}}$

$$= 100 \times 20 \times \cos (-143.13° + 90°) = 1200 \text{ W}$$

power supplied by phase B is $V_{\text{BN}} I_{\text{B}} \cos \phi_{\text{B}}$

$$= 100 \times 20 \cos (126.87° - 90°) = 1600 \text{ W}$$

Hence,

$$\text{total power supplied} = 2000 + 1200 + 1600 = 4800 \text{ W}$$

12.3 Unworked Problems

Problem 12.1

Three impedances of $2\angle 30°$ ohm are connected in star to a balanced 440 V, 3-phase supply of phase sequence RYB. Calculate the line currents, and draw the phasor diagram for the circuit.
$[I_{\text{R}} = 127\angle -30° \text{ A}; I_{\text{Y}} = 127\angle -150° \text{ A}; I_{\text{B}} = 127\angle 90° \text{ A}]$

Problem 12.2

If the phase sequence of the supply in Problem 12.1 is reversed, calculate the line currents.
$[I_{\text{R}} = 127\angle -30° \text{ A}; I_{\text{Y}} = 127\angle 90° \text{ A}; I_{\text{B}} = 127\angle -150° \text{ A}]$

Problem 12.3

If the impedances in Problem 12.1 are connected in delta, determine the current in each phase of the load, and the line currents. Draw the phasor diagram for the system.
$[I_{\text{RY}} = 220\angle 0° \text{ A}; I_{\text{BR}} = 220\angle 120° \text{ A}; I_{\text{YB}} = 220\angle -120° \text{ A}; I_{\text{R}} = 381\angle -30° \text{ A}; I_{\text{Y}} = 381\angle -150° \text{ A}; I_{\text{B}} = 381\angle 90° \text{ A}]$

Problem 12.4

A 3-phase, 4-wire, 500 V balanced supply of phase sequence RYB is connected to a star-connected load containing the following impedances.

$$Z_{RS} = 10\angle 0° \text{ ohm}, \quad Z_{YS} = 4 + j3 \text{ ohm}, \quad Z_{BS} = 3 - j4 \text{ ohm}$$

If V_{RN} lies in the reference direction, calculate the current in each line and in the neutral wire.

$[I_R = 28.9\angle 0° \text{ A}; I_Y = 57.74\angle -156.9° \text{ A}; I_B = 57.7\angle 173.1° \text{ A}; I_N = 83.1\angle 190.9° \text{ A}]$

Problem 12.5

For Problem 12.4, determine the symmetrical components of the currents.

$[I_{R1} = 36.77\angle 6° \text{ A}; I_{R2} = 19.54\angle 4.1° \text{ A}; I_{R0} = 27.69\angle 190.9° \text{ A}]$

Problem 12.6

A balanced 3-phase, 3-wire, 240 V supply of phase sequence RYB is connected to an unbalanced delta-connected load with the following impedances.

$$Z_{RY} = 10\angle 20° \text{ ohm}, \quad Z_{YB} = 5\angle 90° \text{ ohm}, \quad Z_{BR} = 8\angle -20° \text{ ohm}$$

Determine the current in each phase of the load, and in each line. Draw the phasor diagram for the load.

$[I_{RY} = 24\angle 10° \text{ A}; I_{YB} = 48\angle 180° \text{ A}; I_{BR} = 30\angle 170° \text{ A}; I_R = 53.19\angle -1.1° \text{ A}; I_Y = 71.76\angle 183.33° \text{ A}; I_B = 19.18\angle 15.76° \text{ A}]$

Problem 12.7

An unbalanced 3-phase, 3-wire supply of phase sequence RYB has the following phase voltages.

$$V_{RN} = 100\angle -80° \text{ V}, \quad V_{YN} = 120\angle 180° \text{ V}, \quad V_{BN} = 90\angle 90° \text{ V}$$

It supplies power to an unbalanced set of star-connected impedances whose values are as follows.

$$Z_{RS} = 10 + j2 \text{ ohm}, \quad Z_{YS} = -j5 \text{ ohm}, \quad Z_{BS} = 8 - j3 \text{ ohm}$$

Calculate the line currents, the voltage of the star point of the load with respect to the neutral point of the supply, and the voltage across each phase of the load.

$[I_R = 9.82\angle -44.1° \text{ A}; I_Y = 13.84\angle -129.77° \text{ A}; I_B = 17.56\angle 84.1° \text{ A}; V_{BN} = 80.15\angle -146.47° \text{ V}; V_{RS} = 100.1\angle -32.78° \text{ V}; V_{YS} = 69.2\angle 140.2° \text{ V}; V_{BS} = 150\angle 63.55° \text{ V}]$

Problem 12.8

Calculate the symmetrical components of the voltages and currents in Problem 12.7.

$[V_{R1} = 97.37\angle-57.9°$ V; $\quad V_{R2} = 13.19\angle-90.8°$ V; $\quad V_{R0} = 34.33\angle184.7°$ V;
$I_{R1} = 13.33\angle-29.2°$ A; $I_{R2} = 4.6\angle184.2°$ A; $I_{R0} = 0$ A$]$

Problem 12.9

Calculate the power in kW, the reactive power in kVAr, and the kVA consumed by the circuits in Problems 12.1 and 12.3.

[83.8 kW; 48.4 kVAr; 96.8 kVA; 251.5 kW; 145.2 kVAr; 290.4 kVA]

Problem 12.10

In Problem 12.4, determine the power consumed by each phase of the load and by the complete circuit.

$[P_R = 8.33$ kW; $P_Y = 13.34$ kW; $P_B = 10$ kW; $P_T = 31.67$ kW$]$

Problem 12.11

Calculate the power supplied by each of the symmetrical components in Problem 12.5, hence determine the total power consumed.

$[P_{ZPS} = 0; P_{PPS} = 31.67$ kW; $P_{NPS} = 0; P_T = 31.67$ kW$]$

Problem 12.12

Calculate the power consumed by each phase of the load in Problem 12.7, and also the total power consumed. Determine also the power supplied by each of the symmetrical components.

$[P_R = 0.96$ kW; $P_Y = 0; P_B = 2.47$ kW; $P_T = 3.43$ kW; $P_{ZPS} = 0;$
$P_{PPS} = 3.43$ kW; $P_{NPS} = 16$ W$]$

Problem 12.13

If the power consumed by the circuit in Problem 12.1 is measured by two wattmeters, one having its current coil in the R-line, the other having its current coil in the Y-line, determine the indication on each instrument.

$[P_R = 55.88$ kW; $P_Y = 27.94$ kW$]$

Problem 12.14

Evaluate the reading on each of two wattmeters connected to read the power consumed by the circuit in Worked Example 12.6, one having its current coil in the Y-line, the other having its current coil in the B-line.
$[P_Y = 5.69 \text{ kW}; P_B = 7.61 \text{ kW}]$

Problem 12.15

Determine the indication on each of two wattmeters connected to read the total power consumed by the circuit in Problem 12.7, with the current coils connected in (a) the R and Y lines, (b) the Y and B lines, (c) the R and B lines.
[(a) $P_R = 1.41 \text{ kW}$, $P_Y = 2.02 \text{ kW}$; (b) $P_Y = 0.17 \text{ kW}$, $P_B = 3.26 \text{ kW}$;
(c) $P_R = 1.64 \text{ kW}$, $P_B = 1.79 \text{ kW}$]

Problem 12.16

A star-connected load comprises two 15 000 ohm resistors and a voltmeter of resistance 15 000 ohm, the supply being a balanced 250 V, 3-phase, 3-wire system of phase sequence RYB. Determine the reading on the voltmeter. If the voltmeter is shunted by a 5000 ohm resistor, calculate the new indication on the voltmeter.
[144.3 V; 72.17 V]

Problem 12.17

An unbalanced star-connected load is supplied by a symmetrical 3-phase, 3-wire source of phase sequence RYB. The voltage of the R-line relative to the star point of the load is $145.6\angle 35°$ V, and the voltage of the Y-line relative to the star point is $255.4\angle 207°$ V. Calculate the line voltage of the supply, the voltage across the B-phase of the load, and the voltage of the star point of the load relative to the neutral point of the supply.
[400 V; $363.4\angle 128.7°$ V; $139.5\angle -36.8°$ V]

Problem 12.18

A resistor of 500 ohm and a capacitor of 5.5 microfarad are connected in series between lines R and Y of a 440 V, 50 Hz balanced 3-phase supply, the resistor being connected to the R-line, and the capacitor to the Y-line. Determine the modulus of the voltage between line B and the junction of the capacitor and resistor for the phase sequence (a) RYB, (b) RBY.
[RYB 600 V; RBY 166 V]

Problem 12.19

The current flowing in phase BR of a delta-connected load is 25 A at a power factor of 0.866 lagging, the current in phase YB is 20 A at unity power factor, and the current in phase RY is 30 A at a power factor of 0.7071 leading. Calculate the current in each line if the phase sequence is RYB, and V_{RN} lies in the reference direction.
$[I_R = 21.6\angle 19.9° \text{ A}; I_Y = 49.6\angle -99° \text{ A}; I_B = 43.5\angle 106.7° \text{ A}]$

Problem 12.20

If, in Problem 12.19, the magnitude of the line voltage is 300 V, calculate the impedance in each phase of the load.
$[Z_{BR} = 12\angle 30° \text{ ohm}; Z_{YB} = 15\angle 0° \text{ ohm}; Z_{RY} = 10\angle -45° \text{ ohm}]$

Problem 12.21

A 440 V, 3-phase symmetrical supply of phase sequence RYB is connected to a delta-connected load with the following phase impedances.

$$Z_{RY} = j10 \text{ ohm}, Z_{YB} = -j20 \text{ ohm}, Z_{BR} = 10 \text{ ohm}$$

Calculate the current in each line. The power consumed by the load is measured by means of two wattmeters, one having its current coil in the R-line, the other having its current coil in the B-line. Determine the power indicated on each instrument, and also the total power consumed by the circuit.
$[I_R = 85\angle -45° \text{ A}; I_Y = 38.1\angle 90° \text{ A}; I_B = 64\angle 160° \text{ A}; P_R = 9.68 \text{ kW};$
$P_B = 9.63 \text{ kW}; P_T = 19.31 \text{ kW}]$

Problem 12.22

If, due to a fault, the common connection between the two wattmeter voltage coils in problem 12.21 becomes isolated from the Y-line (the two voltage coils remaining connected together), calculate the reading on each of the two wattmeters.
$[P_R = 18.06 \text{ kW}; P_B = 13.87 \text{ kW}]$

Problem 12.23

(a) A delta-connected load contains the following impedances
between R and Y $50\angle -30°$ ohm
between Y and B $50\angle 0°$ ohm
between B and R $50\angle 30°$ ohm
If the line voltage is 400 V, calculate the current in the R-line.

(b) Three $5\angle30°$-ohm impedances are connected in star to a 400 V, 3-phase supply of phase sequence RYB. Calculate the power, the reactive power, and the apparent power consumed.

(Staffordshire Polytechnic)

[**(a)** Assuming that V_{RN} lies in the reference direction, $I_R = 8\angle0°$ A;
(b) 2.77 kW; 1.6 kVAr; 3.2 kVA]

13 Transients and the Laplace Transform

13.1 Fact Sheet

In a circuit which contains one or more energy storage element, a *transient state* will exist whenever the energy condition in the circuit changes, until the new *steady state* is reached. This may be caused by changing the applied voltage or current, or by changing any of the circuit elements, usually by opening or closing switches. This chapter studies the behaviour of such circuits as a function of time after making a change. Both single and double energy transients will be considered and their equations expressed in *standard form*.

(a) First-order Systems

The circuits in Figures 13.1 and 13.2 contain a single energy storage element (see Chapter 1), in which v_S is the supply voltage and i is the circuit current at time t seconds after closing the switch. At this time voltages v_R, v_L, and v_C are across the components.

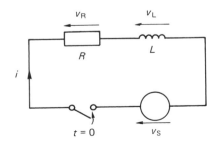

Fig 13.1

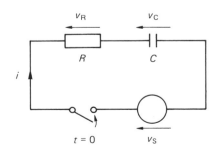

Fig 13.2

294

Inductive Circuit

For Figure 13.1, by KVL,

$$v_S = v_R + v_L$$

But

$$v_L = L \frac{di}{dt}$$

Therefore,

$$v_S = iR + L \frac{di}{dt}$$

or

$$\frac{v_S}{R} = i + \frac{L}{R}\frac{di}{dt} \tag{13.1}$$

Capacitive Circuit

For Figure 13.2, by KVL,

$$v_S = v_R + v_C$$
$$= iR + v_C$$

Now, since

$$i = C \frac{dv_C}{dt}$$

then,

$$v_S = RC \frac{dv_C}{dt} + v_C \tag{13.2}$$

In general,

$$F = x + T \frac{dx}{dt} \tag{13.3}$$

where F = driving function = steady-state value of x, in which x = circuit variable, T = circuit time constant and dx/dt is the first derivative.

Using the D operator, where $D = d/dt$, then $F = x + TDx$.

The solution of linear, first-order equations of this type, where the variables can be separated on the two sides of the equation consists of two parts:

$$x = x_t + x_{SS}$$

where x_t is the *transient solution* obtained by making $F = 0$, and x_{SS} is the *steady-state solution*, i.e., the value of x as $t \to \infty$.

For the transient solution of the equation,

$$x_t + T\frac{dx_t}{dt} = 0$$

x_t is always of the form $Ae^{-t/T}$, where A is a constant to be determined from the circuit's initial conditions, i.e., the value of x at $t = 0$.

In general, the complete solution is of the form

$$x = Ae^{-t/T} + x_{SS} \tag{13.4}$$

(i) ***Constant voltage source, $v_S = E$ volts, and the switch is closed at $t = 0$***

For the inductive circuit shown in Figure 13.1, from Equation (13.1)

$$i + \frac{L}{R}\frac{di}{dt} = \frac{E}{R}$$

or $i + TDi =$ final current   where $T = L/R$

Since the inductor has no voltage across it when the current is steady,

$$i_{SS} = \frac{E}{R}$$

Hence the complete solution for the current in the circuit in Figure 13.1 is

$$i = Ae^{-t/T} + \frac{E}{R} \tag{13.5}$$

For the capacitive circuit shown in Figure 13.2, from Equation (13.2)

$$v_C + RC\frac{dv_C}{dt} = E$$

so,

$$v_C + TDv_C = \text{final voltage}$$

Since the capacitor is fully charged in the steady state, no current flows in it and $v_{SS} = E$.

The complete solution for the capacitor voltage in the circuit in Figure 13.2 is

$$v_C = Ae^{-t/T} + E \tag{13.6}$$

Initial conditions: Substitute the values of i and v at the instant the switches are closed in the two circuits. Let these be zero and V_1 volts respectively.

Since the current through an inductor and the voltage across a capacitor cannot be changed instantly, then, at $t = 0$, in Equation 13.5 for the inductive circuit in Figure 13.1,

$$0 = A + \frac{E}{R}$$

that is,

$$A = -\frac{E}{R}$$

Hence,

$$i = \frac{E}{R}(1 - e^{-Rt/L})$$ (13.7)

In Equation 13.6 for the capacitive circuit in Figure 13.2,

$$V_1 = A + E$$

then

$$A = V_1 - E$$

Hence

$$v = E - (E - V_1)e^{-t/RC}$$ (13.8)

In both cases the solution is of the form:

instantaneous value = final value − step size $\times$ $e^{-t/T}$

which is illustrated graphically for two cases in Figures 13.3(a) and 13.3(b). In Figure 13.3(a), final value $>$ initial value, while in Figure 13.3(b), final value $<$ initial value.

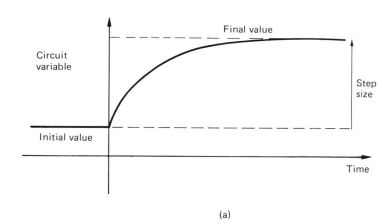

(a)

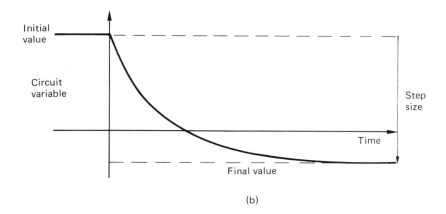

(b)

Fig 13.3

(ii) *Alternating voltage source, $v_S = E_m \sin \omega t$ applied to the series R–L circuit in Figure 13.1*

Refer to the waveform diagram in Figure 13.4. The switch is closed at some time $t = t'$ to make it general, so the circuit equation becomes, from Equation 13.1

$$\frac{E_m}{R} \sin \omega t = i + \frac{L}{R}\frac{di}{dt}$$

Its solution will again be in two parts:

1. the transient solution, $i = Ae^{-Rt/L}$ as before
2. the steady-state solution. From single-phase theory (refer to Chapter 5):

$$i_{SS} = \frac{E_m}{Z}\sin(\omega t - \phi)$$

where

$$Z = \surd(R^2 + \omega^2 L^2) \text{ and } \tan\phi = \frac{\omega L}{R}$$

in which ϕ is the phase angle between the sinusoidal supply voltage and the steady-state current.
So,

$$i = Ae^{-Rt/L} + \frac{E_m}{Z}\sin(\omega t - \phi)$$

For zero initial current, i.e. $i = 0$ at $t = t'$, then

$$0 = Ae^{-Rt'/L} + \frac{E_m}{Z}\sin(\omega t' - \phi)$$

$$A = -\frac{E_m}{Z}e^{Rt'/L}\sin(\omega t' - \phi)$$

Hence,

$$i = \frac{E_m}{Z}\sin(\omega t - \phi) - e^{R(t'-t)/L}\sin(\omega t' - \phi)$$

This is shown graphically in Figure 13.4.

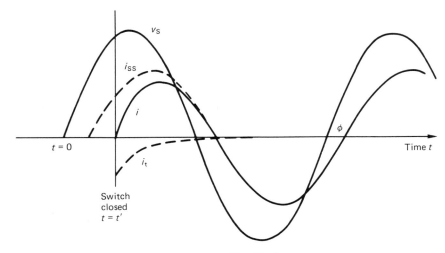

Fig 13.4

(b)   Circuits Reducible to First Order Format

Circuits which have a single energy storage element may be solved by first obtaining Thévenin's equivalent circuit. The circuit time constants then become L/R_{Th} or CR_{Th}.

(c)   Second-order Systems (Double Energy Transients)

(i)   Series Circuit

The voltage equation for the series RLC circuit in Figure 13.5 is given by KVL:

$$v_R + v_L + v_C = v_S$$

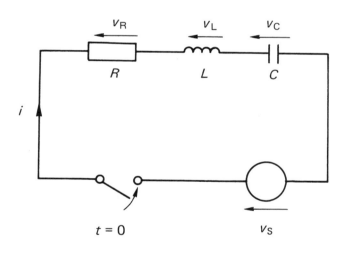

Fig 13.5

that is,

$$iR + L\,\frac{\mathrm{d}i}{\mathrm{d}t} + \frac{1}{C}\int i\mathrm{d}t = v_S$$

Differentiate this equation with respect to time to give

$$R\,\frac{\mathrm{d}i}{\mathrm{d}t} + L\,\frac{\mathrm{d}^2 i}{\mathrm{d}t^2} + \frac{i}{C} = \frac{\mathrm{d}v_S}{\mathrm{d}t}$$

that is,

$$\frac{\mathrm{d}^2 i}{\mathrm{d}t^2} + \frac{R}{L}\,\frac{\mathrm{d}i}{\mathrm{d}t} + \frac{i}{LC} = \frac{1}{L}\,\frac{\mathrm{d}v_S}{\mathrm{d}t}$$

The highest derivative in the output variable, i, is second order and the solution is again made up of two parts: namely

$$i = i_t + i_{SS}.$$

The *steady-state solution* i_{SS} is determined by single-phase theory. For example, when the source is a constant voltage, i_{SS} is zero because of the capacitor.

The *transient solution*, i_t is obtained by equating the left hand side of the equation to zero. For convenience in interpretation, the coefficient of the highest derivative is reduced to unity. Hence, using the D operator for clarity,

$$D^2 i_t + \frac{R}{L} D i_t + \frac{1}{LC} i_t = 0 \tag{13.9}$$

The 'standard form' of this linear second-order differential equation is

$$(D^2 + 2d\omega_n D + \omega_n^2) i_t = 0 \tag{13.10}$$

where ω_n is the undamped natural frequency of the oscillations and d is the damping factor.

Comparing Equations 13.9 and 13.10, shows for the series circuit that

$$\omega_n = \frac{1}{\sqrt{LC}} \quad \text{and} \quad d = \frac{R}{2\omega_n L} = \frac{R}{2} \sqrt{\frac{C}{L}}$$

The condition $d = 0$ implies zero circuit resistance.

The solutions to Equation 13.10 are determined by the value of d as follows:

(i) $d < 1$, damped oscillations
$$i_t = A e^{-d\omega_n t} \sin(\omega_o t + \theta)$$
(ii) $d = 1$, critical damping
$$i_t = (A + Bt) e^{-\omega_n t}$$
(iii) $d > 1$, overdamped response
$$i_t = (A e^{-\omega_o t} + B e^{-\omega_o t}) e^{-d\omega_n t}$$
(iv) $d = 0$, no damping, continuous oscillation
$$i_t = A \sin(\omega_n t + \theta)$$

where A, B, and θ are constants determined by the initial conditions of the circuit, and ω_o is the frequency of the damped oscillations. This is given by $\omega_o = \omega_n \sqrt{|(1 - d^2)|}$

Initial conditions: With constant voltage E volts applied to the circuit in Figure 13.5, by KVL,

$$Ri + LDi + v_C = E$$

Let the voltage across the capacitor be V_1 and the circuit current be zero before closing the switch, hence at $t = 0$

$$LDi + V_1 = E$$

$$Di = \frac{(E - V_1)}{L}$$

Steady-state solution: $i_{SS} = 0$, since the capacitor is fully charged to E.

Hence the complete solution is given by $i = i_t$. Substituting these values into (i), (ii), (iii) and (iv) above leads to

(1) $d < 1$

$$i = \frac{(E - V_1)}{\omega_o L} e^{-d\omega_n t} \sin\omega_o t$$

(2) $d = 1$

$$i = \frac{(E - V_1)}{L} t e^{-\omega_n t}$$

(3) $d > 1$

$$i = \frac{(E - V_1)}{2\omega_o L} e^{-d\omega_n t} (e^{\omega_o t} - e^{-\omega_o t})$$

$$= \frac{(E - V_1)}{\omega_o L} e^{-d\omega_n t} \sinh\omega_o t$$

(4) $d = 0$

$$i = \frac{(E - V_1)}{\omega_n L} \sin\omega_n t$$

(ii) Parallel Circuit

The current equation for the parallel R–L–C circuit in Figure 13.6 is given by KCL:

$$i_R + i_L + i_C = I \tag{13.11}$$

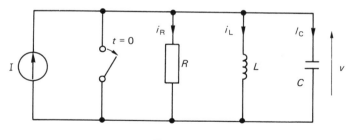

Fig 13.6

or,

$$\frac{v}{R} + i_L + C\frac{dv}{dt} = I \tag{13.12}$$

Now,

$$v = L\frac{di_L}{dt}$$

Hence,

$$\frac{L}{R}\frac{di_L}{dt} + i_L + CL\frac{d^2i_L}{dt^2} = I \tag{13.13}$$

Re-write in *standard form*

$$\left(D^2 + \frac{1}{RC}D + \frac{1}{LC}\right)i_L = \frac{I}{LC}$$

Hence

$$\omega_n^2 = \frac{1}{LC} \quad \text{and} \quad d = \frac{1}{2\omega_n RC} = \frac{1}{2R}\sqrt{\frac{L}{C}}$$

Solution for d > 1

From Equation (iii) above, the transient solution is

$$i_L = (Ae^{\omega_o t} + Be^{-\omega_o t})e^{-d\omega_n t}$$

In the steady state, $i_L = I$, $v = 0$, $i_R = i_C = 0$, so the complete solution is

$$i_L = Ae^{(\omega_o - d\omega_n)t} + Be^{-(\omega_o + d\omega_n)t} + I \qquad (13.14)$$

Initial conditions: At $t = 0$, $i_L = 0$ and $v = 0$
Hence from Equation (13.11) $i_C = I$ at $t = 0$
so in Equation (13.13)

$$\left(\frac{di_L}{dt}\right)_{t=0} = 0$$

Differentiating Equation (13.14) with respect to time gives

$$Di_L = A(\omega_o - d\omega_n)e^{(\omega_o - d\omega_n)t} - B(\omega_o + d\omega_n)e^{-(\omega_o + d\omega_n)t} \qquad (13.15)$$

In Equation (13.14),

$$0 = A + B + I \quad \text{for } t = 0,$$

and in Equation (13.15),

$$0 = A(\omega_o - d\omega_n) - B(\omega_o + d\omega_n)$$

Solving these two equations for A and B gives

$$A = -I\frac{(\omega_o + d\omega_n)}{2\omega_o} \qquad B = -I\frac{(\omega_o - d\omega_n)}{2\omega_o}$$

Hence,

$$i_L = I\left[1 - \frac{(d\omega_n + \omega_o)}{2\omega_o}e^{-(d\omega_n - \omega_o)t} + \frac{(d\omega_n - \omega_o)}{2\omega_o}e^{-(d\omega_n + \omega_o)t}\right] \qquad (13.16)$$

Solution for d < 1

From (i) above, the transient solution is

$$i_t = Ae^{-d\omega_n t}\sin(\omega_o t + \theta)$$

As before, the steady state solution, $i_{L\,SS} = I$, so the complete solution is

$$i_L = Ae^{-d\omega_n t}\sin(\omega_o t + \theta) + I$$

Again $(i_L)_{t=0} = 0$ and $(Di_L)_{t=0} = 0$
where $Di_L = A\,[-d\omega_n e^{-d\omega_n t}\sin(\omega_o t + \theta) + \omega_o e^{-d\omega_n t}\cos(\omega_o t + \theta)]$
which give $\tan\theta = \omega_o/d\omega_n$ and $A = -I/\sin\theta = -\omega_n I/\omega_o$
   Hence,

$$i_L = I\left[1 - \frac{\omega_n}{\omega_o}\,e^{-d\omega_n t}\sin(\omega_o t + \theta)\right] \tag{13.17}$$

(d)   Introduction to Laplace Transforms

The Laplace transform converts a time-domain expression $f(t)$ into a complex frequency-domain expression $F(s)$, where $s = \sigma + j\omega$. A list of Laplace transform pairs relating $f(t)$ and $F(s)$ is given in Table 13.1. $F(s)$ is defined as

$$F(s) = \mathscr{L}f(t) = \int_0^\infty f(t)\,e^{-st}\,dt$$

Circuit Element Representation

(i)   *Resistor (Refer to Figure 13.7)*

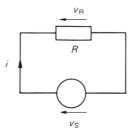

Fig 13.7

The supply voltage v_S applied across the resistor causes current i to flow in the circuit, and $v_S = 0$ for $t < 0$. By KVL, $v_S = v_R$, and by Ohm's law

$$v_R = iR$$

that is $v_S = iR$. Taking the Laplace transform of both sides of the equation gives

$$\bar{v}_S = \bar{i}R$$

where $\bar{i}$ is the current in the s-domain or frequency domain, and $\bar{v}_S$ is the Laplace transform of the supply voltage. For example, if v_S is a constant voltage E volt then, from Table 13.1

$$\bar{v}_S = \frac{E}{s}$$

303

Table 13.1

Function	Laplace transform
$f(t)$	$F(s) = \int_0^\infty e^{-st} f(t) \, dt$
1	$\dfrac{1}{s}$
$e^{-\alpha t}$	$\dfrac{1}{s + \alpha}$
$\sin \omega t$	$\dfrac{\omega}{s^2 + \omega^2}$
$\cos \omega t$	$\dfrac{s}{s^2 + \omega^2}$
t	$\dfrac{1}{s^2}$
$t^n(n + \text{ve integer})$	$\dfrac{n!}{s^{n+1}}$
$\sinh \beta t$	$\dfrac{\beta}{s^2 - \beta^2}$
$\cosh \beta t$	$\dfrac{s}{s^2 - \beta^2}$
$t\sin \omega t$	$\dfrac{2\omega s}{(s^2 + \theta^2)^2}$
$t\cos \omega t$	$\dfrac{s^2 - \omega^2}{(s^2 + \omega^2)^2}$
$\sin \omega t - \omega t \cos \omega t$	$\dfrac{2\omega^3}{(s^2 + \omega^2)^2}$
$e^{-\alpha t} t^n$	$\dfrac{n!}{(s + \alpha)^{n+1}}$
$e^{-\alpha t}\cos \omega t$	$\dfrac{s + \alpha}{(s + \alpha)^2 + \omega^2}$
$e^{-\alpha t} \sin \omega t$	$\dfrac{\omega}{(s + \alpha)^2 + \omega^2}$
$\dfrac{dx}{dt}$	$s\bar{x} - x_0$ where $\bar{x} = \mathscr{L}x$ $x_0 = $ value of x at $t = 0$

(ii)   *Inductor (Refer to Figure 13.8)*

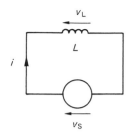

Fig 13.8

For this element,

$$v_S = v_L = L\frac{di}{dt}$$

Taking the transform of each side gives

$$\bar{v}_S = \bar{v}_L = L[s\bar{i} - i(0)]$$

where $i(0)$ is the value of i at $t = 0$; this is often zero but, to allow for the general case, we will assume its value to be I_1. Hence, the time-domain circuit in Figure 13.8 can be replaced by the s-domain equivalent in Figure 13.9.

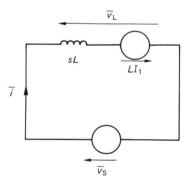

Fig 13.9

(iii)   *Capacitor (Refer to Figure 13.10)*

The capacitor current is

$$i = \frac{dq}{dt} = C\frac{dv_C}{dt}$$

Taking the transform of both sides of the equation gives

$$\bar{i} = C[s\bar{v}_C - v_C(0)]$$

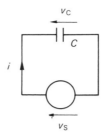

Fig 13.10

where $v_C(0)$ is the value of v_C at $t = 0$: let this be V_1 in the same sense that v_C is shown. Transposing this equation gives

$$\bar{v}_C = \frac{\bar{i}}{sC} + \frac{V_1}{s}$$

which can be used as the s-domain model of the capacitor (see Figure 13.11).

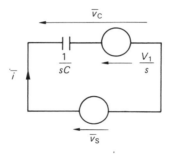

Fig 13.11

(e)   Simple First-order Circuit

Consider the case where a capacitor is charged through a resistor from a constant-voltage source (see Figure 13.2). This can be replaced by the equivalent s-domain elements in Figure 13.12. Applying KVL to the latter yields

$$\frac{E}{s} - \frac{V_1}{s} = \bar{i}\left(R + \frac{1}{sC}\right)$$

Transposing the equation gives

$$\bar{i} = \frac{C(E - V_1)}{1 + RCs} = \left(\frac{E - V_1}{R}\right)\left(\frac{1}{s + 1/T}\right)$$

where $T = RC$. The equation has been expressed in this way, since it has the same form as one of the standard transforms.

Taking the inverse Laplace transform is represented by the symbol $\mathscr{L}^{-1}$, hence

$$\mathscr{L}^{-1}\bar{i} = i = \left(\frac{E - V_1}{R}\right)e^{-t/T}$$

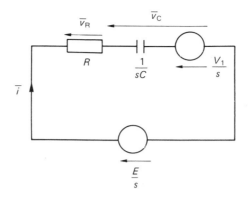

Fig 13.12

Now,

$$v_C = E - iR$$

Hence,

$$v_C = E - (E - V_1)\,e^{-t/T}$$

This result agrees with Equation 13.8.

(f) Second-Order Circuit

Consider the series RLC circuit in Figure 13.5, with a constant voltage E volts applied at $t = 0$ when the capacitor voltage is V_1. The s-domain equivalent circuit is shown in Figure 13.13. Applying KVL to this circuit gives

$$\frac{E}{s} - \frac{V_1}{s} = \left(R + sL + \frac{1}{sC} \right) \bar{i}$$

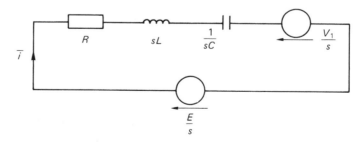

Fig 13.13

Hence,

$$C(E - V_1) = (RCs + s^2 LC + 1)\,\bar{i}$$

or

$$\left(\frac{E - V_1}{L} \right) = \left(s^2 + \frac{R}{L}s + \frac{1}{LC} \right) \bar{i}$$

The right-hand side is in the form

$$(s^2 + 2d\omega_n s + \omega_n^2)\,\bar{\imath}$$

where d and ω_n are constants for a given circuit; ω_n is the *undamped natural frequency* (in rad/s), and d is the *damping factor*. The equation above is similar to Equation 13.10. Equating coefficients shows that

$$\omega_n^2 = \frac{1}{LC} \quad \text{and} \quad 2d\omega_n = \frac{R}{L}$$

That is,

$$d = \frac{R}{2}\sqrt{\frac{C}{L}}$$

Transposing the equation gives

$$\bar{\imath} = \left(\frac{E - V_1}{L}\right)\left(\frac{1}{s^2 + 2d\omega_n s + w_n^2}\right)$$

The solution for $i(t)$ depends on the value of d as follows.

(i) $d = 0$ *(no damping − continuous oscillation)*

The s-domain equation is

$$\bar{\imath} = \left(\frac{E - V_1}{L}\right)\left(\frac{1}{s^2 + \omega_n^2}\right)$$

Using the table of Laplace transforms, $\mathcal{L}^{-1}$ gives the corresponding time-domain equation

$$i = \left(\frac{E - V_1}{\omega_n L}\right)\sin \omega_n t$$

The corresponding waveform is shown in Figure 13.14(i).

(ii) $d < 1$ *(damped oscillations)*

'Complete the square' of the function of s in the $\bar{\imath}$ equation to give

$$\bar{\imath} = \left(\frac{E - V_1}{L}\right)\left[\frac{1}{(s + d\omega_n)^2 + \omega_o^2}\right]$$

where $\omega_o^2 = \omega_n^2(1 - d^2)$.

The inverse transform gives

$$i = \left(\frac{E - V_1}{\omega_o L}\right) e^{-d\omega_n t} \sin \omega_o t$$

where ω_o is the frequency of the damped sine wave bounded by the envelope $\pm e^{-d\omega_n t}$, see Figure 13.14(ii).

308

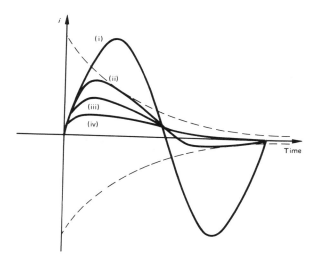

Fig 13.14

(iii)   *d = 1 (critical damping)*

For given values of L and C, this condition represents the minimum value of R for the current not to be oscillatory, i.e., with a positive supply voltage, the current just does not become negative. The s-domain equation is

$$\bar{\imath} = \left(\frac{E - V_1}{L}\right)\left[\frac{1}{(s + \omega_n)^2}\right]$$

The inverse transform gives

$$i = \left(\frac{E - V_1}{L}\right) t \, e^{-\omega_n t}$$

The response is shown in Figure 13.14(iii).

(iv)   *d > 1 (overdamped response)*

The s-domain equation is

$$\bar{\imath} = \left(\frac{E - V_1}{L}\right)\left[\frac{1}{(s + d\omega_n)^2 - \omega_o^2}\right]$$

where $\omega_o^2 = \omega_n^2(d^2 - 1)$.

The inverse transform is

$$i = \left(\frac{E - V_1}{\omega_o L}\right) e^{-d\omega_n t} \sinh \omega_o t$$

or

$$i = \left(\frac{E - V_1}{2\omega_o L}\right) [e^{(\omega_o - d\omega_n)t} - e^{-(\omega_o + d\omega_n)t}]$$

In general, $\omega_o^2 = \omega_n^2|(1 - d^2)|$ to obtain the numerical value of ω_o. A typical response is illustrated in Figure 13.14(iv).

(g)   Transfer Functions

If Xe^{st} is a general input signal to a network, and Ye^{st} is the output, then the ratio

$$\frac{Ye^{st}}{Xe^{st}} = G(s)$$

is called the *transfer function* of the circuit (all initial conditions being set to zero). Depending on the nature of the two signals, the ratio may be a voltage gain, or a current gain, or an impedance, or an admittance.

For example, the time domain circuit in Figure 13.20 can be represented by its s-domain equivalent in Figure 13.15. In the latter case, R_1, R_2 and $1/sC$ are treated as complex impedances, so by potential divider action

$$G(s) = \frac{\overline{v}_o}{\overline{v}_1} = \frac{\overline{Z}_2}{\overline{Z}_1 + \overline{Z}_2}$$

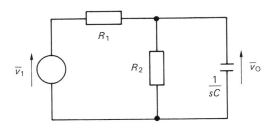

Fig 13.15

where

$$\overline{Z}_1 = R_1 \text{ and } \overline{Z}_2 = \frac{R_2/sC}{R_2 + 1/sC}$$

Substituting these values gives

$$G(s) = \frac{R_2}{R_1 + R_2 + R_1 R_2 C s}$$

Suppose that v_1 is a step input voltage of E volts, then

$$\mathcal{L} v_1 = \overline{v}_1 = E/s$$

That is,

$$\bar{v}_o = \frac{ER_2}{s(R_1 + R_2 + R_1 R_2 Cs)}$$

Using partial fractions (see Appendix 4), we can simplify the expression to allow the inverse Laplace transform to be evaluated and give the transient response of the network.

13.2 Worked Examples

Example 13.1

A coil has a resistance of 2.0 ohm and an inductance of 20 mH. Calculate **(a)** the circuit time constant, **(b)** the steady-state current when a 10 V battery is switched across the coil, **(c)** the value of the current in the coil (i) 5 ms and (ii) 10 ms after applying the battery, assuming there was no initial stored energy, **(d)** the rate of change of current immediately after closing the switch in **(b)**. **(e)** Sketch the response of $i(t)$ with scaled axes.

Solution 13.1

Refer to Figure 13.1 and Equation 13.7

(a) Time constant, $T = \dfrac{L}{R} = \dfrac{20 \times 10^{-3}}{2} = 10$ ms

(b) Steady-state current $= \dfrac{E}{R} = \dfrac{10}{2} = 5$ A

(c) i) $i = 5(1 - e^{-5 \times 10^{-3}/10 \times 10^{-3}})$

$= 5 \times 0.393 = 1.97$ A

ii) $i = 5(1 - e^{-10 \times 10^{-3}/10 \times 10^{-3}})$

$= 5 \times 0.632 = 3.16$ A

(d) $\dfrac{di}{dt} = \dfrac{E}{R} \times \dfrac{R}{L} e^{-Rt/L} = \dfrac{E}{L} e^{-Rt/L}$

Hence at $t = 0$, rate of change of current $= 10/(20 \times 10^{-3}) = 500$ A/s

(e) Refer to Figure 13.16 for current response.

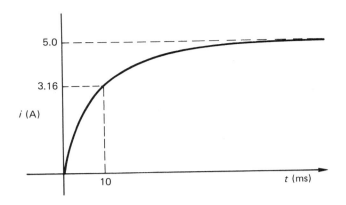

Fig 13.16

Example 13.2

A 100 kΩ resistor and a 0.5 microfarad capacitor are connected in series with a battery as shown in Figure 13.2. The voltage across the capacitor terminals immediately before applying the battery was 20 V assisting that of the battery. Calculate **(a)** the circuit time constant **(b)** the time after $t = 0$ when the voltages across the capacitor and the resistor are the same. **(c)** Sketch a graph of capacitor voltage against time with scaled axes.

Solution 13.2

(a) Time constant, $T = CR = 0.5 \times 10^{-6} \times 100 \times 10^{3}$ s

$$= 50 \text{ ms}$$

(b) Let t_1 be the time when the resistor and capacitor voltages are the same, then $v_R = v_C = v_S/2 = 50$ V at $t = t_1$
From Equation 13.8

$$50 = 100 - [100 - (-20)]e^{-t_1/50}$$

where t_1 is in milliseconds
Then,

$$50 = 100 - 120e^{-t_1/50}$$

$$e^{t_1/50} = \frac{120}{50} = 2.4$$

$$t_1 = 50 \ln 2.4 \text{ s} = 43.8 \text{ ms}$$

(c) The variation of v_C against t is shown in Figure 13.17.

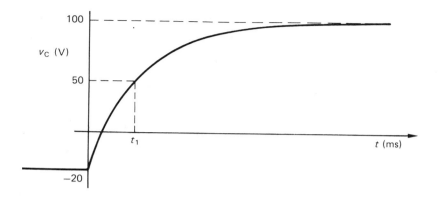

Fig 13.17

Example 13.3

(a) Determine the expression for $v_o(t)$ after the switch in the network in Figure 13.18 is opened at $t = 0$. **(b)** Repeat part **(a)** when the inductor is replaced by a 1/6 mF capacitor.

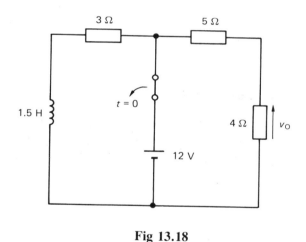

Fig 13.18

Solution 13.3

(a) Before the switch is opened, assume that steady state conditions have been reached, so the current in the inductor is limited only by the 3 ohm resistor; i.e., its current will be $12/3 = 4$ A (downwards).

Immediately the switch is opened, this current must continue to flow in the inductor and through the three resistors in series (R_T). Ultimately the current will decay to zero with a time constant,

$$T = \frac{L}{R_T} = \frac{1.5}{12} = \frac{1}{8} \text{ s}.$$

313

From the observation in section (i) of the Fact Sheet in this chapter, for a single energy transient,

$$\text{Instantaneous value} = \text{final value} - \text{step size} \times e^{-t/T}$$

Hence, current for $t > 0$ is given by

$$i = 0 - (-4)e^{-8t} = 0 + 4e^{-8t} \text{ A}$$

This is the current passing up through the 4 ohm resistor, so

$$v_0 = -4i = -16e^{-8t} \text{ V}.$$

(b) When the inductor is replaced by a capacitor, the steady-state voltage across the capacitor before the switch is opened is 12 V.

After opening the switch, the capacitor voltage decays from 12 V to zero with a time constant, $T = R_T C = 12 \times 1/6 \times 10^{-3} = 2$ ms.

Again, using the equation:

$$\text{instantaneous value} = \text{final value} - \text{step} \times e^{-t/T}$$

gives, capacitor voltage $v_C = 0 - (-12)e^{-500t} = 12e^{-500t} \text{ V}$.

By potential divider action,

$$\text{the output voltage } v_0 = \frac{4}{12} \times v_C$$

Hence, $v_0 = 4e^{-500t} \text{ V}$.

Example 13.4

In the series circuit shown in Figure 13.5, $R = 200$ ohm, $L = 2.0$ H, $C = 50$ microfarad. Derive the expression for the voltage across the capacitor when a constant voltage of 10 V is suddenly applied. Assume zero initial energy conditions.

Solution 13.4

For a series RLC circuit, we obtain Equation 13.9 and comparison with Equation 13.10 gives the undamped natural frequency

$$\omega_n = \frac{1}{\sqrt{(LC)}}$$

and the damping factor is

$$d = \frac{R}{2} \sqrt{\frac{C}{L}}$$

Hence, $\omega_n = 100$ rad/s and $d = 0.5$.
The damped oscillatory frequency is calculated using:

$$\omega_o^2 = \omega_n^2 (1 - d^2)$$

Substituting values gives

$$\omega_o = 86.6 \text{ rad/s.}$$

For $d < 1$, the transient solution is given by

$$v_t = A e^{-d\omega_n t} \sin(\omega_o t + \theta)$$

while the steady-state capacitor voltage is 10 V due to the supply, i.e. $v_{CSS} = 10$. Hence

$$v_C = A e^{-50t} \sin(86.6t + \theta) + 10 \qquad (13.20)$$

Differentiate Equation (13.20) with respect to time to give

$$Dv_C = -50A e^{-50t} \sin(86.6t + \theta) + 86.6A e^{-50t} \cos(86.6t + \theta) \quad (13.21)$$

Initial conditions: The voltage across the capacitor and the current through the inductor cannot change suddenly at the instant the switch is closed. This means (i) at $t = 0$, $v_C = 0$ and (ii) at $t = 0$, $i = 0$, hence

$$\frac{dv_C}{dt} = 0$$

because $i = Cdv_C/dt$.

Substituting in Equations (13.20) and (13.21) gives:
In (13.21),

$$0 = -50A \sin\theta + 86.6A \cos\theta$$

$$\tan\theta = \frac{86.6}{50}, \text{ so } \theta = 60°$$

In (13.20), $0 = A \sin\theta + 10$
Hence,

$$A = \frac{-10}{\sin\theta} = \frac{-10}{0.866} = -11.5$$

The capacitor voltage v_C is given by substituting these in Equation 13.20.

$$v_C = 10[1 - 1.15e^{-50t} \sin(86.6t + 60°)] \text{ V}$$

Example 13.5

The voltage pulse $v_1(t)$, shown in Figure 13.19 is applied to the input of the network in Figure 13.20 in which $R_1 = 30 \text{ k}\Omega$, $R_2 = 60 \text{ k}\Omega$, $C = 0.5$ microfarad. The capacitor is initially uncharged.

(a) Derive the expression for $v_o(t)$

    (i) for $0 < t < 20$ ms

    (ii) for $t > 20$ ms

(b) Hence calculate the time taken for the capacitor voltage to decay to 10 V after the end of the pulse.

(c) Sketch the response $v_o(t)$.

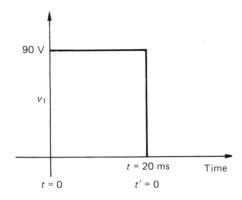

Fig 13.19

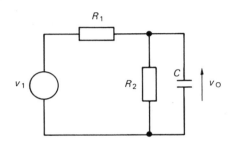

Fig 13.20

Solution 13.5

(a) Thévenin's equivalent circuit for Figure 13.20 is shown in Figure 13.21, where

$$V_{Th} = \frac{60 \times 10^3 \, v_1}{(60 + 30) \times 10^3} = 60 \text{ V for } t < 20 \text{ ms.}$$

$$R_{Th} = \frac{R_1 \times R_2}{R_1 + R_2} = 20 \times 10^3 \text{ ohm.}$$

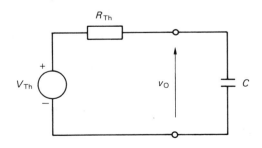

Fig 13.21

The circuit time constant $T = R_{Th}C = 20 \times 10^3 \times 0.5 \times 10^{-6}$

$$= 10 \text{ ms}$$

General solution: $v_0 = v_t + v_{SS}$

(i) *For t < 20 ms, $v_{SS} = V_{Th}$*

Note: At this stage, the capacitor charges from zero volts towards the equivalent supply voltage V_{Th}, therefore $v_0 = Ae^{-t/T} + 60$

Initial conditions: Since there is no initial charge, $v_0 = 0$ at $t = 0$, i.e., $0 = A + 60$, or $A = -60$.

The specific solution for $t < 20$ ms is

$$v_o = 60(1 - e^{-100t}) \text{ V}.$$

This is shown as (i) on the graph in Figure 13.22.

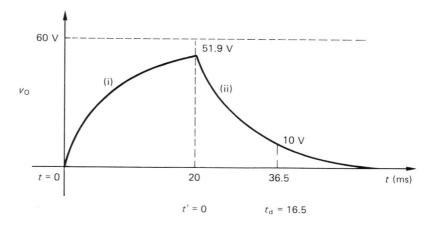

Fig 13.22

(ii) *For t > 20 ms, let t = (0.02 + t') where t' is the time measured after the end of the pulse*

In the steady state, the capacitor will become discharged, so $v_{SS} = 0$, therefore $v_o = Be^{-t'/T} + 0$.

The initial condition of v_o is the value of v_0 at $t = 20$ ms in (i).
At $t = 20$ ms, $v_o = 60(1 - e^{-2}) = 51.9$ V. Substitution gives $B = 51.9$
The specific solution for $t > 20$ ms

$$v_o = 51.9e^{-100t'}, \text{ i.e., } v_o = 51.9e^{(2-100t)} \text{ V}$$

(b) Time to decay to 10 V, t_d, is given by

$$10 = 51.9e^{-100t_d}$$

$$t_d = \frac{\ln 5.19}{100} = 16.5 \text{ ms}$$

Example 13.6

In the parallel RLC circuit shown in Figure 13.6, $L = 0.5$ H and $C = 12.5$ μF. Derive expressions for the inductor current i_L when $I = 100$ mA and (a) $R = 200$ ohm (b) $R = 50$ ohm. Sketch the graphs of i_L against time for both cases.

Solution 13.6

From the Fact Sheet in this chapter, section (b) (ii), the undamped natural frequency is

$$\omega_n = \frac{1}{\sqrt{(LC)}} = 400 \text{ rad/s}$$

(a) For $R = 200$ ohm, the damping factor is

$$d = \frac{1}{2R} \sqrt{\frac{L}{C}} = 0.5$$

Therefore $d\omega_n = 200$; $\omega_o = \omega_n \sqrt{(1 - d^2)} = 346$ rad/s

$$\tan \theta = \frac{\omega_o}{d\omega_n} = 1.732, \text{ hence } \theta = 60°.$$

Using equation 13.17,
$$i_L = 100[1 - 400 \, e^{-200t} \sin(346t + 60°)] \text{ mA}$$

(b) For $R = 50$ ohm, $= \frac{1}{2R} \sqrt{\frac{L}{C}} = 2.0$ so, $d\omega_n = 800$ rad/s.

Hence, $\omega_o = \omega_n \sqrt{(d^2 - 1)} = 693$ rad/s
Using Equation 13.16
$$i_L = 100 \left(1 - \frac{1493}{1386} e^{-107t} + \frac{107}{1386} e^{-1493t}\right) \text{ mA}$$

$$= 100 \, (1 - 1.077 \, e^{-107t} + 0.077 \, e^{-1493t}) \text{ mA}$$

Graphs showing i_L against time are shown in Figure 13.23 for the two cases (i) $R = 200$ ohm and (ii) $R = 50$ ohm.

Example 13.7

A resistor R ohm, a 5.0 mH inductor and a 100 microfarad capacitor are connected in series to a 100 V d.c. supply. Derive the equations relating the instantaneous current to time after the circuit has been completed (i) when $R = 20$ ohm,
(ii) when $R = 10$ ohm, if the capacitor voltage prior to completing the circuit is (a) zero and (b) −100 V.

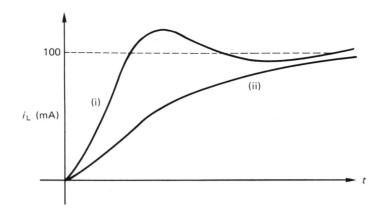

Fig 13.23

Calculate the maximum value of the current for the circuits in (i) **(a)** and in (ii) **(a)**.

Solution 13.7

In Figure 13.5,

$$L = 5 \times 10^{-3} \text{ H}, \ C = 100 \times 10^{-6} \text{ F}, \ \omega_n = \frac{1}{\sqrt{(LC)}} = 1414 \text{ rad/s}$$

(i) $R = 20$ ohm

$$d = \frac{R}{2}\sqrt{\frac{C}{L}} = 1.414$$

$$\omega_o = \omega_n\sqrt{(d^2 - 1)} = 1414$$

(ii) $R = 10$ ohm

$$d = \frac{R}{2}\sqrt{\frac{C}{L}} = 0.707$$

$$\omega_o = \omega_n\sqrt{(1 - d^2)} = 1000$$

Transient Solution for d > 1

$$i_t = e^{-d\omega_n t}\,(Ae^{\omega_n t} + Be^{-\omega_n t})$$

$$i_t = e^{-2000t}\,(Ae^{1414t} + Be^{-1414t})$$

$$i_t = Ae^{-586t} + Be^{-3414t}$$

Transient Solution for d < 1

$$i_t = Ae^{-d\omega_n t}\sin(\omega_o t + \theta)$$

$$i_t = Ae^{-1000t}\sin(1000t + \theta)$$

Now at $t = 0$, $i = 0$

$$A = -B$$

$$0 = A\sin\theta$$

Since A cannot be zero if i_t has a finite value, then $\theta = 0$

$$i_t = A(e^{-586t} - e^{-3414t})$$

$$i_t = Ae^{-1000t}\sin 1000t$$

$$\left(\frac{di}{dt}\right)_{t=0} = -586\,A + 3414\,A$$

$$\left(\frac{di}{dt}\right)_{t=0} = 1000\,A$$

$$= 2828\,A$$

319

From the Fact Sheet in this chapter for the series RLC circuit,

$$\left(\frac{di}{dt}\right)_{t=0} = \frac{(E - V_1)}{L}$$

(a) For $V_1 = 0$ and $d > 1$,

$$\left(\frac{di}{dt}\right)_{t=0} = \frac{100}{5 \times 10^{-3}} = 2828 \text{ A}$$

giving $A = 7.07$

(a) For $V_1 = 0$ and $d < 1$,

$$\left(\frac{di}{dt}\right)_{t=0} = 20 \times 10^3 = 1000 \text{ A}$$

giving $A = 20$

Solutions

(i) (a) For $R = 20$ ohm and $V_1 = 0$

$$i = 7.07(e^{-586t} - e^{-3414t}) \text{ amperes}$$

(ii) (a) For $R = 10$ ohm and $V_1 = 0$

$$i = 20e^{-1000t} \sin1000t \text{ amperes}$$

(b) For $V_1 = -100$ V and $d > 1$

$$A = 14.14$$

(b) For $V_1 = -100$ V and $d < 1$

$$A = 40$$

Solutions

(i) (b) For $R = 20$ ohm
and $V_1 = -100$ V

$$i = 14.14(e^{-586t} - e^{-3414t}) \text{ amperes}$$

(ii) (b) For $R = 10$ ohm
and $V_1 = -100$ V

$$i = 40e^{-1000t} \sin1000t \text{ amperes}$$

Maximum current

For (i) (a)

$$\frac{di}{dt} = 7.07(-586e^{-586t} + 3414e^{-3414t})$$

For (ii) (a)

$$\frac{di}{dt} = 20(-1000e^{-1000t} \sin1000t + 1000e^{-1000t} \cos1000t)$$

Equate both of these to zero to give the time to reach maximum current in each case, as follows

In (i) (a)

$$586e^{-586t_i} = 3414e^{-3414t_i}$$

$$e^{2828t_i} = \frac{3414}{586}$$

$$2828t_i = 1.762$$

and $\quad t_i = 0.623$ ms

In (ii) (a)

$$\sin1000t_{ii} = \cos1000t_{ii}$$

$$1000t_{ii} = \frac{\pi}{4}$$

Thus $t_{ii} = 0.785$ ms

Substitute these times back in their respective current equations to give:

Maximum current = 4.06 amperes   Maximum current = 6.45 amperes

for condition (i) (a)   for condition (ii) (a)

Example 13.8

A 5.0 ohm resistor and a 385 microfarad capacitor are connected in series across voltage source $v = 2000 \sin 300t$ volts at the instant the voltage is a positive maximum. Derive the complete expression for the circuit current i as a function of the time after the voltage is zero going positive. The capacitor was uncharged before the switch was closed.

Solution 13.8

Refer to section (a) (ii) of the Fact Sheet in this chapter.
   Total current

$$i = Ae^{-t/RC} + i_{SS}$$

where,

$$i_{SS} = \frac{2000}{Z} \sin(300t + \phi) \quad \text{and } T = RC = 5 \times 385 \times 10^{-6}$$
$$= 1.925 \text{ ms}$$

The modulus of the circuit impedance, $Z = \sqrt{(R^2 + X^2)}$

$$\text{where the capacitive reactance, } X = \frac{10^6}{300 \times 385} \text{ ohm}$$

This gives $X = 8.66$ ohm and $Z = 10$ ohm.
   The phase angle ϕ, between the steady-state current and the steady-state voltage is calculated using single-phase theory (refer to Chapter 5).
   Then,

$$\tan \phi = \frac{1}{\omega CR} \text{ giving } \phi = 60° = \frac{\pi}{3}$$

Substitution in the i_{SS} equation above results in

$$i_{SS} = 200 \sin\left(300t + \frac{\pi}{3}\right) \text{ amperes}$$

Combining this with the transient current gives the instantaneous current equation

$$i = Ae^{-t/RC} + 200 \sin\left(300t + \frac{\pi}{3}\right) \text{ amperes}$$

At the instant the switch is closed, the voltage is a maximum, where $t = \pi/600$ s, and $i = 2000/5 = 400$ amperes, since initially all of the applied voltage must be dropped across the resistor. Substitute these in the current equation to give

$$400 = Ae^{-\pi/600T} + 200 \sin\left(\frac{\pi}{2} + \frac{\pi}{3}\right)$$

that is,

$$A = 300 \, e^{\pi/600T} = 300e^{2.72} = 4554$$

The complete expression for the current is

$$i = 4554 \, e^{-t/T} + 200 \sin\left(300t + \frac{\pi}{3}\right) \text{ amperes}$$

Example 13.9

For the two-mesh circuit shown in Figure 13.24, derive the equation for the current $i(t)$ in the 5 ohm resistor after the switch is closed at $t = 0$.

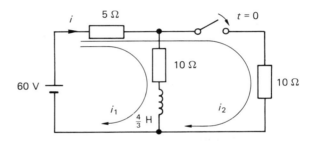

Fig 13.24

Solution 13.9

The current through the inductor, i_1, cannot change at the instant the switch is closed. Let a second circulating current be i_2 as marked in Figure 13.24; the answer required will be $i_1 + i_2$.

By KVL, we see

$$60 = 5(i_1 + i_2) + \left(10 + \frac{4D}{3}\right)i_1$$

Giving,

$$60 = 15i_1 + \frac{4}{3}Di_1 + 5i_2 \tag{13.22}$$

$$60 = 5i_1 + 15i_2 \tag{13.23}$$

Also,
Hence,

$$i_2 = 4 - \frac{i_1}{3}$$

Substitute in Equation (13.22) to give

$$40 = \frac{40}{3} i_1 + \frac{4}{3} i_1$$

Hence,

$$3 = (1 + 0.1\mathrm{D})i_1$$

Compare with the standard Equation (13.4) to see $i_1 = A\mathrm{e}^{-10t} + 3$. Now at $t = 0$, $i_1 = 60/15 = 4$ amperes, therefore $A = 1$ and $i_1 = \mathrm{e}^{-10t} + 3$.

Substituting this into the expression for i_2 above, gives

$$i_2 = 3 - \frac{\mathrm{e}^{-10t}}{3}$$

The current in the 5 ohm resistor $= i_1 + i_2$

$$= 6 + \frac{2}{3}\mathrm{e}^{-10t} \text{ amperes}$$

Note: The reader will find it an interesting exercise to show that the voltage across the coil changes instantaneously from 40 V to 26.7 V when the switch is closed.

Example 13.10

Use the Laplace transform method to derive the equation of the capacitor voltage in Worked Example 13.2.

Solution 13.10

The s-domain circuit is shown in Figure 13.25. Applying KVL to this circuit yields

$$\frac{100}{s} + \frac{20}{s} = \left(R + \frac{1}{sC}\right)\bar{i}$$

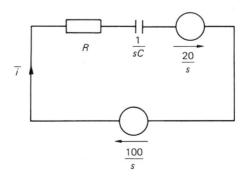

Fig 13.25

323

That is,

$$\bar{i} = \frac{120C}{1 + RCs} = \frac{120}{R(s + 1/RC)}$$

Substituting values for R and C gives

$$\bar{i} = \frac{1.2 \times 10^{-3}}{s + 20}$$

The inverse transform gives $i = 1.2 \times 10^{-3}\,e^{-20t}$ A
and $v_C = 100 - iR = 100 - 120e^{-20t}$ V.

Example 13.11

Solve Worked Example 13.9 using the Laplace transform method.

Solution 13.11

The s-domain circuit is shown in Figure 13.26. Before closing the switch the current, I_1, in the 4/3 H inductor is $60/(5 + 10) = 4$ A. This initial condition is represented by an s-domain voltage of $LI_1 = 16/3$ V, as shown. If the current in the 5 ohm resistor is i_A, then for the left-hand mesh

$$\frac{60}{s} + \frac{16}{3} = \left(5 + 10 + \frac{4s}{3}\right)\bar{i}_A - \left(10 + \frac{4s}{3}\right)\bar{i}_B$$

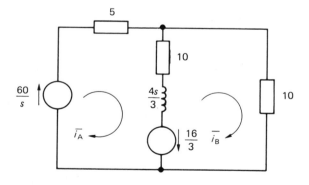

Fig 13.26

and for the right-hand mesh

$$\frac{-16}{3} = -\left(10 + \frac{4s}{3}\right)\bar{i}_A + \left(10 + 10 + \frac{4s}{3}\right)\bar{i}_B$$

Adding these equations gives

$$\frac{60}{s} = 5\,\bar{i}_A + 10\,\bar{i}_B$$

or

$$\bar{i}_B = \frac{6}{s} - \frac{\bar{i}_A}{2}$$

Substituting this into the right-hand mesh equation yields

$$\frac{-16}{3} = -10\bar{i}_A - \frac{4s}{3}\bar{i}_A + \frac{120}{s} - 10\bar{i}_A + 8 - \frac{2s}{3}\bar{i}_A$$

which reduces to

$$\bar{i}_A = \frac{60}{s(s+10)} + \frac{20}{3(s+10)}$$

The inverse transform gives

$$i_A = 6(1 - e^{-10t}) + \frac{20}{3} e^{-10t}$$

$$= 6 + \frac{2}{3} e^{-10t} \text{ amperes}$$

This agrees with the solution obtained in Worked Example 13.9.

Example 13.12

For the series RLC circuit in Figure 13.5, $L = 2$ mH, $C = 0.05$ microfarad, and there is no initial stored energy. **(a)** Calculate the minimum value of R so that the current waveform does not become negative after applying a constant voltage of $+E$ volts. **(b)** For the value of R in part **(a)**, what is the peak voltage across R when $E = 100$ V?

Solution 13.12

(a) This condition corresponds to critical damping where $d = 1$. From the Fact Sheet, for the series circuit,

$$d = \frac{R}{2}\sqrt{\frac{C}{L}},$$

or

$$R = 2d\sqrt{\frac{L}{C}} = 2\sqrt{\left(\frac{2 \times 10^{-3}}{0.05 \times 10^{-6}}\right)} = 400 \text{ ohm}$$

(b) From the Fact Sheet for $d = 1$ and $V_1 = 0$,

$$i = \frac{E}{L} t\, e^{-\omega_n t} \quad \text{where } \omega_n = \frac{1}{\sqrt{(LC)}} = 10^5 \text{ rad/s}$$

The voltage across R will be a maximum when i is a maximum, i.e., when $di/dt = 0$. This is at time t_m, when

$$\frac{di}{dt} = \frac{E}{L}(e^{-\omega_n t_m} - \omega_n t_m e^{-\omega_n t_m}) = 0$$

or

$$\omega_n t_m = 1$$

Hence,

$$t_m = 1/10^5 \text{ s} = 10 \; \mu\text{s}$$

Substituting this value into the equation for current yields

$$i_m = \frac{E}{\omega_n L}e^{-1} = \frac{100}{10^5 \times 2 \times 10^{-3}} \times 0.368 = 0.184 \text{ A}$$

and the peak voltage across R is $i_m R = 73.7 \text{ V} = V_m$.

It should be noted that

$$V_m = \frac{ER}{\omega_n L}e^{-1}$$

which simplifies to $2Ee^{-1}$, i.e., it varies only with the magnitude of the step input voltage when the critical damping case is considered.

Example 13.13

(a) Obtain the voltage transfer function function $\dfrac{V_o}{V_1}(s)$ for the circuit in Figure 13.27. (b) If v_1 is a step input of 10 V, derive equations for $v_o(t)$ when (i) $R = 1.0$ ohm, (ii) $R = 2.0$ ohm, (iii) $R = 0.5$ ohm.

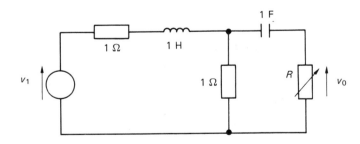

Fig 13.27

Solution 13.13

(a)   The s-domain circuit is shown in Figure 13.28. By mesh analysis

$$\overline{V}_1 = (2 + s)\overline{I}_1 - \overline{I}_2$$

$$0 = -\overline{I}_1 + (1 + R + 1/s)\overline{I}_2$$

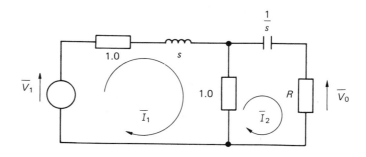

Fig 13.28

From the second of these equations $\bar{I}_1 = (1 + R + 1/s)\bar{I}_2$; substituting this in the first equation gives

$$\bar{V}_1 = (2 + s)(1 + R + 1/s)\bar{I}_2 - \bar{I}_2$$

But $\bar{V}_o = \bar{I}_2 R$, hence

$$\bar{V}_1 = \frac{\bar{V}_o}{R}\left[2 + 2R + \frac{2}{s} + s + sR\right]$$

so that the required transfer function is

$$\frac{\bar{V}_o}{\bar{V}_1} = \frac{sR}{s^2(1 + R) + s(2 + 2R) + 2}$$

(b)   For a step function of 10 V, $\bar{V}_1 = 10/s$ and

$$\bar{V}_o = \frac{10R}{s^2(1 + R) + s(2 + 2R) + 2}$$

(i)   When $R = 1.0$ ohm

$$\bar{V}_o = \frac{10}{2s^2 + 4s + 2} = \frac{5}{(s + 1)^2}$$

The inverse transform gives $v_o = 5\,t\,e^{-t}$ V.

(ii)   For $R = 2.0$ ohm

$$\bar{V}_o = \frac{20}{3s^2 + 6s + 2} = \frac{20}{3}\left(\frac{1}{s^2 + 2s + 2/3}\right)$$

Now compare the function of s with that in the Fact Sheet in this chapter, i.e., $1/(s^2 + 2d\omega_n s + \omega_n^2)$, and comparing coefficients we see that $\omega_n^2 = 2/3$ or $\omega_n = \sqrt{(2/3)} = 0.816$ rad/s, and $2d\omega_n = 2$ or $d = \sqrt{(3/2)} = 1.225$. Hence $\omega_o = \omega_n\sqrt{(d^2 - 1)} = 0.577$ rad/s.

For $d > 1$, the time domain solution is

$$v_o = \frac{20}{0.577}\,e^{-t}\,\sinh 0.577t\ \text{V}$$

(iii) For $R = 0.5$ ohm

$$\overline{V}_o = \frac{5}{1.5s^2 + 3s + 2} = \frac{5}{1.5}\left(\frac{1}{s^2 + 2s + 4/3}\right)$$

Comparing this with the quadratic function in s shows that $\omega_n^2 = 4/3$ or $\omega_n = 2/\sqrt{3} = 1.155$ rad/s, and $2d\omega_n = 2$ hence $d = \sqrt{3}/2 = 0.866$. The oscillatory frequency is $\omega_o = \omega_n\sqrt{(1 - d^2)} = 0.577$ rad/s, and $d\omega_n = 1$.

For $d < 1$, the time-domain solution is

$$v_o = \frac{10}{3 \times 0.577} e^{-t} \sin 0.577t = 5.78\, e^{-t} \sin 0.577t \text{ V}$$

Example 13.14

A coil has a resistance of 1600 ohm and an inductance of 10 H. It is connected across the terminals of a 10 microfarad capacitor, which had previously been charged to 100 V. Derive an expression for the voltage between the terminals of the coil after the connection is made.

Solution 13.14

The s-domain circuit is drawn in Figure 13.29. By potential divider action

$$v_{\text{COIL}} = \frac{1600 + 10s}{1600 + 10s + 10^5/s} \times \frac{100}{s}$$

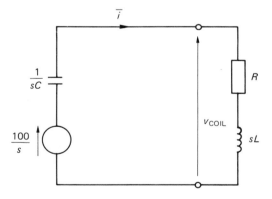

Fig 13.29

This simplifies to

$$v_{\text{COIL}} = 100\left(\frac{160 + s}{s^2 + 160s + 10^4}\right)$$

$$= 100\left[\frac{s + 80}{(s + 80)^2 + 60^2} + \frac{80}{(s + 80)^2 + 60^2}\right]$$

The inverse transform gives

$$v_{COIL} = 100\left(e^{-80t}\cos 60t + \frac{80}{60}e^{-80t}\sin 60t\right)$$

$$= (100\cos 60t + 133.3\sin 60t)\,e^{-80t}$$

$$= 166.7\,e^{-80t}\sin(60t + 36.9°)\text{ V}$$

Note: At $t = 0$, $V_{COIL} = 100$ V.

13.3 Unworked Problems

Problem 13.1

(a) In Figure 13.30 the switch is closed at $t = 0$, when $v_C = 0$. Calculate v_C when $t = 1.0$ s. [Suggest using Thévenin's theorem.]
(b) Repeat part (a) when $v_C(0) = 2.0$ V.
[2.36 V; 3.57 V]

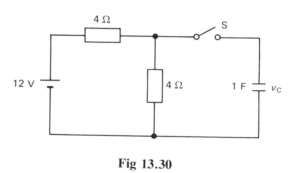

Fig 13.30

Problem 13.2

Initially the switch S in Figure 13.31 is open and $v_C(0) = 0$. From then on, S automatically closes when $v_C(t)$ rises to $2V_S/3$ and opens when it falls to $V_S/3$. Sketch $v_C(t)$. Show that the frequency of oscillation is given by

$$f = \frac{1.443}{C(R_1 + 2R_2)}\text{ Hz}$$

[Note: This is the principle of operation of the 555 astable multivibrator.]

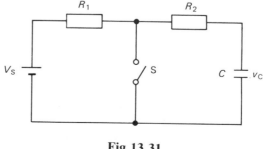

Fig 13.31

329

Problem 13.3

A capacitor is charged through a resistor from a constant voltage source V_S as shown in Figure 13.2. For zero initial energy, the capacitor voltage v_C and the current i are given by:

$$v_C(t) = V_S(1 - e^{-t/T}) \text{ and}$$

$$i(t) = \frac{V_S}{R} e^{-t/T} \quad \text{where } T = RC$$

(a) Derive an expression for the total energy stored by the capacitor using $W = \int v_C(t)i(t)\,\mathrm{d}t$
(b) Derive an expression for the total energy dissipated in the resistor while charging the capacitor in part **(a)**.

$$[\tfrac{1}{2} CV_S^2; \tfrac{1}{2} CV_S^2]$$

Problem 13.4

The capacitor in Figure 13.32 is initially uncharged. Switch S is closed at $t = 0$. Develop an expression for the time variation of the current i for $t > 0$, given that the time constant at the capacitor terminals is 2 seconds.

(Liverpool Polytechnic)

$$[i = 1.4 + 0.6e^{-t/2} \text{ mA}]$$

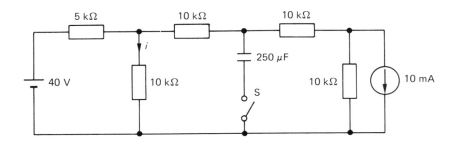

Fig 13.32

Problem 13.5

For a single transient, represented by the circuits in Figures 13.1 and 13.2 and Equations (13.7) and (13.8), show that if the rate of change of the circuit variable, e.g., current, remained constant at any instant, it would reach the steady-state value after a time equal to one time constant.

Problem 13.6

A coil has a resistance $R = 10$ ohm and inductance $L = 0.1$ H.
(a) Derive the expression for the instantaneous value of the current in the coil after it has been connected to a 240 V, 50 Hz sinusoidal supply, assuming that at the instant the circuit is completed the voltage is zero and becoming positive.
(b) Calculate the value of the instantaneous current 8 ms after completing the circuit.
[**(a)** $i = 10.38 \sin(100\pi t - 72.3°) + 0.953 e^{-100t}$ A; **(b)** 14.3 A]

Problem 13.7

In Figure 13.33, $E = 10$ V, $R_1 = 2.0$ ohm, $R_2 = 6.0$ ohm, and $L = 0.5$ H. The switch is closed at $t = 0$.
(a) What is the circuit current before closing the switch?
(b) What is the steady-state current after closing it?
(c) Derive the expression for the instantaneous current for $t > 0$.
[**(a)** 1.25 A; **(b)** 5.0 A; **(c)** $i = 5(1 - 0.75 e^{-4t})$ A]

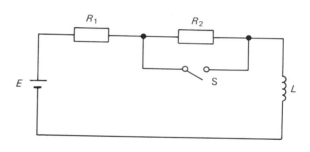

Fig 13.33

Problem 13.8

In Figure 13.34, the switch is closed at $t = 0$. Determine **(a)** the steady-state values of i_1 and i_2 before closing the switch and **(b)** the steady-state values of i_1 and i_2 after closing the switch. Hence derive expressions for $i_1(t)$ and $i_2(t)$
[**(a)** 4.5 mA, 4.5 mA; **(b)** 5.0 mA, 0; $i_1 = 5 + e^{-5t}$ mA; $i_2 = 4.5 e^{-200t}$ mA]

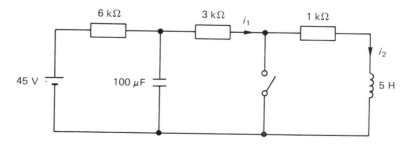

Fig 13.34

Problem 13.9

A 40 ohm resistor, a 5 mH inductor and a 100 microfarad capacitor are connected in series with a 100 V d.c. supply. The capacitor is initially uncharged. Derive the equation relating the instantaneous current to time after the circuit has been completed. Calculate the current after 0.4 ms. Determine the circuit resistance for a critically damped current response.

(Staffordshire Polytechnic)

$[i = 2.67(e^{-260t} - e^{-7740t})$ A; 2.28 A; 14.1 ohm.$]$

Problem 13.10

A coil of 200 turns has a resistance of 25 ohm and is wound on a magnetic material which has a magnetisation characteristic represented by the linearised graph shown in Figure 13.35. Calculate the time taken for the current to rise to 5.5 A if a d.c. supply of 150 V is switched on to the coil.
Note: The self inductance of the coil is given by the flux linkages per ampere, i.e., the slope of the given characteristic multiplied by the number of turns. So, for $i < 1.0$ A, $L = 4$ H and for $i > 1.0$ A, $L = 0.25$ H.
[Time to reach 1 A = 29.2 ms; total time to reach 5.5 A = 52.2 ms.]

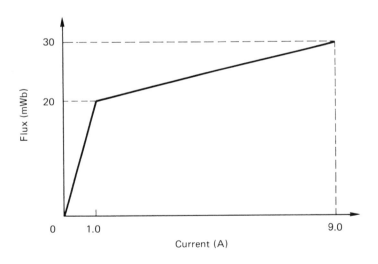

Fig 13.35

Problem 13.11

(a) For the circuit shown in Figure 13.36, derive the expression for the battery current after the switch is closed at $t = 0$, assuming no initial stored energy.
(b) What is the equation for the current in the 3 ohm resistor if the switch is opened after steady state conditions have been reached?
$[$(a) $2 - 2e^{-4t}$ A; (b) $-2e^{-6t}$ A$]$

332

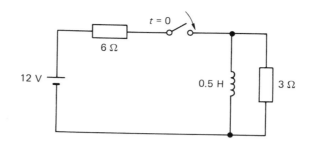

Fig 13.36

Problem 13.12

The voltage transform of a network is given by

$$\frac{V_o}{V_1} = G(s) = \frac{16(s + 2)}{s^2 + 12s + 32}$$

Derive the transient response for a step input of 1.0 V to the network.

(Staffordshire Polytechnic)

$[v_o = 1 + 2e^{-4t} - 3e^{-8t} \text{ V}]$

Problem 13.13

For the network in Figure 13.37, $R = 50$ ohm and $C = 100$ microfarad. Derive the equation for $v_o(t)$ when a 100 V d.c. source of zero internal resistance is connected across AB at time $t = 0$. There is no initial stored energy.

(Staffordshire Polytechnic)

$[v_o = 117 \, e^{-524t} - 17 \, e^{-76t} \text{ V}]$

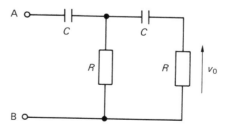

Fig 13.37

Problem 13.14

In Problem 13.13 above, calculate the instant when v_o first becomes negative.
$[t = 4.3 \text{ ms}]$

333

Problem 13.15

For the operational amplifier circuit in Figure 13.38, derive the voltage transfer function $\frac{V_o}{V_1}(s)$, assuming the amplifier to be ideal (Refer to Worked Example 7.7).

(Staffordshire Polytechnic)

$$\left[\frac{V_o}{V_1}(s) = \frac{2}{(s+2)(s+1)}\right]$$

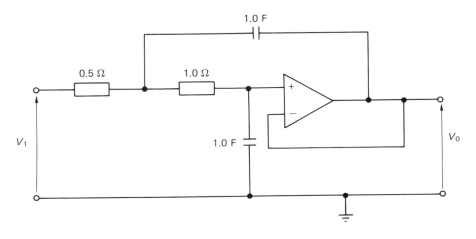

Fig 13.38

Appendix 1
Complex Numbers

(a) Imaginary Numbers

The concept of imaginary numbers was introduced by mathematicians to allow them to express the square root of a negative number. For example, if $x^2 = -9$, the solution is given by saying

$$x = \text{imaginary operator} \times \sqrt{9}$$

The imaginary number is useful to electrical engineers, who gave the imaginary operator the symbol j so that, in the above case

$$x = j3$$

(Mathematicians use the symbol i to represent the imaginary operator, but as this symbol is used by electrical engineers to represent electrical current, the symbol j is used.)
Thus

$$j = \sqrt{(-1)}$$
$$j^2 = (\sqrt{(-1)})^2 = -1$$
$$j^3 = j \times j^2 = -j$$
$$j^4 = j^2 \times j^2 = 1, \text{ etc.}$$

The reader should note that

$$\text{imaginary number} = \text{imaginary operator (j)} \times \text{real number}$$

(b) Complex Numbers

A *complex number* is the sum of a real number and an imaginary number, and is either written in bold Roman type (as in this book), or has a bar drawn over it (as is often the case in hand-written material). Thus

$$\mathbf{V} = a + jb$$

or

$$\bar{V} = a + jb$$

335

It is important to note that both *a* and *b* are *real numbers*, but the component j*b* is an *imaginary number* since *b* is multiplied by the imaginary operator j.

(c) Representation of Complex Numbers

There are four ways of representing a complex number, namely

rectangular or Cartesian form $V = a + jb$

polar form $V = r\angle\theta$

exponential form $V = r \times e^{j\theta}$

trigonometric form $V = r(\cos\theta + j\sin\theta)$

The last three forms above are, from Euler's identity, generally the same form. The relationship between them is

$$r = \sqrt{(a^2 + b^2)} \qquad \theta = \tan^{-1}(b/a)$$

The rectangular and polar forms are most widely used in electrical engineering. The seven complex numbers V_1 to V_7 represented in Figure A1.1 are written in polar and rectangular form as follows.

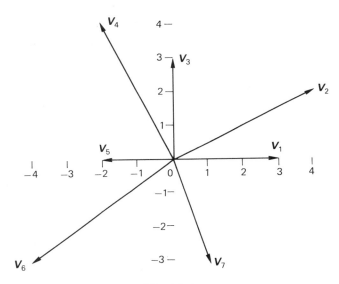

Fig A1.1

$V_1 = 3 = 3 + j0 = 3\angle 0°$

$V_2 = 4 + j2 = 4.47\angle 26.57°$

$V_3 = j3 = 0 + j3 = 3\angle 90°$

$V_4 = -2 + j4 = 4.47\angle 116.57°$

$V_5 = -2 = -2 + j0 = 2\angle 180°$ (or $2\angle -180°$)

$V_6 = -4 - j3 = 5\angle 216.87°$ (or $5\angle -143.13°$)

$V_7 = 1 - j3 = 3.16\angle -71.57°$

(d) Conjugate of a Complex Number

The conjugate, V^*, of the complex number $V = a + jb = r\angle\theta$ is

$$V^* = a - jb = r\angle-\theta$$

where $r = \sqrt{(a^2 + b^2)}$ and $\theta = \tan^{-1}(b/a)$.

If $V = 3 + j4 = 5\angle53.13°$, then $V^* = 3 - j4 = 5\angle-53.13°$. Also $(V^*)^* = V$. A complex number and its conjugate are said to form a *conjugate complex pair* of numbers. Other useful properties are

$$(V_1V_2)^* = V_1^*V_2^*$$

$$(V_1 \pm V_2)^* = V_1^* \pm V_2^*$$

$$\left(\frac{V_1}{V_2}\right)^* = \frac{V_1^*}{V_2^*}$$

(e) Sum and Difference of Complex Numbers

To perform addition (or subtraction) of complex numbers, the numbers must first be converted into rectangular form, and the real parts must be added together (or subtracted from one another), and then the imaginary parts added together (or subtracted from one another) as follows.

If $V_1 = 5 + j6$ and $V_2 = -3 - j8$, then

$$V_1 + V_2 = (5 + j6) + (-3 - j8) = 2 - j2$$

$$V_1 - V_2 = (5 + j6) - (-3 - j8) = 8 + j14$$

(f) Multiplication of Complex Numbers

When the numbers are expressed in polar form, the multiplication proceeds as follows

$$r_1\angle\theta_1 \times r_2\angle\theta_2 = r_1r_2\angle(\theta_1 + \theta_2)$$

In general, it is more convenient to carry out multiplication of complex numbers using the polar form than it is using rectangular form. However, when numbers are expressed in rectangular form, the multiplication can be carried out as follows.

$$(a + jb)(c + jd) = (ac + j^2bd) + j(ad + bc)$$

$$= (ac - bd) + j(ad + bc)$$

If $V_1 = 3 + j4 = 5\angle53.13°$ and $V_2 = -5 - j5 = 7.07\angle-135°$, then

$$V_1 \times V_2 = 5\angle53.13° \times 7.07\angle-135° = 35.35\angle-81.87°$$

or

$$V_1 \times V_2 = (3 + j4)(-5 - j5) = (-15 + 20) + j(-15 - 20) = 5 - j35$$

337

The *product of a conjugate complex pair* of rectangular numbers is

$$(a + jb)(a - jb) = a^2 + b^2$$

and the *product of a conjugate complex pair* of polar numbers is

$$r\angle\theta \times r\angle-\theta = r^2\angle(\theta - \theta) = r^2$$

both giving a real number and no imaginary term. For example, if $V = 3 + j4 = 5\angle53.13°$, then

$$V \times V^* = (3 + j4)(3 - j4) = 9 + 16 = 25$$

or

$$V \times V^* = 5\angle53.13° \times 5\angle-53.13° = 25\angle0°$$

(g) Division of Complex Numbers

If V and I are complex numbers then, using polar values, division is carried out as follows.

$$\frac{V}{I} = \frac{r_1\angle\theta}{r_2\angle\phi} = \frac{r_1}{r_2}\angle(\theta - \phi)$$

In general, it is more convenient to use polar values rather than rectangular values when performing division.

Using rectangular complex values, division is carried out as follows

$$\frac{V}{I} = \frac{V \times I^*}{I \times I^*}$$

The product $I \times I^*$ gives a real number with no imaginary part (see section f), and the process of dividing by $(I \times I^*)$ is known as *rationalizing the denominator*. For example

if $V = a + jb$ and $I = c + jd$, then

$$\frac{V}{I} = \frac{(a + jb)(c - jd)}{(c + jd)(c - jd)} = \frac{(ac + bd) + j(bc - ad)}{c^2 + d^2}$$

Suppose $V = 4 + j4 = 5.66\angle45°$ and $I = 3 + j4 = 5\angle53.13°$, then

$$\frac{V}{I} = \frac{5.66\angle45°}{5\angle53.13°} = 1.132\angle-8.13°$$

or

$$\frac{V}{I} = \frac{(4 + j4)(3 - j4)}{(3 + j4)(3 - j4)} = \frac{(12 + 16) + j(12 - 16)}{9 + 16}$$

$$= \frac{28 - j4}{25} = 1.12 - j0.16$$

(h) Powers and Roots of Complex Numbers

The Nth power of a complex number is calculated as follows.

$$(R\angle\theta)^N = R^N\angle N\theta$$

For example,

$$(2\angle 60°)^3 = 8\angle 180°$$

There are N roots of the complex number $R\angle\theta$ as follows

$$(R\angle\theta)^{1/N} = R^{1/N}\angle\frac{\theta + [n \times 360]}{N}$$

where n has a value in the range $0, 1, 1 \ldots, (N-1)$.

For example $\sqrt[3]{(8\angle 60°)}$ has the values $2\angle 20°$, $2\angle 140°$ and $2\angle 260°$.

Appendix 2
Matrices and Determinants

(a) Matrix Representation

Consider the equations

$$V_1 = Z_{11}I_1 + Z_{12}I_2 + Z_{13}I_3$$
$$V_2 = Z_{21}I_1 + Z_{22}I_2 + Z_{23}I_3$$
$$V_3 = Z_{31}I_1 + Z_{32}I_2 + Z_{33}I_3$$

These can be written in *matrix form* of ordered rows and columns of elements of the same kind as follows.

$$
\begin{bmatrix} V_1 \\ V_2 \\ V_3 \end{bmatrix} =
\begin{bmatrix} Z_{11} & Z_{12} & Z_{13} \\ Z_{21} & Z_{22} & Z_{23} \\ Z_{31} & Z_{32} & Z_{33} \end{bmatrix}
\begin{bmatrix} I_1 \\ I_2 \\ I_3 \end{bmatrix}
$$

or, alternatively, in the even more ordered form

$$[V] = [Z][I]$$

where $[V]$ is a voltage matrix, $[Z]$ is an impedance matrix, and $[I]$ is a current matrix. The formalized matrix representation is well suited to calculator and computer solution of equations.

The double subscript notation is used to identify the position of an element within a matrix. The first subscript denotes the row in which the element is found, and the second denote the column. Thus Z_{23} is the element in the second row of the third column. A simple mnemonic to remember the order of the subscripts is **R**oman **C**atholic (**R**ows, **C**olumns).

Both the voltage and the current matrix, above, are written in the form of a column, and each is described as a *column matrix* or *vector*. These have only one column, but may contain any number of rows (in the case considered, both have the same length). Since there is only one column in a column matrix, only one subscript is necessary to define the position of an element within it.

The impedance matrix is a *square matrix*, in which the number of rows is equal to the number of columns.

The *major diagonal* of a square matrix is the diagonal line of elements going from the top leftmost element to the bottom rightmost element, i.e., the elements Z_{11}, Z_{22}, Z_{33} in the impedance matrix above lie on the major diagonal.

A *diagonal matrix* is a rectangular matrix in which all the elements are zero except those on the major diagonal.

An *identity matrix* or *unit matrix* is a diagonal matrix in which the value of each of the elements on the major diagonal is unity.

Other forms include the following. A *row matrix* has only one row containing a number of columns as follows.

$$[a_{11} \quad a_{12} \quad a_{13} \quad ... \quad a_{1N}]$$

A *rectangular matrix* is one having M rows and N columns ($M \neq N$), and is described as an *M by N* or $M \times N$ matrix, as shown below.

$$\begin{bmatrix} a_{11} & a_{12} & ... & a_{1N} \\ a_{21} & a_{22} & ... & a_{2N} \\ ... & ... & ... & ... \\ a_{M1} & a_{M2} & ... & a_{MN} \end{bmatrix}$$

A *null matrix* is one in which every element is zero.

(b) Matrix Addition and Subtraction

Two matrices can either be added together or subtracted from one another *if they are of the same order*. If $A = [a_{ij}]$ and $B = [b_{ij}]$ are two $M \times N$ matrices, their sum (or difference) is the matrix $C = [c_{ij}]$, where each element of C is the sum (or difference) of the corresponding elements of A and B. That is

$$A \pm B = [a_{ij} \pm b_{ij}]$$

If $A = \begin{bmatrix} -3 & 4 & 5 \\ 0 & -6 & 7 \end{bmatrix}$ and $B = \begin{bmatrix} 3 & 4 & -5 \\ 6 & -7 & 8 \end{bmatrix}$ then

$$A + B = \begin{bmatrix} -3+3 & 4+4 & 5-5 \\ 0+6 & -6-7 & 7+8 \end{bmatrix} = \begin{bmatrix} 0 & 8 & 0 \\ 6 & -13 & 15 \end{bmatrix}$$

$$A - B = \begin{bmatrix} -3-3 & 4-4 & 5-(-5) \\ 0-6 & -6-(-7) & 7-8 \end{bmatrix} = \begin{bmatrix} -6 & 0 & 10 \\ -6 & 1 & -1 \end{bmatrix}$$

(c) Matrix Multiplication

The matrix product AB (which *must be carried out in that order*) can be computed only if the *number of columns in A* is equal to the *number of rows in B*. B is not necessarily conformable to A for multiplication, i.e., the product BA may not be defined. The following should be observed.

1. $AB \neq BA$ generally.
2. $AB = 0$ does not always imply $A = 0$ or $B = 0$.
3. $AB = AC$ does not always imply $B = C$.

If matrices are conformable, multiplication is performed on a *row by column* basis; each element in a row is multiplied by the corresponding element of a column, and the products are summed.

If A is a $1 \times M$ row matrix, and B is a $M \times 1$ column matrix, then

$$AB = [a_{11} \quad a_{12} \quad \ldots \quad a_{1M}] \begin{bmatrix} b_{11} \\ b_{21} \\ \cdot \\ \cdot \\ \cdot \\ b_{M1} \end{bmatrix}$$

$$= [a_{11}b_{11} + a_{12}b_{21} + \ldots + a_{1M}b_{M1}]$$

$$= \left[\sum_{k=1}^{M} a_{1k}b_{k1} \right]$$

Note: BA is not defined.

Suppose that $A = [-1 \quad 2 \quad 3]$ and $B = \begin{bmatrix} -6 \\ 0 \\ 7 \end{bmatrix}$ then

$$AB = [-1 \quad 2 \quad 3] \begin{bmatrix} -6 \\ 0 \\ 7 \end{bmatrix} = [-1(-6) + 2(0) + 3(7)] = [27]$$

If $A = \begin{bmatrix} a_{11} & a_{12} \\ a_{21} & a_{22} \\ a_{31} & a_{32} \end{bmatrix}$ and $B = \begin{bmatrix} b_{11} & b_{12} \\ \\ b_{21} & b_{22} \end{bmatrix}$ then

$$AB = \begin{bmatrix} a_{11}b_{11} + a_{12}b_{21} & a_{11}b_{12} + a_{12}b_{22} \\ a_{21}b_{11} + a_{22}b_{21} & a_{21}b_{12} + a_{22}b_{22} \\ a_{31}b_{11} + a_{32}b_{21} & a_{31}b_{12} + a_{32}b_{23} \end{bmatrix}$$

Note: BA is not defined.

Suppose that $A = \begin{bmatrix} -1 & 0 \\ 3 & -4 \\ 5 & 6 \end{bmatrix}$ and $B = \begin{bmatrix} 4 & 5 \\ -6 & 7 \end{bmatrix}$ then

$$AB = \begin{bmatrix} -1(4)+0(-6) & -1(5)+0(7) \\ 3(4)+(-4)(-6) & 3(5)+(-4)(7) \\ 5(4)+6(-6) & 5(5)+6(7) \end{bmatrix} = \begin{bmatrix} -4 & -5 \\ 36 & -13 \\ -16 & 67 \end{bmatrix}$$

Also, if $R = \begin{bmatrix} 5 & -3 & 0 \\ -3 & 12 & -5 \\ 0 & -5 & 11 \end{bmatrix}$ and $I = \begin{bmatrix} I_1 \\ I_2 \\ I_3 \end{bmatrix}$ then

$$RI = \begin{bmatrix} 5I_1 & -3I_2 & -0I_3 \\ -3I_1 & 12I_2 & -5I_3 \\ -0I_1 & -5I_2 & 11I_3 \end{bmatrix}$$

A *matrix may be multiplied by a scalar k* (which should not be confused with the 1×1 matrix $[k]$), to give

$$kA = Ak = [ka_{ij}]$$

that is, each element in the matrix is multiplied by k.

(d) The Determinant of a Square Matrix

A matrix is simply an ordered array of elements, and *has no numerical value*. On the other hand, the *determinant* of a square matrix has a numerical value, which is given the symbol Δ, or det A or $|A|$. This value can be used in the computation of the value of unknown variables in the equations represented by the matrix equations.

The value of a determinant of order 2 is calculated as follows.

$$\begin{vmatrix} a_{11} & a_{12} \\ a_{21} & a_{22} \end{vmatrix} = a_{11}a_{22} - a_{12}a_{21}$$

For example,

$$\begin{vmatrix} 2 & 4 \\ -5 & -3 \end{vmatrix} = 2(-3) - 4(-5) = 14$$

For a determinant of order 3

$$\begin{vmatrix} a_{11} & a_{12} & a_{13} \\ a_{21} & a_{22} & a_{23} \\ a_{31} & a_{32} & a_{33} \end{vmatrix} = \begin{aligned} & a_{11}a_{22}a_{33} + a_{12}a_{22}a_{31} + a_{13}a_{21}a_{32} - a_{13}a_{22}a_{31} - a_{12}a_{21}a_{33} \\ & - a_{11}a_{23}a_{32} \end{aligned}$$

For example,

$$\begin{vmatrix} 2 & -3 & 4 \\ 5 & 6 & -2 \\ -3 & -4 & 7 \end{vmatrix} = \begin{aligned} & 2.6.7 + (-3).(-2).(-3) + 4.5.(-4) \\ & - 4.6.(-3) - (-3).5.7 - 2.(-2).(-4) \\ & = -63 \end{aligned}$$

(e) Minors and Cofactors

The *minor* of the element a_{ij} (row i, column j) of a determinant is obtained by deleting row i and column j of the determinant; the minor of this element is given the symbol M_{ij}. The value of the minor is multiplied by $(-1)^{i+j}$ to give the *cofactor* of a_{ij}; the cofactor is given the symbol Δ_{ij}.

For example, in the determinant of order 3 above

$$M_{22} = \begin{vmatrix} a_{11} & a_{13} \\ a_{31} & a_{33} \end{vmatrix}$$

and

$$\Delta_{22} = (-1)^{2+2} \begin{vmatrix} a_{11} & a_{13} \\ a_{31} & a_{33} \end{vmatrix} = + \begin{vmatrix} a_{11} & a_{13} \\ a_{31} & a_{33} \end{vmatrix} = + a_{11}a_{33} - a_{13}a_{31}$$

(f) Evaluating a Determinant

The value of a determinant of order N is the sum of the N products of each element in a selected row (or column) and its cofactor (great care should be taken in ensuring that the cofactor has the correct mathematical sign, see section (e) above).

Consider the following determinant of order 3, which can be evaluated by (for example) selecting the elements in the first row as follows.

$$\begin{vmatrix} a_{11} & a_{12} & a_{13} \\ a_{21} & a_{22} & a_{23} \\ a_{31} & a_{32} & a_{33} \end{vmatrix} = a_{11}\Delta_{11} + a_{12}\Delta_{12} + a_{13}\Delta_{13}$$

$$= a_{11} \begin{vmatrix} a_{22} & a_{23} \\ a_{32} & a_{33} \end{vmatrix} - a_{12} \begin{vmatrix} a_{21} & a_{23} \\ a_{31} & a_{33} \end{vmatrix} + a_{13} \begin{vmatrix} a_{21} & a_{22} \\ a_{31} & a_{32} \end{vmatrix}$$

$$= (a_{11}a_{22}a_{33} - a_{11}a_{23}a_{32}) - (a_{12}a_{21}a_{33} - a_{12}a_{23}a_{31}) + (a_{13}a_{21}a_{32} - a_{13}a_{22}a_{31})$$

Alternatively, if the elements in the second column are selected, then the value of the determinant is calculated from

$$a_{12}\Delta_{12} + a_{22}\Delta_{22} + a_{32}\Delta_{32}$$

Both of the above calculations produce the result given earlier in section (d).

(g) The Rule of Sarrus

A determinant of order 3 can be evaluated using the rule of Sarrus as follows.

The determinant is written down, and the first two columns are repeated to the right of the determinant. Diagonal lines are drawn joining sets of three elements together; the product of the diagonally downwards terms are given a positive sign, and the product of the diagonally upwards terms are given a negative sign. The value of the determinant is the sum of these products. For example, by the rule of Sarrus

$$\begin{vmatrix} 5 & 6 & 7 \\ 2 & -3 & 4 \\ 1 & -2 & 3 \end{vmatrix} \begin{array}{l} = 5.(-3).3 + 6.4.1. + 7.2.(-2) - 7.(-3).1 - 6.2.3 - 5.4.(-2) \\ \\ = -45 + 24 - 28 + 21 - 36 + 40 = -24 \end{array}$$

(h)   Cramer's Rule

Linear simultaneous equations can be solved by *Cramer's rule* as follows. Consider the following matrix form of equation

$$\begin{bmatrix} y_1 \\ y_2 \\ . \\ . \\ . \\ y_M \end{bmatrix} = \begin{bmatrix} a_{11} & a_{12} & \ldots & a_{1N} \\ a_{21} & a_{22} & \ldots & a_{2N} \\ . & . & \ldots & . \\ . & . & \ldots & . \\ . & . & \ldots & . \\ a_{M1} & a_{M2} & \ldots & a_{MN} \end{bmatrix} \begin{bmatrix} x_1 \\ x_2 \\ . \\ . \\ . \\ x_N \end{bmatrix}$$

The value of x_K in the Kth row is obtained from the computations

$$x_K = \frac{1}{\det A} \begin{vmatrix} a_{11} & \ldots & a_{1(K-1)} & y_1 & a_{1(K+1)} & \ldots & a_{1N} \\ a_{21} & \ldots & a_{2(K-1)} & y_2 & a_{2(K+1)} & \ldots & a_{2N} \\ . & \ldots & . & . & . & \ldots & . \\ . & \ldots & . & . & . & \ldots & . \\ . & \ldots & . & . & . & \ldots & . \\ a_{M1} & \ldots & a_{M(K-1)} & y_M & a_{2(K+1)} & \ldots & a_{MN} \end{vmatrix}$$

For example, solve for I_2 in the following

$$5 = 10I_1 - 3I_2 - 5I_3$$
$$10 = -3I_1 + 7I_2 - 4I_3$$
$$-15 = -5I_1 - 4I_2 + 9I_3$$

The matrix form of the equation is

$$\begin{bmatrix} 5 \\ 10 \\ -15 \end{bmatrix} = \begin{bmatrix} 10 & -3 & -5 \\ -3 & 7 & -4 \\ -5 & -4 & 9 \end{bmatrix} \begin{bmatrix} I_1 \\ I_2 \\ I_3 \end{bmatrix}$$

From Cramer's rule

$$I_2 = \begin{vmatrix} 10 & 5 & -5 \\ -3 & 10 & -4 \\ -5 & -15 & 9 \end{vmatrix} \Big/ \begin{vmatrix} 10 & -3 & -5 \\ -3 & 7 & -4 \\ -5 & -4 & 9 \end{vmatrix}$$

and using the rule of Sarrus

$$I_2 = \frac{10.10.9 + 5.(-4).(-5) + (-5).(-3).(-15) - (-5).10.(-5) - 5.(-3).9 - 10.(-4).(-15)}{10.7.9 + (-3).(-4).(-5) + (-5).(-3).(-4) - (-5).7.(-5) - (-3).(-3).9 - 10.(-4).(-4)}$$

$$= \frac{60}{94} = 0.638$$

(i) Matrices and Determinants Containing Complex Numbers

Matrices and determinants containing complex numbers can be handled by the methods described above, but the reader must use the methods described in sections (e) to (h) of appendix 1 when dealing with complex numbers.

Appendix 3
Computer Software
for Circuit Analysis

Introduction

A range of software packages is available for the analysis of circuits using mainframe, mini and personal computers. The attention of the reader is directed here to one of the most popular of them, namely the *Simulation Program with Integrated Circuit Emphasis* or *SPICE*, developed at the University of California, Berkeley, which is widely available.

With the space available, only an introduction can be given here; for more details, the reader should study a copy of the *User Guide* for the version of SPICE employed in his computer system.

SPICE enables circuit analysis to be performed on d.c. and a.c. circuits (or a combination of the two) which include elements such as resistors, inductors, coupled circuits, capacitors, semiconductor devices, dependent and independent sources, transmission lines, etc. SPICE can also be used to perform frequency response analysis, Fourier analysis, transient analysis, and can handle problems involving electronic noise, temperature effects, etc.

The reader should note that some of these features may not be available in some versions of SPICE for personal computers.

The circuit to be analysed is described using a *text editor*, which allows the user to creak and modify the *input file* (one program line per circuit component). The first line of the file normally contains a title statement, and the file is terminated by a ".END" statement. Such element as voltage sources, current sources, resistors, inductors, transformers, capacitors, diodes, transistors, etc., can be included in the input file.

Next, the input file is read by an *analyser*, which checks the file for errors; if none are present, it performs the required analysis and supplies the results. On completion, control is returned to the editor.

Depending on the type of analysis required, the results may either be in numerical form, or graphical form, or both.

Circuit Description

Each terminal of each element in the circuit being analysed is connected to a node, the nodes being numbered in the range 0, 1, 2, 3 .... n; the value of n is only limited by the version of SPICE being used. Node 0 is the reference (or ground) node. A two-terminal element, such as a resistor, an inductor, a capacitor, etc, is connected between two nodes, and a three-terminal element such as a transistor is connected between three nodes.

The value of a component, such as the resistance of a resistor, can be specified either by entering its actual value (usually a maximum seven figures), or by expressing the value in exponent form, e.g., 1.5E-6, or by writing it in symbolic form as shown in Table A3.1. Thus, the resistance of a 1200 ohm resistor may be specified either as 1200, or as 1.2E3, or as 1.2K.

Table A3.1
SPICE symbolic values

Value	SPICE Symbolic form	Exponent form
10^{-15}	F	1E–15
10^{-12}	P	1E–12
10^{-9}	N	1E–9
10^{-6}	U	1E–6
10^{-3}	M	1E–3
10^{3}	K	1E3
10^{6}	MEG	1E6
10^{9}	G	1E9
10^{12}	T	1E12

Element Description

In the following, the SPICE specifications of a number of the more important circuit elements are described.

Resistors

The general specification is of the form

RXXXXXXX   N1   N2   VALUE

in which RXXXXXXX is the designation of the resistor in the circuit being analysed; the XXXXXXX part of the designation is an alphanumeric string from one to seven characters. For example, this could be R2, R23, or R3AC4XY, etc. N1 and N2 are the nodes between which the resistor is connected, and VALUE is the resistance of the resistor in ohms. A typical specification may be

R2   1   2   3.5

The reader should note that SPICE does not accept conductance values, and that a resistance of zero ohms is not allowed.

Capacitors

These are specified in the form

$$\text{CXXXXXXX} \quad \text{N+} \quad \text{N-} \quad \text{VALUE} \langle \text{IC=ICOND} \rangle$$

where N+ is the positive node, N− is the negative node, and VALUE is the capacitance in farads. The $\langle \; \rangle$ brackets indicate that the contents are optional and, where present, give the initial charge on the capacitor between N+ and N− in volts.

Examples include

$$\text{C3} \quad 1 \quad 0 \quad 0.5\text{E-6}$$

$$\text{C29} \quad 4 \quad 5 \quad 0.7\text{U} \quad \text{IC}=-2.3$$

Inductors

The general specification is

$$\text{LXXXXXXX} \quad \text{N+} \quad \text{N-} \quad \text{VALUE} \langle \text{IC=ICOND} \rangle$$

where N+ is the positive node, N− is the negative node, and VALUE is the inductance in henrys. Where present, the initial current (in A), flows inside the inductor from N+ and N−.

Examples include

$$\text{L4} \quad 4 \quad 5 \quad 5.6\text{M}$$

$$\text{L6} \quad 2 \quad 3 \quad 4 \quad \text{IC}=1.5$$

Where an inductor is part of a coupled circuit (see the following section), node N+ is the end marked by a 'dot' using the dot notation (see Chapter 11).

Coupled circuits

A coupled circuit is presented as a non-ideal device with a specified magnetic coupling coefficient betwen the windings. It is specified in the form

$$\text{KXXXXXXX} \quad \text{LYYYYYYY} \quad \text{LZZZZZZZ} \quad \text{VALUE}$$

where XXXXXXX, YYYYYY and ZZZZZZZ are alphanumeric strings from one to seven characters in length. KXXXXXXX is the designation of the coupled circuit, e.g., K8, while LYYYYYY and LZZZZZZZ are the designation of the windings of the coupled circuit; the designation of each of the windings is given separately. If the transformer has two windings of self-inductance L_1 and L_2, and a mutual inductance M, the coupling coefficient between the windings is $k = M/\sqrt{(L_1 L_2)}$, where $0 < k \leq 1$; the value of the coupling coefficient is given in the VALUE section of the transformer specification. A complete specification of a two-winding coupled circuit may be

$$\text{K3} \quad \text{L1} \quad \text{L2} \quad 0.65$$

$$\text{L1} \quad 4 \quad 0 \quad 2$$

$$\text{L2} \quad 5 \quad 0 \quad 4$$

This represents a nonideal transformer with a coupling coefficient of 0.65, having a coil L_1 (of inductance 2 H) connected between nodes 4 and 0, and coil L_2 (of inductance 4 H) connected between nodes 5 and 0. The 'dotted' end of coil L_1 being connected to node 4, and the 'dotted' end of L_2 connected to node 5.

Independent Voltage Source

The general specification of an independent constant (d.c.) voltage source has the form

$$VXXXXXXX \quad N+ \quad N- \quad \langle DC \; VALUE \rangle$$

e.g., V4 1 0 DC 7.5
and for a sinusoidal a.c. source it has the form

$$VXXXXXXX \quad N+ \quad N- \quad \langle AC \; \langle ACMAG \; \langle ACPHASE \rangle \rangle \rangle$$

e.g., VS 3 4 AC 6.7
where VXXXXXXX designates the voltage source in the circuit, N+ is the positive node, and N− the negative node. In the case of the constant (d.c.) source, VALUE is the direct voltage produced by the source; in the a.c. case, the voltage is given by ACMAG, and ACPHASE is the phase angle of the source. If ACMAG is omitted, a value of one volt is assumed; if ACPHASE is omitted, a phase angle of zero is assumed.

SPICE also allows a selected range of other independent sources such as a pulse, an exponential wave, etc, to be used.

Linear Dependent Voltage Sources

The general form of a *linear voltage-controlled* (or *voltage-dependent*) *voltage source* is

$$EXXXXXXX \quad N+ \quad N- \quad NC+ \quad NC- \quad VALUE$$

where N+ and N− are the positive and negative nodes, respectively, of the controlled source, whilst NC+ and NC− are the respective positive and negative nodes of the dependent (or controlling) voltage source. VALUE is the voltage gain from the controlling to the controlled source.

The general form for a *linear current-controlled* (or *current-dependent*) *voltage source* is

$$HXXXXXXX \quad N+ \quad N- \quad VNAM \quad VALUE$$

where N+ and N− have the meaning given above, and VNAM is the name of the voltage source through which the controlling current flows. The direction of positive controlling current flow is from the positive node, through the source, to the negative node of VNAM. VALUE is the transresistance (ohms) between the controlling current and the controlled voltage.

Independent Current Source

For a constant (d.c.) source the general specification has the form

IYYYYYY   N+   N−   ⟨DC⟩ VALUE

e.g.,   I5   1   0   DC   5.3
and for an a.c. source it has the form

IYYYYYY   N+   N−   ⟨AC   ⟨ACMAG   ⟨ACPHASE⟩⟩⟩

e.g.,   I42   5   3   AC   5.6

IYYYYYY designates the current source within the circuit, and the arrow designating the direction of current flow through the source is from node N+ to N−. VALUE is the value of the current. In the case of an a.c. source, if ACMAG is omitted a current of 1 A is assumed, and if ACPHASE is omitted a phase angle of zero is assumed.

Linear Dependent Current Sources

The general form for a *linear voltage-dependent* (or *voltage-controlled) current source* is

GXXXXXX   N+   N−   NC+   NC−   VALUE

where N+ and N− are the positive and negative nodes, respectively, of the controlled source, NC+ and NC− are the respective positive and negative nodes of the controlling source, and VALUE is the transconductance (in S) between the two. Current flow is from N+, through the source, to N−.

The general form for a *linear current-dependent* (or *current-controlled) current source* is

FXXXXXX   N+   N−   VNAM   VALUE

where N+ and N− are as defined above, VNAM is the name of the voltage source through which the controlling current flows, and VALUE is the current gain between the two.

Print-out Analysis

The general form of statement is

.PRINT   PRTYPE   VAR1   ⟨VAR2 .... VAR8⟩

in which PRTYPE is the type of analysis to be performed, e.g., d.c., a.c., transient, noise, etc. For example

.PRINT   DC   V(1)   V(3,4)

In the above example, V(1) is the voltage at node 1 (with respect to node 0), and V(3,4) is the voltage at node 3 with respect to node 4.

In the case of an a.c. analysis, five form of output can be obtained as follows:

$$VR \ - \text{real part}$$

$$VI \ - \text{imaginary part}$$

$$VM \ - \text{magnitude}$$

$$VP \ - \text{phase shift}$$

$$VDB - 20 \times \log_{10}(\text{magnitude})$$

As with the d.c. case, differential voltage can be printed, e.g.,

$$\text{.PRINT} \quad \text{AC} \quad VP(1,2) \quad VR(4,5)$$

The current flowing in an independent voltage source can be specified as follows

$$I(VXXXXXXX)$$

and the current in the voltage source can be printed, e.g.,

$$\text{.PRINT} \quad \text{AC} \quad IM(VS) \quad IP(VS)$$

A voltage source must be present in a branch before the current in the branch can be printed; it is sometimes useful to insert an independent voltage source of zero volts in a branch in order to determine the current in that branch.

Plotting

The general form of plot is produced by the .PLOT statement described below

$$\text{.PLOT} \quad \text{PLTYPE} \quad OV1\langle PLO1, PHI1\rangle \quad \langle OV2\rangle\langle PLO2, PHI2\rangle 4 ....\langle OVB\rangle$$

Up to eight output variables (OV1 to OV8) may be plotted; the type of analysis is specified by PLTYPE (which may be DC, AC, or TRAN(SIENT)). The low and high boundaries for the independent variables may be specified by the user (PLO,PHI), but if the plot limits are not specified, the SPICE program will automatically determine suitable minimum and maximum scale values.

Figure 7.25 shows a typical plot of two variables (gain and phase) plotted against frequency. Both of the vertical scales were chosen automatically. Note also that the value of the first specified output variable (gain) has its values printed alongside the independent variable (frequency) values. There is no limit to the number of .PLOT lines specified for each type of analysis.

Transient Analysis

The general form of statement is

$$\text{.TRAN} \quad \text{TSTEP} \quad \text{TSTOP} \quad \langle\text{TSTART}\rangle \quad \langle\text{TMAX}\rangle \quad \langle\text{UIC}\rangle$$

where TSTEP is the plotting and/or printing increment of time for the output. TSTOP is the final value of time, and TSTART is the initial value of time used in computing the transient response; the default value of the latter is zero. Using TMAX enables the computing time step to be smaller than TSTEP. The optional parameter UIC means 'Use Initial Conditions', whose values are specified using IC=... with inductors or capacitors, or a .IC line to specify initial node voltages.

.PRINT TRAN and .PLOT TRAN are two lines which are respectively used to print out a table of node voltages, and to plot a graph of these as a function of time. For example, the lines

$$.TRAN\ 0.1M\ \ 5M$$

$$.PLOT\ \ TRAN\ \ V(4)\ V(1)$$

produces a graph of the voltages at nodes 4 and 1 in a network, starting at zero time and incrementing in steps of 0.1 ms for a duration of 5 ms. The graph abscissa will be those of time and the value of node 4 voltages at these times. The scales of both voltages will be calculated and marked automatically.

Programming Examples

Example 1

Here we analyse a simple d.c. resistive circuit containing two independent voltage sources (see Worked Example 2.1). The circuit is shown in Figure A3.1, and the corresponding input file is

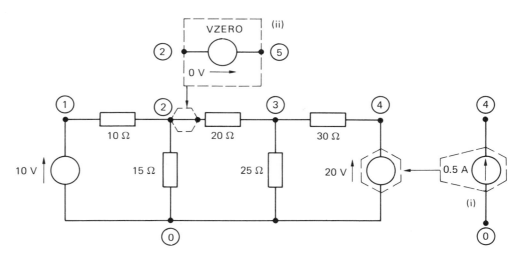

Fig A3.1

```
EXAMPLE 1
V10  1  0  DC  10
V40  4  0  DC  20
R12  1  2  10
R23  2  3  20
R34  3  4  30
R20  2  0  15
R30  3  0  25
.END
```

In this case, the independent voltage sources are simply specified in terms of the nodes they are connected between; thus V10 is connected between node 1 and node 0 (node 1 being positive), and V40 is connected between node 4 and node 0. The resistors are specified in the same way. Since no type of analysis is specified in the program then, when SPICE is run, it simply performs a d.c. analysis, and it calculates the voltage at each node in the circuit relative to node 0, as follows:

NODE VOLTAGE   NODE VOLTAGE   NODE VOLTAGE   NODE VOLTAGE
  (1) 10.0000   (2) 6.4679   (3) 8.0275   (4) 20.0000

Certain versions of SPICE automatically provide other information such as the following.

VOLTAGE SOURCE CURRENTS

NAME   CURRENT

V10   −3.532D-01

V40   −3.991D-01

TOTAL POWER DISSIPATION 1.15D+0.1 WATTS

The version of SPICE used by the authors produces an exponent term preceded either by D (see above results) or E, e.g., 1.234D+02 or 1.234E+02, both corresponding to the value 123.4. It also calculates the current *entering* the positive node of each voltage source, i.e., in the above case, 0.3532 A *leaves* the positive node of V10.

Example 2

In this case, the circuit in Figure A3.1 is modified as shown in inset (i), in which the 20 V independent voltage source is replaced by a 0.5 A independent current source. The input file is identical to that given above with the exception that the second line is replaced by

I04 0 4 DC 0.5

The node voltages are printed by SPICE as follows:

NODE VOLTAGE   NODE VOLTAGE   NODE VOLTAGE   NODE VOLTAGE
  (1) 10.0000   (2) 6.7647   (3) 9.3137   (4) 24.3137

Example 3

Assuming that the version of SPICE used by the reader does not provide the current in the voltage sources in the circuit, we return to the circuit in Programming Example 1, to illustrate how mesh current analysis can be performed on the circuit. To do this, we insert the independent voltage source VZERO, having a value of zero volts, between node 2 and the 20 ohm resistor, as shown in inset (ii) in Figure A3.1. In so doing, it is necessary to add node 5 to the circuit. The input file now becomes

EXAMPLE 3
```
V10    1   0   DC   10
V40    4   0   DC   20
VZERO  5   2   DC   0
R12    1   2   10
R53    5   3   20
R34    3   4   30
R20    2   0   15
R30    3   0   25
.PRINT   DC   I(V10)   I(VZERO)   I(V40)
.END
```

The corresponding mesh currents are printed by SPICE as follows.

VOLTAGE SOURCE CURRENTS

NAME	CURRENT
V10	$-3.532D-01$
V40	$-3.991D-01$
VZERO	$7.798D-02$

Once again, the reader should note that the calculated value of current enters the positive node of the source in question.

Example 4

This program introduces a current-controlled voltage source into a circuit (see Figure A3.2). Since it is necessary for the controlling current to flow in a voltage source, a zero-valued independent source (VZERO) is introduced in the branch in which the controlling current flows. The input file for the circuit is

EXAMPLE 4
```
V10    1   0   DC   25
V32    3   2   DC   2
VZERO  2   4   DC   0
H30    3   0   VZERO   3
R12    1   2   6
R40    4   0   2
.PRINT   DC   I(V10)   I(VZERO)   I(V32)
.END
```

The .PRINT control statement results in the current in each branch of the circuit being printed as follows.

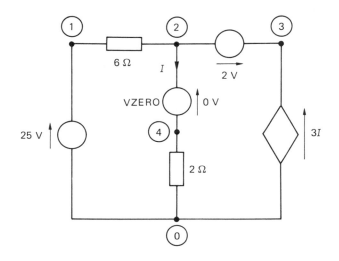

Fig A3.2

VOLTAGE SOURCE CURRENTS

NAME   CURRENT

V10   −3.500D+00

V32   −1.500D+00

VZERO   2.000D+00

Example 5

Here SPICE is asked to calculate the polar form of the complex voltage at node 2 of the a.c. circuit in Figure A3.3, together with the polar and rectangular form of the current drawn from the supply. The input file for the circuit is

```
EXAMPLE 5
VS   1   0   AC   10
L12  1   2   1
C20  2   0   10U
R20  2   0   200
.AC   LIN   1   50   50
.PRINT   AC   VM(2)   VP(2)   IM(VS)   IP(VS)   IR(VS)   II(VS)
.END
```

There are several points the reader should note at this time. Firstly, SPICE does not accept values of inductive and capacitive reactance (it only accepts inductance and capacitance). Secondly, it only accepts frequency in hertz (not in rad/s) and, finally, it only deals with phase shift in degrees (not in radians).

This is the first time we have encountered the method of supplying information to SPICE about the frequency of an a.c. source. The general form is

.AC   VAR   NO   FSTART   FSTOP

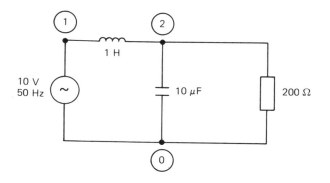

Fig A3.3

There are several points the reader should note at this time. Firstly, SPICE does not accept values of inductive and capacitive reactance (it only accepts inductance and capacitance). Secondly, it only accepts frequency in hertz (not in rad/s) and, finally, it only deals with phase shift in degrees (not in radians).

This is the first time we have encountered the method of supplying information to SPICE about the frequency of an a.c. source. The general form is

$$\text{.AC} \quad \text{VAR} \quad \text{NO} \quad \text{FSTART} \quad \text{FSTOP}$$

in which FSTART and FSTOP are respectively the frequency at which the analysis starts and stops (clearly, this is the way in which the user can perform a frequency analysis over a range of frequencies). VAR is the method of variation between these two frequencies; SPICE accepts linear variation (LIN), decade variation (DEC), and octave variation (OCT). NO is the number of points to be calculated per decade over the frequency range.

The .PRINT instruction requests SPICE to provide the appropriate complex values of voltage and current, which are

FREQ	VM(2)	VP(2)	IM(VS)	IP(VS)	IR(VS)	II(VS)
5.000E+01	6.366E+00	−8.952E+01	3.759E−02	1.226E+02	−2.026E−02	3.166E−02

As before, the current calculated is that which enters the positive terminal of VS.

Example 6

If, as in many engineering examples, inductive and capacitive reactance rather than inductance and capacitance are provided as data, it is merely necessary to let the frequency be 0.1592 Hz (or 1 rad/s). Each SPICE inductor then has an inductance equal to X_L henrys, and each capacitor has a capacitance of $1/X_C$ farads.

Consider the circuit in Figure A3.4 (see also Worked Example 11.6), in which we need to calculate the complex current flowing in the capacitor. The inductive and capacitive reactances in the circuit are given in ohms and, assuming a supply frequency of 0.1592 Hz (1 rad/s), the corresponding inductances and capacitance are

$$L_{12} = 4 \text{ H} \quad L_{32} = 8\text{H} \quad M = 3 \text{ H} \quad C = 0.1 \text{ F}$$

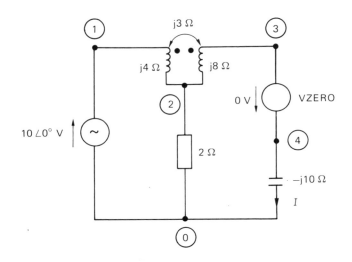

Fig A3.4

The magnetic coupling coefficient between the windings is

$$k = M/\sqrt{(L_{12}L_{32})} = 3/\sqrt{(4 \times 8)} = 0.5303$$

The input file for the circuit is

```
EXAMPLE 6
VS   1   0   AC   10
VZERO   3   4   AC   0
R20   2   0   2
C40   4   0   0.1
K1   L12   L32   0.5303
L12   1   2   4
L32   3   2   8
.AC   LIN   1   0.1592   0.1592
.PRINT   AC   IM(VZERO)   IP(VZERO)
.END
```

The resulting output file contains the following

FREQ	IM(VZERO)	IP(VZERO)
1.592E-01	1.921E+00	8.151E+01

The current calculated is that flowing from node 4 to node 0 downwards through the capacitor (see also Worked Example 11.6).

Example 7

The frequency response of the circuit shown in Figure 7.26(b) for the data given in Problem 7.2 is plotted using the program

*: VDB(2)
+: VP(2)

FREQ	VDB(2)					
*)------------------	-6.000D+01	-4.000D+01	-2.000D+01	0.000D+00	2.000D+0
+)------------------	-5.000D+01	0.000D+00	5.000D+01	1.000D+02	1.500D+0
1.000D-03	-4.404D+01	. *	.	.	+	.	.
1.259D-03	-4.204D+01	. *	.	.	+	.	.
1.585D-03	-4.004D+01	. *	.	.	+	.	.
1.995D-03	-3.804D+01	. *	.	.	+	.	.
2.512D-03	-3.605D+01	. *	.	.	+	.	.
3.162D-03	-3.405D+01	. *	.	.	+	.	.
3.981D-03	-3.206D+01	.	*	.	+	.	.
5.012D-03	-3.007D+01	.	*	.	+	.	.
6.310D-03	-2.810D+01	.	*	.	+	.	.
7.943D-03	-2.613D+01	.	*	.	+	.	.
1.000D-02	-2.419D+01	.	.	*	+	.	.
1.259D-02	-2.227D+01	.	.	*	+	.	.
1.585D-02	-2.041D+01	.	.	*.	+	.	.
1.995D-02	-1.861D+01	.	.	*	+	.	.
2.512D-02	-1.691D+01	.	.	* +	.	.
3.162D-02	-1.536D+01	.	.	+*	.	.
3.981D-02	-1.398D+01	.	.	+ *	.	.
5.012D-02	-1.281D+01	.	.	+ *	.	.
6.310D-02	-1.186D+01	.	. +	.	*	.	.
7.943D-02	-1.114D+01	.	+	.	*	.	.
1.000D-01	-1.062D+01	.	+	.	*	.	.
1.259D-01	-1.025D+01	.	+	.	*	.	.
1.585D-01	-1.000D+01	.	+	.	*	.	.
1.995D-01	-9.839D+00	.	+	.	*	.	.
2.512D-01	-9.732D+00	.	+	.	*	.	.
3.162D-01	-9.663D+00	.	+	.	*	.	.
3.981D-01	-9.619D+00	.	+	.	*	.	.
5.012D-01	-9.591D+00	.	+	.	*	.	.
6.310D-01	-9.573D+00	.	.+	.	*	.	.
7.943D-01	-9.562D+00	.	.+	.	*	.	.
1.000D+00	-9.555D+00	.	.+	.	*	.	.
1.259D+00	-9.550D+00	.	.+	.	*	.	.
1.585D+00	-9.547D+00	.	.+	.	*	.	.
1.995D+00	-9.545D+00	.	.+	.	*	.	.
2.512D+00	-9.544D+00	.	.+	.	*	.	.

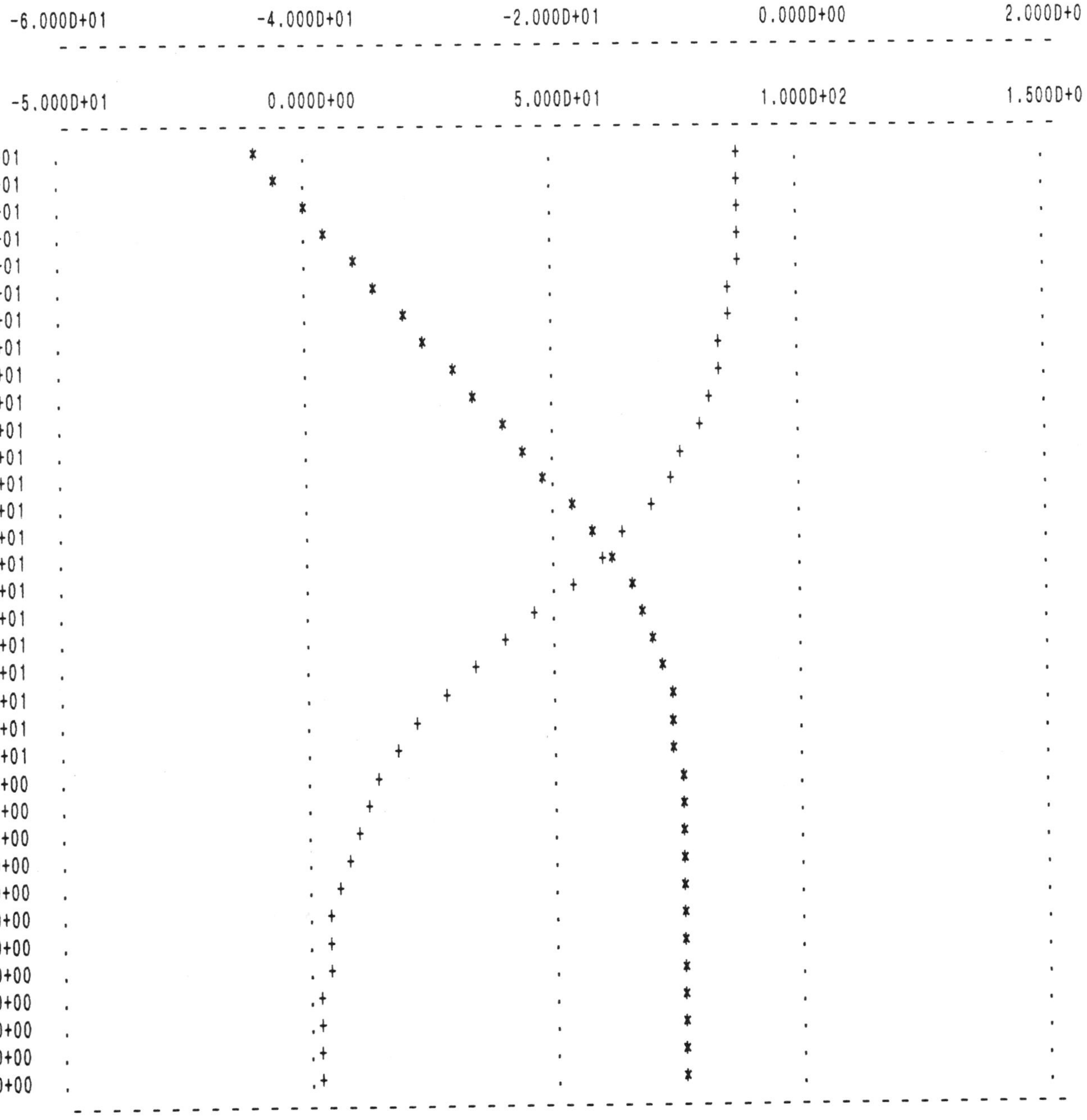

Fig A3.5

EXAMPLE 7
V1   1   0   AC   1

C1   1   2   1

C2   2   0   2

R   2   0   1

.AC   DEC   10   0.01   2.0

.PLOT   AC   VDB(2)   VP(2)

.END

The .AC line asks for ten points per decade to be used to plot the graph over the frequency range 0.01 Hz to 2.0 Hz. Since the input voltage is 1 volt, the gain of the network at node 2 in dB is given by VDB(2), and the phase shift by VP(2) (both relative to node 0). The response is shown in Figure A3.5, which should be compared with the result obtained in Problem 7.2.

Example 8

This example illustrates the transient solution of the parallel RLC circuit in Figure A3.6, with a resistance value of $R = 200$ ohms (see also Worked Example 13.6). The input file is written as follows.

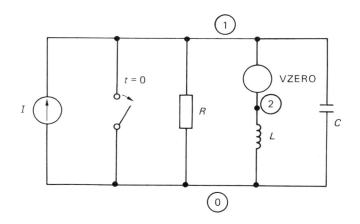

Fig A3.6

EXAMPLE 8
I   0   1   DC   100M

R   1   0   200

L   2   0   0.5   IC=0

C   1   0   12.5U   IC=0

VZERO   1   2   DC   0

.TRAN   1.0M   20M   UIC

.PLOT   TRAN   I(VZERO)

.END

The inductor current is sensed in the zero-voltage source VZERO. Since the switch initially short-circuits both the inductor and the capacitor, the initial condition in both is set to zero.

The .PLOT TRAN command causes i_L to be plotted for time increments of 1.0 ms for a period of 20 ms, and is shown in Figure A3.7 (which should be compared with Figure 13.23(i)).

TIME   I(VZERO)

TIME	I(VZERO)
0.0000D+00	-2.1490-08
1.000D-03	7.039D-03
2.000D-03	2.366D-02
3.000D-03	4.475D-02
4.000D-03	6.608D-02
5.000D-03	8.482D-02
6.000D-03	9.937D-02
7.000D-03	1.092D-01
8.000D-03	1.146D-01
9.000D-03	1.164D-01
1.000D-02	1.154D-01
1.100D-02	1.128D-01
1.200D-02	1.093D-01
1.300D-02	1.058D-01
1.400D-02	1.027D-01
1.500D-02	1.002D-01
1.600D-02	9.857D-02
1.700D-02	9.763D-02
1.800D-02	9.731D-02
1.900D-02	9.745D-02
2.000D-02	9.787D-02

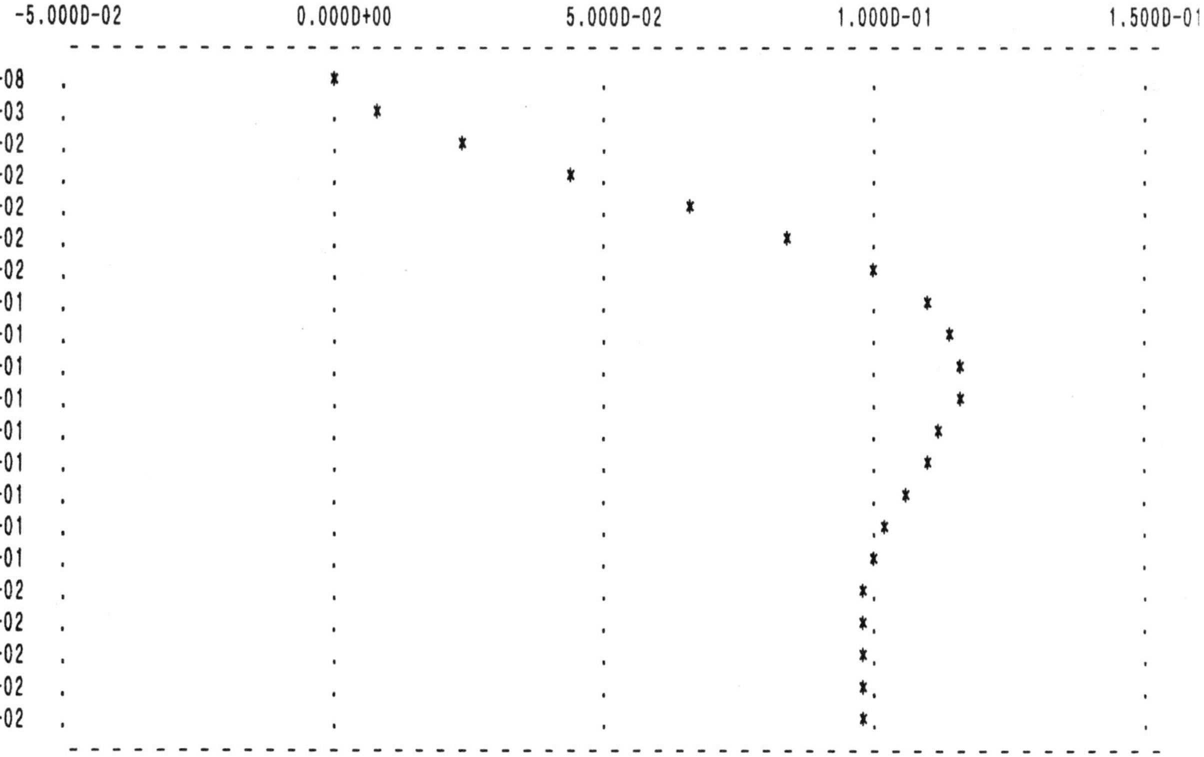

-5.000D-02   0.0000D+00   5.000D-02   1.000D-01   1.500D-01

Fig A3.7

Appendix 4 Partial Fractions

Functions of s can be transformed directly using integral calculus but, in practice, it is easier to arrange the functions so that they fit one or more of the terms in a table of Laplace transforms. One method of doing this is by the use of *partial fractions*.

Analysis of electrical problems by the Laplace transform method generally requires the derivation of the inverse transform from a result which, usually, is in the form of the ratio of two polynomials in s.

If

$$F(s) = \frac{N(s)}{D(s)}$$

where $N(s)$ and $D(s)$ are polynomials in s, and the degree of $N(s)$ is less than the degree of $D(s)$, then:

1. For every linear factor $(As + B)$ in $D(s)$ there is a corresponding partial fraction

$$\frac{1}{As + B}$$

2. For every quadratic factor $(As^2 + Bs + C)^2$ in $D(s)$ which has real roots, there is a corresponding partial fraction

$$\frac{Ps + Q}{As^2 + Bs + C}.$$

3. For every repeated factor $(As + B)^2$ in $D(s)$ there is a corresponding partial fraction

$$\frac{P}{As + B} + \frac{Q}{(As + B)^2}.$$

4. For every repeated quadratic factor $(As^2 + Bs + C)^2$ in $D(s)$ there is a corresponding partial fraction

$$\frac{Ps + Q}{As^2 + BS + C} + \frac{Rs + T}{(As^2 + Bs + C)^2}.$$

5. For every thrice-repeated character $(As + B)^3$ in $D(s)$ there is a corresponding partial fraction

$$\frac{P}{As + B} + \frac{Q}{(As + B)^2} + \frac{R}{(As + B)^3}.$$

6. For every cubic factor $As^3 + Bs^2 + Cs + D$ in $D(s)$ there is a corresponding partial fraction

$$\frac{Ps^2 + Qs + R}{As^3 + Bs^2 + Cs + D}.$$

Example A4.1

Determine the partial fraction expansion of

$$\frac{200}{s(s + 1)(s + 2)}.$$

Applying the rules laid down above

$$\frac{200}{s(s + 1)(s + 2)} = \frac{A}{s} + \frac{B}{s + 1} + \frac{C}{s + 2}$$

A, B and C in the above expression are known as the *residues*. The residues are quickly evaluated in this case by the *cover-up rule* as follows.

(i) Determine the *value* of s which makes the denominator of that particular term zero.
(ii) Substitute this *value* into the full expression (both numerator and denominator) and, ignoring or 'covering up' the factor in question, the *residue* is the result of the calculation.

The residue A is calculated by letting $s = 0$. Substituting this value in the original equation whilst 'covering up' the factor s gives

$$A = \left.\frac{200}{(s + 1)(s + 2)}\right|_{s=0} = \frac{200}{((0) + 1)((0) + 2)} = 100$$

The residue B is calculated by letting $s = -1$, as follows

$$B = \left.\frac{200}{s(s + 2)}\right|_{s=-1} = \frac{200}{(-1)((-1) + 2)} = -200$$

and the residue C is calculated by letting $s = -2$ as follows

$$C = \left.\frac{200}{s(s + 1)}\right|_{s=-2} = \frac{200}{(-2)((-2) + 1)} = 100$$

That is

$$\frac{200}{s(s + 1)(s + 2)} = \frac{100}{s} - \frac{200}{s + 1} + \frac{100}{s + 2}$$

Example A4.2

Determine the partial fraction expansion of

$$\frac{54}{(4s^2 - 5s + 1)^2}$$

This can be re-written in the form

$$\frac{54}{(4s^2 - 5s + 1)^2} = \frac{54}{(1 - s)^2(1 - 4s)^2}$$

Since there are repeated factors in the denominator, the partial fraction expansion is written as follows

$$\frac{A}{1 - s} + \frac{B}{(1 - s)^2} + \frac{C}{1 - 4s} + \frac{D}{(1 - 4s)^2}$$

Since $(1 - s)^2$ and $(1 - 4s)^2$ appear in the original equation, we can evaluate the residues B and D by the cover-up rule as follows.

$$B = \frac{54}{(1 - 4s)^2}\bigg|_{s=1} = \frac{54}{(1 - 4(1))^2} = 6$$

$$D = \frac{54}{(1 - s)^2}\bigg|_{s=0.25} = \frac{54}{(1 - 0.25)^2} = 96$$

The residues A and C are calculated by substituting the known residues, and multiplying both sides of the equation by the denominator of the polynomial as follows.

$$54 = A(1 - s)(1 - 4s)^2 + 6(1 - 4s)^2 + C(1 - s)^2(1 - 4s) + 96(1 - s)^2$$

Equating coefficients of s^3 gives $-16A - 4C = 0$, and equating coefficients of s^2 gives $8A + 3C = -64$. Solving for A and C yields $A = 16$, $C = -64$. That is

$$\frac{54}{(4s^2 - 5s + 1)^2} = \frac{16}{1 - s} + \frac{6}{(1 - s)^2} - \frac{64}{1 - 4s} + \frac{96}{(1 - 4s)^2}$$

Bibliography

There are many excellent texts in the field of circuit analysis, the following being a representative selection. In particular, the attention of the reader is directed towards those marked with a *. These texts contain introductory material on the computer program SPICE. A valuable text devoted to solving circuits using SPICE is W. Banzhaf, *Computer-Aided Circuit Analysis using SPICE*, Prentice-Hall, 1989.

1. L. S. Bobrow, *Elementary Linear Circuit Analysis*, 2nd Edition, Holt, Rinehart and Winston, 1987*
2. S. A. Boctor, *Electric Circuit Analysis*, Prentice-Hall, 1987*
3. R. L. Boylestad, *Introductory Circuit Analysis*, 5th Edition, Merrill Publishing Co., 1987
4. M. D. Ciletti, *Introduction to Circuit Analysis and Design*, Holt, Rinehart and Winston, 1988. Supplement available on SPICE
5. T. L. Floyd, *Principles of Electric Circuits*, 2nd Edition, Merrill Publishing Co., 1985
6. J. D. Irwin, *Basic Engineering Circuit Analysis*, 2nd Edition, Macmillan, 1987*
7. M. C. Kelly and B. Nichols, *Introductory Linear Electrical Circuits and Electronics*, John Wiley, 1988
8. J. W. Nilsson, *Electric Circuits*, 3rd Edition, Addison-Wesley, 1990*

PSPICE software suitable for personal computers is available both in full and in evaluation versions from ARS Microsystems Ltd, Dorman Road, Camberley, Surrey, GU15 3DF. Other versions of SPICE including SPICE.AGE and ECA-2 are obtainable from Those Engineers Ltd., 106a Fortune Green Road, West Hampstead, London, NW6 1DS.

Index